W1

THIS IDLE TRADE

ON DOCTORS WHO WERE WRITERS

By the same Author:

Dickens's Doctors   1979
Castles In Kent   1980
Jane Austen in Kent   1981
"Therefore Imagine"; The Works of Clemence Dane   1988
Not a Moment to Lose: Some Reminiscences   1989

THIS IDLE TRADE

ON DOCTORS WHO WERE WRITERS

DAVID WALDRON SMITHERS

The Dragonfly Press
TUNBRIDGE WELLS KENT

First published 1989
by the Dragonfly Press
2 Charlton Cottages, Barden Road, Speldhurst
Tunbridge Wells, Kent TN3 0LH

British Library Cataloguing in Publication Data
Smithers, David Waldron
This idle trade : on doctors who were writers.
1. English literature. Writers. Doctors
I. Title
820 . 9'9261

ISBN 0-9513500-1-3

Designed and set by Words & Images, Speldhurst, Kent
Printed and bound by Antony Rowe, Chippenham, Wiltshire

"I left no calling for this idle trade."

Alexander Pope in his *Epistle to Doctor Arbuthnot*

"Reader, I here put into thy hands, what has been the diversion of some of my idle and heavy hours."

Doctor John Locke in the introduction to his *Essay Concerning Human Understanding*

"Such and so various are the tastes of men."

Doctor Mark Akenside in his *The Pleasures of the Imagination*

Day after day
In vain we labor -
And grow old.

So come,
Empty a cup of wine
With me.
Waste no pity
On the falling blossoms.
Year after year
They will come again
With Spring.

Doctor Wang Wei (699-759) translated by Henry Hersch Hart in Mary McDonough's *Poet Physicians*

DEDICATION

To Elizabeth and Andrew with love

CONTENTS

CHAPTER ELEVEN
Tales of Human Behaviour
William Somerset Maugham 1874-1965

APPENDIX
References to papers on British doctor-writers

ILLUSTRATIONS

ACKNOWLEDGEMENTS

I am obliged to John Halperin, William Ober and Charles Sharp for reading the manuscript, correcting errors and making valuable suggestions. To have been able to call on the help of a Professor of English Literature, a doctor noted for his outstanding contributions to Medical History and a man who has read widely in four languages has been a great privilege.

Professor Franco Crainz, an expert on Princess Charlotte and her confinement and an old friend of mine in Rome has kindly commented on Chapter 9. A copy of the letter from Dr. William Beeston on smallpox inoculation, written only three years after its introduction into England in 1721, was kindly sent to me by Dr. David van Zwanenberg, who tells me that it is quoted in C.W. Dixon's 1962 monograph on smallpox. Ruth Fisher reminded me of an appropriate Hobbes quotation used in Chapter 2. I am grateful to Rosemary Angel, until recently Officer in Charge of Museums at Kew, for help with Chapter 10 and to Doctors Oliver Mayo and Alvin Rodin with Chapter 11.

I have received most valuable assistance from the staff of The London Library, and the libraries of New Scotland Yard, The Royal College of Physicians, The Royal College of Surgeons, The Royal Society, The Royal Society of Medicine and the Wellcome Foundation. The National Portrait Gallery has kindly supplied information and most of the illustrations, the one of William Denton came from Sir Ralph Verney, that of John Arbuthnot from the Scottish National Portrait Gallery, the one of William Wilde from the National Gallery of Ireland, one of Somerset Maugham from the Tate Gallery, and that of Austin Freeman from Mr. Austin Briant.

Mrs. D. Lambert did most of the typing with unfailing patience and cheerfulness and Mrs. J. Pelham did the rest and gave me valuable help with the revision. Work on this project has been pursued intermittently for seven years since it was started in 1983.

Extracts were incorporated in the Thomas Vicary Lecture given before The Royal College of Surgeons of England and the Worshipful Company of Barbers in October 1984, a shortened version of which appeared in the 1985 Christmas number of the *British Medical Journal*.

PREFACE

Medico-Literary Associations

THE SUBJECT of medico-literary associations and the varied circumstances which have produced author/physicians, has recently been arousing much interest particularly in America where two journals, *Literature and Medicine* from the John Hopkins University Press and *Medical Heritage* from W.B. Saunders, have been devoted to it and where two-day conferences on Literature and Medicine have been held at The University of Connecticut School of Medicine. This book considers the life and work of a few famous doctor-writers selected from a wide-ranging compass spread over two hundred and fifty years. They were all engaged at one time in medical practice: four of them, William Denton, John Arbuthnot, Sir David Hamilton and Mark Akenside, were physicians to Kings and Queens; two, William Wilde and Oliver Gogarty, were well known surgeons; two, Charles Lever and Sir Arthur Conan Doyle, were successful general practitioners; Austin Freeman was a colonial surgeon and a prison medical officer; John Keats practised hospital medicine for five of the twenty-six years of his short life; some, such as Tobias Smollett, Oliver Goldsmith and Somerset Maugham were better fitted to literature than to medicine, and a few, like John Locke, Thomas Young and Sir Joseph Hooker, devoted most of their time with great success to other pursuits.

These brief lives of literary doctors include extracts from their work and comments on important questions being asked to-day about subjects which were of special interest to them. A peculiar significance is attached to the literary achievements of this distinguished group of men, since the scientific training and humanitarian practice of their particular age had a profound influence on the widely varied expressions of their creative work, whether in poetry, philosophy, biography or fiction. However, throughout their diverse writing, you keep bumping into that combination of the sensible and the sensitive which is so characteristic of the good doctor. While a collection of brief biographies does not readily provide an insight into the circumstances, opportunities, motives and struggles which go to the creation of great doctor-writers, nevertheless each unique character adds to the pattern, vividly illuminating a small portion of the tapestry.

The long-standing association between medicine and literature goes back at least to the time of Hippocrates. Nearly five hundred years later St. Luke, "the beloved physician" of Antioch, of the third Gospel and *The Acts of the Apostles*, was a medical author who told his story in lyrical prose which both expressed his gentle, humane nature and communicated his love of poetry. It is to him that we owe *The Magnificat* and the preservation of *Nunc Dimittis*, so it is from a doctor that we inherit some of the best remembered words in the English language, both the beauty and conviction of Mary's spontaneous hymn when the babe leaped in her womb:

> My soul doeth magnify the Lord,
> And my spirit hath rejoiced in God my Saviour,

and Simeon's thankful song for the promise fulfilled when he took the child Jesus in his arms:

> Lord, now lettest thou they servant depart in peace,
> According to thy word;
> For mine eyes have seen thy salvation
> Which thou hast prepared before the face of all people;
> A light to lighten the Gentiles,
> And the glory of thy people Israel.

The medico-literary connection is of particular interest because, over the years, more doctors have achieved fame in literature than have members of any other profession; Apollo, the god of poetry, was after all the father of Aesculapius, the god of the healing art, – nevertheless, there could be other reasons for this concurrence. Medicine became a learned profession by easy stages. From the middle of the seventeenth century there was a rise in the status of those engaged in therapeutics as a motley collection of dispensers of nostrums, panaceas, elixirs, balms and placebos slowly merged into a broadly identifiable association.

A new financial and social position was attained by those graduate doctors of physic who had been expensively trained in one of the famous medical schools in the Universities of Europe – Edinburgh, Glasgow, Leyden, Paris, Rheims, Utrecht. The stress placed by physicians on education embodied a genuine desire to be the guardians of quality and professional excellence both in performance and in conduct, even if accompanied by a degree of lofty condescension. The early part of the eighteenth century was the beginning of a long-running pamphlet – controversy about the need for a liberal education for physicians. Bernice Hamilton in *The Medical Profession in the Eighteenth Century* (1951), wrote "The real point at issue was whether the education of a gentleman was necessary to a physician, or merely ornamental".

During the eighteenth century the advance of other parts of the profession was achieved through the skills and indispensable contribution of surgeons and the improved academic standard of apothecaries. Physicians were, however, seriously handicapped by the general futility of the remedies at their command. The vast change that has occurred in the effectiveness of treatment is a quite recent development. Even well into the twentieth century, after dramatic advances in the recognition of disease entities, in classification, laboratory tests and x-rays leading to more accurate diagnosis, much of therapeutics remained ineffectual. Diagnosis, prognosis, comfort and explanation to patient and to relatives, based on experience, were supported by a few drugs such as aspirin, morphine and digitalis, and later by the advent of replacement therapy with the vitamins and insulin. There has been a revolution in treatment since then, particularly of the infections brought about by sulphonamides and antibiotics, which were not with us until the 1950's. So it is that the medical curriculum and post-graduate study to-day leave less and less time for doctors to engage in any studious application to the arts.

There was, therefore, a long period between the rise of the educated man in medicine and the sudden overwhelming demands made on the modern doctor which provided, for the more fortunate, an atmosphere of prosperity and leisure conducive to the study and practice of literature. Even then many of the more famous doctor-writers were unable to apply themselves successfully to a life both of letters and of medicine. Nevertheless, for some three hundred years the climate was propitious for the establishment of a medico-literary tradition.

13

The gains resulting from the intensive modern training of doctors are naturally immense and the losses may be small, but a tendency to develop a reductionist turn of mind and to produce an excess of convergent, narrow specialists in the profession does exist, and should be a matter for concern amongst those responsible for medical education. An interest in, and some appreciation of, the arts is an advantage, and perhaps a necessity, in the successful pursuit of understanding in science where an artistic leap of the mind is so often the preliminary to the critical challenge of an idea by observation and experiment.

Whatever the general background may have been, the individual reasons for the development of each doctor-writer relationship were probably as varied and as numerous as the doctors who took to non-medical writing. Some started early in their careers, either from natural inclination or in an attempt to supplement a meagre income, others became authors in retirement and a few drifted into medicine after lacking success as writers. Sir James Clark (1788-1870), who attended Keats when he was dying in Rome and who became Queen Victoria's physician, is said to have taken up medicine when he failed as a writer for *The Signet*. Some went, or were pushed, into medicine but, like Charles Lever (1806-1872) and Somerset Maugham (1874-1965), escaped to their chosen way of life.

One dramatic example is to be found in the story of George Crabbe (1754-1832); of humble origin, the son of a Suffolk saltmaster, he worked as a labourer, was self-educated and, by apprenticeship, made himself into a rural physician. At the age of 26, certain that he was really a poet, he "determined to go to London and venture all". Rejected by publishers, with no money left, near to starvation, he wrote to Edmund Burke (1729-1797) enclosing some verses. He was immediately summoned to Burke's house and, in a moment, in a generous, farsighted act of patronage, was set on the road to success, even though William Hazlitt (1778-1830) wrote with some justification: "His song is one sad reality, one unraised, unvaried note of unavailing woe", and Peter Levi in *The Quarterly Magazine* of the Folio Society (Spring 1986) wrote: "No other English poet is so interesting, so deeply nourishing, and yet so unexciting. He makes Wordsworth, at his dullest, look like pyrotechnics". Crabbe's work is solemnly unexpected. Commenting on his poem *The Newspaper*, Levi wished he had lived long enough to write about television:

> A master Passion in the Love of News
> Not Music so commands, nor so the Muse;
> Give Poets Claret, they grow idle soon;
> Feed the Musician, and he's out of tune;
> But the sick Mind of his Disease posses'd
> Flies from all Cure, and sickness when at rest.

Crabbe's son was to write of his father:

> His person and countenance peculiarly led the mind from the suspicion of any but a highly cultivated and polished education, venerable, clerical, intellectual – it seemed a strange inconsistency to imagine him, even in early youth occupied as a warehouseman.

There are however, a surprisingly large number of people who have made a success both in medicine and in literature for which no very obvious reason for the duality springs to mind. Opportunities for the close observation of a great variety of men and women under conditions of stress, suffering, relief and bereavement have been theirs, indeed they have seen more of the triumph of the human spirit than most, but curiously these advantages, with exceptions on occasions such as Somerset Maugham's for example, do not seem to have been those most widely exploited by the doctor-novelists.

Some Fictional Doctors

Lay authors have often chosen doctors for their fictional characters. George Meredith (1828-1909) in *Poems and Lyrics of the Joy of Earth* (1883), wrote of the physician, Melampus, who used observations of the simple things of nature to improve his understanding of his patients, combining, harmoniously if rather obscurely, science with humanity. Sir Walter Scott (1771-1832) in *The Surgeon's Daughter* (1827) has Gideon Gray:

> Under whose rough coat and blunt exterior you find professional skill and enthusiasm, intelligence, humanity, courage and science.

Dr John Brown (1810-1882) in *Horae Subsecivae* took Dr Dray as the epitome of his class in a defence of country doctors and said that Scott had based him on his friend and adviser Dr Ebenezer Clarkson of Selkirk. John Stuart Blackie in his *Life of Roberts Burns* (1888), says that Dr Clarkson used to tell of the arrival of Mr Ainslie and Burns at Veitch's Inn in Selkirk looking so like "twa drookit craws" that he refused to take a glass with them. He did not find out who they were until they had left the next day – "That refusal hangs about the doctor's heart like a dead-weight to this day, and will do till the day of his death, for the bard had not a more enthusiastic admirer". Scott wrote of Gideon Gray that

> He had not himself found out nor had any friend hinted to him, that a slight touch of the cynic, in manner and habits, gives the physician, to the common eye, an air of authority which greatly tends to enlarge his reputation.

There is not, however, a great deal about Dr Gray in the story, his two assistants, Adam Hartley and Richard Middlemas, occupy the stage in an extravagant Indian drama in which the surgeon's daughter is saved from a fate worse than death but neither gets the girl. Thackeray (1811-1863) in *Pendennis* (1848), dedicated to Dr John Elliotson (1786-1868), who used mesmerism in treatment and hypnosis for minor operations, has Sam Huxter of Bartholomew's, who despite his odious apologies, worse than his abuse, even turns out better than expected. He failed to appreciate his lowly position in society.

> Mr. Samuel Huxter was not aware there was any great social difference between Mr. Arthur Pendennis and himself. Mr. Huxter's father was a surgeon and apothecary at Clavering, just as Mr. Pendennis's papa had been a surgeon and apothecary at Bath. But the impudence of some men is beyond all calculation.

There are over fifty medical students and doctors in the works of Charles Dickens (1812-1870) (*Dickens's Doctors*, 1979), forming a wondrous array of eccentrics varying from the dull and virtuous Allan Woodcourt, the impetuous and quick-witted Mr Losberne and the kindly Mr Chillip to Dr Dundey who robbed a bank, Lewsome who supplied Jonas Chuzzlewit with the poison to kill his father, and that most amusing if often drunken scrounger Joshua Lirriper.

Doctors were not often treated kindly in fiction, in fact they had had a rough ride before Trollope. His *Dr Thorne* (1858) was quite a turning point for here was an honest, capable, conservative, kind and sensible man, despised by his colleagues for charging small fees and for making up his own ointments and medicines in a front room for all to see *(The Barsetshire Doctors,* 1982). This new attitude to doctors in literature was carried a step further, each in their best novels, by two ladies who wrote to each other but never met, Mrs. Gaskell (1810-1865) and George Eliot (1819-1880). When *Adam Bede* was published in 1859, Mrs Gaskell, the wife of a Unitarian Minister, wrote to the author whose real identity she did not know:

> Dear Mr Gilbert Elliott,
> Since I came up from Manchester to London I have had the greatest compliment paid me I ever had in my life, I have been suspected of having written "Adam Bede". I have hitherto denied it; but really I think, that as you want to keep your real name a secret, it would be very pleasant for me to blush acquiescence. Will you give me leave?... So, although to my friends I am known under the name of Mrs Gaskell, to you I will confess that I am the author of Adam Bede, and remain very respectfully and gratefully,
> Yours Gilbert Elliot.

Alas when she found out that Gilbert Elliot was George Eliot who was really Mary Anne Evans who was living with George Lewes, it was a shock to her sense of propriety though she retained her deep regard for the author.

Although Elizabeth Gaskell's Dr Gibson is overshadowed by his daughter Molly, the heroine and centre-piece of *Wives and Daughters* (1864), he holds the book together by dealing with the problems of his family and his busy practice, consulting with the great physician Dr Nicholls, undisturbed by having Dr Roscoe settle on the very verge of his territory and being proved right in opposition to two great names from London over Lady Cumnor's operation. He is the very model of an admirable general practitioner, even though no babies ever seem to be born in Hollingford. Mrs Gaskell's doctor in *Cranford* (1853) was low in the social scale, for Mr Hoggins was wanting in refinement of manner, but the ladies were rather proud of him as a doctor. His sister

Mary, after being away for many years, reappeared in Cranford as a well-to-do widow, dressed in rustling black silk, to raise the doctor's social status in some eyes, even though the great Mrs Jamieson found it hard to accept him. When he married Lady Glenmire, she referred to them as "those Hogginses" and thought their happiness an insult to the Glenmire family.

Dr Lydgate in Middlemarch (1871) is a further development of the doctor in fiction. Unlike Dr Thorne he is not censured for his attitude to dispensing nor for the fees he charges but for something far more serious, for the new ideas he entertains. He is an example of the professional and social advance of the new men in medicine so that neither Dr Minchin, Dr Sprague, Mr Wrench nor Mr Toller can approve of him. George Eliot lived with G.H. Lewes for 26 years. He was in some measure responsible for her becoming a successful novelist and she acquired many of her scientific ideas through his interests, especially that in physiology; his *The Physiology of Common Life* (1859) designed for the student and the general reader with its light manner and illustrative stories, was widely read and created great interest. George Eliot presented Lydgate's research projects and ideas on general practice sympathetically, and she brilliantly developed the effects of the weaknesses which trapped him into a disastrous marriage with the selfish and ambitious Rosamond who slowly destroyed his integrity in a way that Dr Gibson's wife, Hyacinth, was never able to do for her husband. Lydgate's interest in reducing the structure of organs to their component tissues and his theory of fever may have been derived from the work of Marie Bichat (1771-1802) and his follower François Broussais (1772-1838) in Paris. His own research on the "fundamental tissue" was stimulated by François Raspail (1794-1878), (now remembered for his political rather than his physiological achievements), who thought he had discovered one fundamental structural component of all living tissues (*George Eliot and Physiology*, 1971). George Eliot could not have known it, but the choice she made for her doctor's research was one that was bound to fail even if persisted in, however, she did allow Lydgate the consolation of financial success in a new practice alternating between London and a Continental bathing-place.

Medical developments in the fight again infections were taken further in a lesser novel, *Martin Arrowsmith* (1925), for Sinclair Lewis wisely sought sounder professional advice than was available to George Eliot when he consulted Paul De Kruif. Here, through Max Gottlieb, Terry Wickett and Martin Arrowsmith himself, he brought out the absorption, discipline and flair demanded for medical research as well as that element of chance which may come to the aid of a well prepared mind, Crabbe's "deep study of the lucky guess" and, as Jane Austen has Emma say to Mr Knightley, "Depend upon it, a lucky guess is never merely luck, there is always some talent in it". The work on bacteriophage in *Martin Arrowsmith* anticipated some aspects of the triumph of antibiotics. Paul De Kruif, described by H.L. Menken as "a huge and sturdy Dutchman with a neck like John L. Sullivan's", contributed much to the book and was himself to write some of the best accounts of medical discovery for the layman, such as *The Microbe Hunters* (1927) and *Men Against Death* (1933), which fired the imagination of a generation of medical students.

Sir Henry Rider Haggard (1856-1925) wrote *Doctor Therne* (1898), "my only novel with a purpose", after *King Solomon's Mines* (1885) had made his name. *Doctor Therne* was written as a powerful piece of propaganda because Rider Haggard was concerned about the decline in vaccination for smallpox, one of the great killing diseases down the ages, responsible for many millions of deaths; even as late as 1967 about two million people died that year of smallpox.

Before the days of vaccination a curious situation arose over smallpox prevention. Lady Mary Wortley Montagu (1689-1762), the wife of the Ambassador at Constantinople, introduced into England in 1721 the inoculation of pus from infected patients into the skin of those at risk. This method was largely successful in prevention but had the disadvantage that some of those so inoculated died of the disease the treatment was designed to prevent. A conclusive, uncontrolled trial of smallpox inoculation was carried out by an unlikely experimental group, those traders in human life who were shipping slaves to America. Sure of its value in protecting their interest, they arranged for routine inoculation to take place on slave ships and in West Indian plantations with good effect, while thousands of the unprotected population of Britain continued to die of the disease. Dr William

Beeston, the founder of the Physic Garden in Ipswich, wrote a letter in 1724 in which he said,

> The practice of inoculation in this town, has so inflamed the angry passions and stirred up the bitter zeal of the bigoted High Churchmen and Dissenters to such a degree, that they sentence to damnation, all that are in any way connected with it. They say that the practice is heathenish and diabolical; it is distrusting providence and taking the power out of God's hand; it will draw down divine judgement, and for the proof of this point, they are so stupid as to urge, that God has begun to show his displeasure against it and us by that great mortality that is amongst us, tho not one that has been in the practice has fallen by it. This and a great deal more they say, but reason they do not, upon the subject.

Vaccination in 1796, the result, like "the dog in the night-time", of one of the great negative observations, the absence of smallpox among dairy-maids, began to solve the problem. The last victim of smallpox in Britain was in 1978, a photographer working in a laboratory from which the virus had escaped. In 1979 the World Health Organisation announced the global eradication of smallpox, a triumph of international cooperation and medical persistence achieved in the face of ignorance and stubborn resistance. Primary vaccination of infants had become compulsory by 1853 but the usual outcry led to a "conscience clause" being inserted in the Vaccination Acts Amendment Act of 1898 and to a sharp drop in the number of infants vaccinated. In his introduction to *Doctor Therne* Rider Haggard wrote with more sense and less prejudice than was displayed by Bernard Shaw:

> Some months since the leaders of the Government dismayed their supporters and astonished the world by a sudden surrender to the clamour of the anti-vaccinationists. In the space of a single evening, with a marvellous versatility, they threw to the agitators the ascertained results of generations of medical faculty, the report of a Royal Commission, what are understood to be their own convictions, and the President of the Local Government Board. After an ineffectual fight the House of Lords answered to the Whip, and, under the guise of a "graceful concession" the health of the country was given without appeal into the hand of the "Conscientious Objector".

Doctor Therne is pure melodrama, but it does contain some good medicine with descriptions of deaths from puerperal fever and pulmonary embolism. It centres round the tragedy of James Therne whose wife dies in childbirth and who is ruined by a vengeful doctor. Rescued by a businessman, he is sponsored for Parliament through his patron's obsession with the anti-vaccination crusade and is eventually left a fortune by his saviour's widow. His successful parliamentary career, based on his anti-vaccination support, comes to a dramatic end in a smallpox epidemic. There is a terrible scene in his study when he is discovered by his already-infected, never-vaccinated daughter, vaccinating himself – "Father what are you doing to your arm?" After her death, her fiancé, Dr Merchison, challenges Therne at an election meeting, where he is speaking against vaccination, to affirm his change of heart and, as he hesitates, Merchison mounts the platform rips the clothes from Therne's shoulder exposing his bare arm so that every eye can read the proof of his infamy, announcing "Murderer of your own child, I reveal that which you hide!"

To attempt any survey of the progress of medicine through an analysis of the work of a succession of fictional doctors, even if unwise, would be futile without some consideration of Sir Roderick Glossop (*Great Doctors in English Literature*, 1983). One of the outstanding doctors of English literature, P.G. Wodehouse's Sir Roderick, of 6b Harley Street and Ditterage Hall, Hants., had been to school with Clarence 9th Earl of Emsworth. He was impersonated on one occasion by Frederick, Altamont, Cornwallis Twistleton, 5th Earl of Ickenham and himself (in the course of duty) was once disguised as a butler. Moving in the highest social circles this eminent brain specialist went as far as New York for consultation. Sir Roderick's practice as a nerve specialist was broadly in accord with standard psychiatric procedure, for his method was to "start topice and observe reactions". His daughter, Honoria, was briefly engaged to Bertie Wooster, as was her cousin Eloise, remembered with shocked discommendation for her intention to be rid of Jeeves. Sir Roderick was a greater man than Dr George Mulliner of Bingley-on-Sea.

Some Literary Doctors

Doctors have written on a variety of subjects outside medicine, real and fictional, some becoming more famous for their literary invention than for their medicine, like Dr Henry Vaughan (1622-1695), for example, the twin brother of an alchemist Thomas Vaughan, who practiced in Brecon and wrote admirable poetry on grand themes. In *The World*, he said:

> I saw Eternity, the other night
> Like a great ring of pure and endless light,
> All calm, as it was bright; –
> And round beneath it, Time, in hours, days, years,
> Driven by the sphers,
> Like a vast shadow moved, in which the world
> And all her train were hurl'd.

There has been a wide range in their non-medical writing with a literary performance ranging from the sublime to the monotonous, extending from that of poets and writers such as Keats and Goldsmith to more humble performers in the art of the drama or the novel (Joanne Trautman and Carol Pollard in *Literature and Medicine* 1975). The founder of The London Medical Society, a great Quaker physician, John Coakley Lettsom (1744-1815), was a voluminous writer, but the well remembered lines were not written by him but about him. These have appeared in many versions but the one attributed to Sheridan is:

> If patients call, both one and all
> I bleeds 'em and I sweats 'em
> And if they die, why what care I –
>
> I. LETTSOM

One quite extraordinary doctor was a great diarist, said by Robert Innes-Smith (1989) to rank with Parson Woodforde, Gilbert White and Henry Kilvert. He was John Henry Salter (1841-1932) and he kept a diary from the age of eight until he died aged 91. This filled a large number of exercise books which were bought after Dr Salter's death by Alderman J.O. Thompson of the *Essex Chronicle* who published extracts from them, however Thompson's house was destroyed by a bomb in the Second World War and the original diary was lost. Dr Salter was a large, fine-looking, sporting man who kept meticulous records: he shot 62,504 head of game from 104 species, bred hunters and dogs, with which he won 611 prizes, his botanical specimens won many awards, he hunted wolves in Russia as a guest of the Tsar and claimed to have brought more than 10,000 babies into the world in his practice on the Essex marshes. He had a bare-knuckle fight with Jack Sullivan, presumably one of the Sullivan twins, which detached the retina in his left eye so that he had to learn to shoot left handed. We can only get a glimpse of this remarkable doctor's life with his Essex practice, his visits to Russia and his extraordinary energy. Only two months before his death in his 90's, Prince Galitzine the grand-nephew of the former Tsar was inviting him to shoot and talk of old times.

Two doctors became Professors of English Literature at University College, London, Robert Latham (1812-1888) and Henry Morley (1822-1894). Sir William Mitchell Banks in *Physic and Letters* (1893) discussing medical education, referred to twelve great doctor-writers and W. Sampson Handley in *Medicine as a Liberal Education* (1913) discussed the careers of over twenty doctors who had adopted another profession mostly that of letters. W.H. Maidlow in *Some British Medical Men of Letters* (1915 and 1916), gave brief notes on some doctor- writers born between 1567 and 1859. Thomas Monro in *The Physician as a Man of Letters, Science and Action* (1933 and 1951) found 135 medical poets and prose writers from Britain up to the time of his second edition. This, though neither complete (omitting many well known doctor-writers, over fifty British and American, including such curious examples as A.J. Cronin, Somerset Maugham, Gertrude Stein and Francis Brett Young) nor up to date, is a valuable book of reference on the general subject of doctors as men of letters. Of Monro's 63 British entries under Fiction and General Literature, twenty-one were Scots and only two were women. Arabella Knealy wrote *Dr Janet of Harley St.* (1893), and Margaret Todd, who qualified in 1894, wrote novels under the name of "Graham Travers", she also published *The Life of Sophia Jex-Blake* (1918) one of the great pioneer women in medicine. Monro left out Helen Ashton, who wrote many novels but is best remembered for Parson Austen's Daughter (1949). Louis Nesbit in *Physician - Authors of the Past and Present* (1935) gave a long list including many of the German doctor-writers. Lord Moynihan, in an expansion of his Linacre Lecture, *Truants, The Story of Some who Deserted Medicine Yet Triumphed* (1936), beautifully reproduced by the Keynes Press in 1983, gave short sketches of many of those doctors who attained to literary fame. In *Poet Physicians* (1944), Mary Lou McDonough gave extracts from the poetry of each of her selection, from Wang Wei (699-759), including thirty from British doctor-writers. The list of doctor-writers continues to grow: in 1983 Dr David Wheldon was the winner of the Graham Greene Triple First Award for his novel *The Viaduct*, Dr Dannie Abse, Chairman of the Poetry Society, published his autobiography *A Strong Dose of Myself*, and Dr John Collee produced his first, highly commended, novel *Kingsley's Touch* in 1984.

The medical writers of fiction and general literature include novelists, those concerned with wide aspects of literature, biographers, and a fine variety of contributors on such divergent topics as astrology, gardening, history, humour, philosophy, politics, theology and travel. There have, of course, been many famous foreign doctor-writers such as those contemporaries Paracelsus (1493-1541) from Switzerland, about whom Browning wrote a poem, and François Rabelais (1495-1553) from France, with Axel Munthe (1857-1949) for Sweden, Oliver Wendell Holmes (1809-1894) for America, Anton Chekhov (1860-1904) for Russia, and George Duhamel (1884-1966), French novelist and army surgeon, to pick just a few. Chekhov wrote of his two professions:

> Medicine is my lawful wife and literature my mistress. When I get tired of one I spend the night with the other. Though its disorderly, its not dull and, besides, neither of them loses anything from my infidelity. If I did not have my medical work, it would be hard to give my thought and liberty of spirit to literature.

Then there has been a notable batch of students who felt another call and became famous by taking to literature or other pursuits before they had qualified in medicine, including such disparate characters as Robert Southey, Sydney Smith, Charles Darwin and Francis Thompson. John Donne only just escaped; his stepfather was President of the College of Physicians, but after some study of medical literature he thought medicine too mercenary.

Attribution of Disease in Biography

Another aspect of the medico-literary association has been the influence attributed in biography to illness. Biographers have not been noted in general for the reliability of their medical assessments. The facts are not easily come by, for most doctors have, quite properly, been reserved about the disclosure of information concerning their patients' health. Some biographers, as a result, striving to add consequence, astonishment, piquancy or just plain interest to their tale, have been apt to select stories to suit their theories instead of searching out evidence to refute them. They have succumbed to the temptation to repeat, or to suggest for themselves, the allocation of dramatic diagnoses, particularly insanity and syphilis, on doubtful or even non-existent evidence, especially when they have disapproved of the subjects whose lives they were recording. The nonsense written about Swift's illness is a fine example, for it seems to have covered most of this popular field: epilepsy, insanity, syphilis and alcoholism. Sir William Wilde (1799-1869) in *The Closing Years of Dean Swift's Life* (1849), effectively destroyed the then current opinion that Swift was mad and carefully assembled the known facts about his medical history. Unfortunately he read too much into the death-mask appearances suggesting a left sided facial weakness, a diagnosis that led later biographers to assume that Swift had had a right sided stroke. Wilde's main assessment, however, was sound; the middle ear disease with vertigo, tinnitus and progressive deafness, with vomiting, which was not unnaturally attributed to a stomach complaint, soon to become known as Ménière's disease (Prosper Ménière, 1799-1862), was the condition from which it is now generally agreed that Swift suffered and to which was added a terminal arteriosclerotic senility.

Poor Oscar Wilde was also the victim of a biographically imposed diagnosis for, with a charming wife and two normal children, he was nevertheless awarded syphilis by some of his biographers. Even the latest and greatest of his biographies (Charles Ellmann 1987) expands on the attribution of syphilis because it fits in with Ellmann's ideas of Oscar Wilde's behaviour. There is no evidence whatsoever that he died of neurosyphilis;

indeed Sir Terrence Cawthorne, (*The Last Illness of Oscar Wilde*, 1959), produced a good deal of evidence to suggest that the likely cause of death was meningitis, a well recognised complication of acute otitis media. Merlin Holland (*The Spectator* Dececember 1988) reviewed the evidence against the attribution of syphilis to Oscar Wilde.

A case has been made out for the idea that George Eliot suffered from slowly progressing acromegaly, a disorder of the pituitary gland which changes the growth pattern in parts already developed, such as the head, face, lower jaw, hands and feet. Her known symptoms would fit, but they would also do for other diagnoses. It was sixteen years after her death that Pierre Marie (1853-1940), a Paris neurologist, recognised that a set of varied symptoms were all attributable to one disease which he named acromegaly from the Greek *akron* extremity *megas* great. The transformation in George Eliot's appearance in the Mayall photograph of February 1858 from those of the previous portraits is perhaps suggestive as Professor Roland Anderson pointed out in *George Eliot: A Case of Acromegaly?* (1982), but though the nose and jaw appear to be enlarged the hands look normal and show no spatulate fingers. Henry James on first meeting George Eliot wrote to his father that there is "a great feminine dignity and character in these massively plain features". J.W. Cross, to whom she was married for the last few months of her life, wrote of the "organ like tones of her voice" and of her fine brows and musician's hands.

While biographers have been inclined to invent diagnoses to fit their theories they have tended to underestimated the influence of severe physical disabilities, which require little fancy on their part, on the minds of their subjects, like those of Pope or Byron for example.

Omissions and Inclusions

Some of the greatest medical writers have not been considered in this study for a variety of reasons. Sir Thomas Browne (1605-1682), for example, that great rarity, a tolerant, sceptical, happy genius, had much study devoted to him at his tercentenary with extensive comments on his life and work, the grandeur of his prose and his deep concern for the integration of religion, science and literature. Coleridge said of him "He has brains in his Head, which is all the more interesting for a little twist in the Brains". There is a peculiar delight to be had from little twists in the intellect and a man who can survey those "commonly presumed Truths which examined prove but Vulgar and Common Errors" is a very special benefactor. The medical best-seller, Peter Mark Roget (1779-1869) has also been left out, his *Thesaurus of English Words and Phases* (1852) published when he was 73, sold twenty-eight editions in his lifetime (he died in his 91st year). Dr A.M. Cooke (*Out of School*. 1974). in another review of medical truants, tells us that one bookshop in Oxford was still selling 750 copies of the *Thesaurus* a year, and that, in all over 21 million copies had been sold. In its (1982) edition, it was in the best seller list for 1983. Samuel Smiles (1812-1904) sold 20,000 copies of *Self Help* (1850) in its first year, before it was translated into seventeen languages. I have included the best-seller doctor in fiction, Somerset Maugham, whose books sold some four million copies world wide.

One of my resolutions has to be broken. I had decided to omit consideration of recent doctor writers. There is no way however that I can leave out Richard Asher; he was four years younger than I, died not long before I started this study and collections of his work were not published until 1972 and 1983. Most of his writing was basically medical, nevertheless, all his writing was glorious common sense and enchantingly presented in a form not only well suited to, but highly salutary for, the layman. Richard Asher was unusual, a modern-day Scriblerian, for, like Swift, Pope and Arbuthnot commenting on social, literary and political life at the end of the seventeenth century, Asher used his talents in the twentieth to ridicule pretentious moralising, debunk the pompous, deride complacent assertions devoid of evidence, satirise dull generalisations and castigate bad writing. He blew great gales of good sense through medicine and did not hesitate to label some unworthy publications as "P.U.B." "pure unadulterated bolony". He found the medical journals dull, which he never was, and thought that they contrasted glumly with the glossy productions of the big drug houses and with the "Woman's Weeklies". He maintained that

The meaning of words has a profound effect on the progress of medicine, that words unsuitable for their purpose damaged the transmission of accurate meaning, that words, though they provide a vehicle to which thought can travel, seldom allow it to arrive intact at its destination.

He defined common sense as "the capacity to see the obvious even amid confusion, and to do the obviously right thing rather than working to rule, or by deadreckoning". He reminded us that "despair is best treated by hope not dope". I am partial to a little therapeutic hymn of his:

> How well a tranquiliser works
> With a believer's ear.
> It sooths all sorrows, all that irks
> And drives away all fear.
>
> It makes the grip of care unclench
> And calms the troubled breast;
> 'Tis manna to Smith Kline and French
> And to the weary rest.
>
> Weak is the effort of my pen
> To voice my coldest thought
> But I feel doctors now and then
> Prescribe more than they ought.

The doctor-writers selected for discussion in the chapters which follow were chosen because of their eminence and to secure a fairly even spread over the seventeenth to nineteenth centuries spanning changing times over some 350 years.

This book is not intended to be a dry academic exercise, sidelines have been followed, digressions pursued, a few absurdities included and quotations and anecdotes added to enliven the more serious considerations. In his preface to *The Vicar of Wakefield*, Dr. Goldsmith wrote: "A book may be amusing with numerous errors, or it may be very dull without a single absurdity".

Abse. D.   *White Coat, Purple Coat: Collected Poems 1948-1988* Hutchinson 1989
Anderson. R.F.   *George Eliot: A Case of Acromegaly* Literature and Medicine, 1982. 1, 87-102

Asher, Richard   *Richard Asher Talking Sense*   Edited by Sir Francis Avery Jones, Pitman Medical. 1972.

Asher, Richard   *A Sense of Asher*,   Keynes Press 1983 and British Medical Journal Paperback 1984.

Banks, Sir William Mitchell   *Physic and Letters*   Trans. Med. Soc. London, 1983. 16, 327-342

Bennett, P.M.J.   *Great Doctors in English Literature*:   Sir Roderick Glossop Brit. Med. J. 1983. 2. 1962-1964.

Cawthorne, T.   *The Last Illness of Oscar Wilde*   Proc. Roy. Soc. Med. 1958. 52. 123-127

Cooke, A.M.   *Out of School*   J. Roy. Coll. Physicians, London, 1974, 9.51-62

Ellmann, Richard   *Oscar Wilde*   Hamish Hamilton, London. 1987

Forrester, J.M.   *George Eliot and Physiology*   Proc. Roy. Soc. Med. 1971, 64, 724-726

Hamilton, Bernice   *The Medical Profession in the Eighteenth Century*   Econ. Hist. Review, Second Series. 1951 4, 141-169

Handley, W. Sampson   *Medicine as a Liberal Education*   Lancet. 1913. 2, 980-983

Innes-Smith, Robert   *A Doctor Digresses. The Salter Diaries*   Country Life. April 20th 1989.

Maidlow, W.H.   *Some British Medical Men of Letters*   Med. Press and Circ. 1915, 283-285 1916, 29-32

Holland, Merlin   *What Killed Oscar Wilde?*   The Spectator. December 24/31 1988. 34.

Monro, T.K.   *The Physician as a Man of Letters, Science and Action*   2nd Edition, E. and S. Livingstone, Edinburgh, 1951.

Moynihan, Lord   *Truants*   Cambridge University Press 1936 and Keynes Press, British Medical Journal 1983.

Nesbit, Louis   *Physician - Authors of the Past and Present*   Med. Life 1935, 42, 643-670

Salter, John Henry   *Diary*   Compiled by J.O. Thompson, John Lane, London 1933.

Smithers, D.W.   *Dicken's Doctors*   Pergamon Press, Oxford, 1979.

Smithers, D.W.   *The Barsetshire Doctors*   Brit. Med. J. 1982 2. 1806-1808.

Smithers, D.W.   *On Some Medicoliterary Alliances*   Brit. Med. J. 1985. 291. 1796-1801.

Thomson, W.A.R.   *Rider Haggard and Smallpox*   Proc. Roy. Soc. 1984. 77, 506-512.

Trautmann, Joanne and Pollard, Carol   *Literature and Medicine*   Society for Health and Human Values. Philadelphia, 1975.

Wilde, Sir William   *The Closing Years of Dean Swift's Life*   Hodges and Smith, Dublin, 1849.

WILLIAM DENTON

CHAPTER ONE

The Dear Doctor and his Nephew

THE ACCOUNT given here of some celebrated doctor-writers starts with a little known, genial, seventeenth-century gentleman most of whose story has come to us through the letters he wrote to his nephew, Sir Ralph Verney, giving an intimate picture of their families and a perceptive commentary on the turbulent times in which they lived. As so often happens with correspondence, being personal affairs addressed to an understanding audience of one, it is the writer, unaffected by any reason to dissemble, rather than the recipient who comes to life. Doctor William Denton (1605-1691) emerges as a shrewd, bustling, humorous, infinitely kind-hearted man to whom everyone turned in time of trouble to be received with instant aid and comfort. He responded to all requests for help and advice except that, as he said, "I will not teach my grandam to shoe goslings". He neglected his own affairs to see to his nephew's interests while he was in exile, and was finding jobs for some, working for the promotion of others and shielding the unfortunate while losing money on his own transactions. Fortunately he had a large income from a good practice. His last letter, written in 1691, was signed "Yours body and bones, Wm. D."

He was obviously a good doctor much in demand and a great success in his profession – becoming physician-in-ordinary to both Charles I and Charles II. In *The Memoirs of the Verney Family* (1892) started by Parthenope Verney the second wife of Sir Harry Verney and completed by Margaret Verney (1899), he is described as

> Rushing about just as our great doctors do today... It would be a very great hindrance to him if he should be absent from the towne but tenn dayes, for he hath been offered a great deale of money to goe but fivety miles out of towne, and he could nott.

Parthe Verney was the sister of Florence Nightingale, their father, William Nightingale, was a wealthy landowner with ideas on women's education in advance of his time, who taught his daughters Latin, Greek, Italian, philosophy, history, mathematics and writing. Parthenope (born in Naples) was Florence's (born in Florence) rather hysterical elder sister of whom the dedicated, forceful and temperamental Florence said that she "knows nothing of human life but the drawing room".

Doctor Denton became a writer on politics and religion, his works were produced in fine style and his letters provide racy descriptions of the life around him. A.L. Rowse (1951) claimed to have re-discovered him and wrote:

> He deserves not to be forgotten. But, in fact, he has to be called back from oblivion. With such a personality it is a pleasure to bring him back to life and give him once more a name.

Of his literary attainment Rowse said:

> And indeed he has a certain historical importance, in that his writings - even if few seem ever to have read them - express the plain man's point of view, though tricked out with a good deal of contemporary erudition... He wrote an admirable prose style, direct and simple, in the new manner of the Restoration... Perhaps he was a bit old-fashioned even in his day, and that accounts for his having been insufficiently regarded. But his character comes through his writing: his moderation, his sense, his plain Protestantism, his humanity, his whimsical humour. And a writer who in one of his tracts replies effectively to a work of Milton's and in another provides an interesting parallel to Locke's *Treatise on Civil Government*, has his place.

Dr Denton lies with his ancestors in the fine old church at Hillesden in Buckinghamshire, once used as an armoury in the defence of his family home, Hillesden House, where the oak door of the church can be seen to-day still pitted with the holes made by bullets fired from the muskets of Cromwell's soldiers as they stormed the defences, took the ammunition and forced the surrender. The Doctor's epitaph proclaims:

> He was blessed with that happy composition of Body and mind that preserved him chearful, easy and agreeable to the last, and endeared his to all that knew him.

Doctor William Denton was the youngest son and eighth child in the family of thirteen of Sir Thomas Denton of Hillesden and his wife Susan Temple. So vast were their families that William's grandmother, Lady Temple, lived to see three hundred and seventy of her descendants. William Denton was born at his mother's home of Stowe seventy-five years before the great house was built for Sir Richard Temple and enlarged, to a design by Sir John Vanburgh, for his son Richard, who became Baron Cobham in 1718. Here the magnificent landscape garden grew with the help of such famous designers as Charles Bridgeman, William Kent and "Capability" Brown, who started there as under-gardener.

At sixteen William Denton went up to Magdalen Hall, Oxford. His much older sister, Margaret, had married, at eighteen, Sir Edmund Verney of Claydon House, which was not far from Hillesden, but they lived at her home for the first years of their married life as Claydon was leased to the Giffards, and Sir Edmund had to negotiate the surrender of the remainder of this lease with the sub-tenant Martin Lister, who had dared to cut the timber and plough the pastures. Sir Edmund and Lady Verney's son Ralph, who became Sir Ralph Verney (1613-1696), was William Denton's nephew and became his life-long friend.

Only a few years younger than his uncle, Ralph came up to Oxford in 1630 to join him at Magdalen Hall. William had matriculated in 1621 and taken his M.A. in 1627, but was staying on at Oxford to study medicine. He qualified there in 1634 and started medical practice in Oxford under Dr Henry Ashworth, but left in 1636 to set up for himself in London.

The Dentons and the Verneys were united as relations, neighbours and friends, Margaret returned to Hillesden for the birth of her children. All twelve were born there. The families were caught up in the Civil War, which cut across their old unity of interest. Some were on one side, some on the other, their family devotion at times in conflict with their judgement or their loyalty. The commitment of some was weakened when they saw the extremes of intolerance, fanaticism and belief in divine right which both sets of protagonists embraced. Each side was in the dangerous position of feeling answerable at the same time both to a higher power and to an intellectual belief. (This predicament of the Dentons and the Verneys was presented in a B.B.C. television series based on John Adair's book *By the Sword Divided*, (1983.) The differences between King and Parliament were deep and of long standing, fed by those two old provocateurs, belief and distrust. All the ingredients necessary to estrange and to enrage were there: both sides believed themselves to be in the right, both claimed to be defending the constitution; the lines were drawn by religion and by two quite different views of liberty, freely advocated but firmly restricted on either side.

The Dentons and the Verneys were both Protestant in religion and Royalist in sympathy. Sir Alexander Denton, a staunch Royalist, had, however, married John Hampden's cousin Mary. Sir Edmund Verney, who had no liking for bishops or for Henrietta Maria, the Queen, and had misgivings about the Royalist cause, nevertheless found it unthinkable to oppose his King. One son, Edmund, went to Ireland to fight for the King, while another, Ralph, sided with Parliament. Dr. Denton, understanding and sensible – devoted to his nephew Ralph, but of Royalist stock and physician to the King – had no liking for this tragic conflict. He attended Charles I on his ill-fated Scottish expedition of 1639. The Scots were demanding the abolition of hated innovations in worship, full re-establishment of Presbyterianism, and the deposing of the bishops. The King made terms at Berwick to gain time and summoned Parliament to raise funds. Parliament, seeing the struggle in terms of English liberty as much as Scotch, refused, and "The Short Parliament" was immediately dissolved. The Earl of Strafford commanding the Royal forces, nevertheless, tried to pursue "The Bishop's War", but his inadequate army turned into a rabble, and the King had to recall Parliament in 1640 to sort things out. The Doctor's letters, philosophical and practical as usual, commented on the folly of the Court and asked to be sent a copy of Dr Read's treatise on wounds. Ralph Verney appealed to the Doctor to help keep his father out of trouble since Sir Edmund Verney had joined the Scottish expedition determined to be involved in the fighting for his King. Ralph and the Doctor managed to get him home safely but only after he had had a taste of battle in a minor skirmish.

"The Long Parliament", now in session, embarked on its programme of reforms designed to curb the King's exercise of power. The King, with that fatal Stuart combination of bad judgement and bad luck, accused Pym, Hampden and others in the House of Commons of treason, and made his famous march from Whitehall Palace to Parliament to arrest them himself. The five members concerned had been warned, and the King with his soldiers entered the chamber to find his selected victims flown. Ralph Verney, now a Member of Parliament, was there on the crowded bench of the House of Commons when the King swept up to the Speaker's chair, saying that treason had no privilege and demanding that the accused be handed over to him. He had to depart empty handed ("Pity he didn't get them!" once wrote that Cornish Royalist, A.L. Rowse). The Queen went to Holland for the marriage of their daughter Mary to William Prince of Orange and to try to raise money for men and arms. The King refused to meet Parliament's ultimatum, which would deprive him of most of his power and give it the right to reform the Church and to prosecute laws against Roman Catholics. The War was on.

The Dentons and the Verneys, despite their divisions, all gathered at Claydon for the christening of Alexander Denton's son. The Doctor's sisters, Mrs. Isham and Susan Denton, as well as others of both families, were together at Hillesden. Their happy family life was to be roughly shaken. The first casualty was Sir Edmund Verney, killed in the battle of Edgehill, carrying the Royal Standard. One of the doctors attending the King at this engagement and given charge of his two sons, the Prince and the Duke of York, there to see the battle, was William Harvey, who was later to become famous for describing the circulation of the blood, of which Sir Thomas Browne, his junior by only 27 years, wrote "be sure you make yourself master of Dr Harvey's piece *De Circul Sang*; which discovery I prefer to that of Columbus".

In 1644 Hillesden, placed between the King's forces at Oxford and the Parliamentarians at Aylesbury, was fortified and given a garrison under Colonel William Smith. Colonel Oliver Cromwell appeared with a large force before the fortifications were completed; capitulation was refused but the Church with the Royalist arsenal was soon taken. Forty of the defenders fell and Colonel Smith was forced to surrender. The Roundheads stripped the house, took the horses and cattle and confined Sir Alexander Denton in the Tower of London where he died. Colonel Smith, who had fallen in love with Sir Alexander's daughter Margaret, was captured but escaped with the help of Mrs Isham and Susan Verney to live to be a baronet and die in his bed. The Doctor commenting as always wrote in 1646 that "women were never soe useful as now". Another romance blossomed in this battle-scarred old house to add to the complications of family loyalties. Susan Denton became attached to one of the Parliamentary commanders, Jecamiah Abercrombie, half Scotch half Irish, married him and left for his quarters at Addington. He was killed by the Cavaliers the next year, and she brought his body back to Hillesden to be buried in the church near the great house he had helped to plunder. John Denton, another of Sir Alexander's sons who had married Penelope Verney, was killed leading an attack on Parliamentary forces at Abingdon in 1644. The Cavaliers advanced on Hillesden too late to save the garrison or the house to which the Roundheads set fire before they left. The ladies fled to Claydon. Ralph Verney's brother, Edmund, was left penniless in London and, as usual, it was "Uncle Doctor" who came to the rescue – to little avail, however, since Edmund got away to serve with the Marquis of Ormonde in the last stand against Cromwell in Ireland and was killed at Drogheda in 1649. The war caused terrible destruction of life and property amongst Dentons and Verneys. After the war, however, a small house was built at Hillesden where the old one had stood and family life was resumed once more.

Ralph Verney got himself into trouble in 1643 because he was the only Member of Parliament who refused to take the Covenant; he was not prepared to commit England to Presbyterian Church Government, one of the agreements Parliament had made to secure peace with the Scots. He withdrew from Parliament and, as a result, was suspected and endangered from both sides. In one of those convenient, arranged marriages of the day, Ralph had taken Mary Blackhall as his bride. She had lost both parents in 1625 in the plague when she was but nine years old and was an heiress under the Court of Wards. She had been purchased from the Court as a prospective bride for his son by Sir Edmund when she was only thirteen years old. He had to fight off the claims of her relatives to secure the match. When Ralph's estates were sequestered he took her and two of their children with him into exile in France.

The Doctor generously and without self-interest took charge of Ralph's affairs, sent him books and kept him in touch with his family, with some assistance from Ralph's acquisitive and egoistic brother Henry. One of the many tragedies in the family involved Ralph's sister Cary. In June 1642 she had been married, at the age of fifteen, to Sir Thomas Gardiner's eldest son. Sir Thomas was Solicitor-General and the King's candidate for the Speakership. A hot-headed, violent Royalist he was impeached for opposing the proceedings of Parliament on the militia in Common Council and getting petitions signed against the Ordinance. The son, Captain Gardiner, was captured in an affray near Windsor but Ralph was able to obtain his release. He was, however, killed near Aylesbury in July 1645. Cary was left at eighteen, pregnant and penniless. Her brother-in-law, Harry Gardiner, who would have helped, was also killed. The baby born in October 1645 was a girl. Sir Thomas Gardiner, who had welcomed his son's marriage to Sir Edmund Verney's daughter, an important connection, disliked the new head of the family, her brother Ralph, who had so well befriended his son, because of his Parliamentary attachment. He found Cary, with a daughter and no heir for him, of little account and did nothing to help her. The Doctor told Ralph, now in exile, that Sir Thomas made complaints about Cary which she did not deserve and wrote to him:

> Ill instruments there will be, and she has suffered much from them, but I hope God in his due time will make her innocent carage appear. I am extremely cozened if she be not much her father's daughter. In your absence I doe what I can for her, but I should be glad you were here to doe the businesse better. I pray write to her, for she hath need enough of comfort, and I know it would please her.

Cary took refuge with her sisters at Claydon, in anxiety, poverty and some peril from the lawless soldiers of both armies. Marriage was the one way for the sisters to secure a livelihood and the Doctor worked to help the girls who had no proper dowry to secure husbands. It was just as well that he had a good practice, a lot of money could be made in medicine at that time. The Doctor wrote "Sir Theodore Mayerne is buryed and died worth 140,000 l.", and *The Verney Memoirs* said "Dr Radcliffe's regular fees were estimated to bring him in a income of at least 4,000 l. a year; Dr Mead's were valued at between 5,000 and 6,000 l." Cary was fortunate, for a few years later she married a kindly, amiable man, Mr Stewkeley with a fine property in Hampshire.

As the war neared its end the Doctor struggled to save Ralph's estates, not helped by Ralph's refusal to acknowledge any fault or to confess to having ever helped the King, as others in like circumstances were doing to further their cause. To do so, Ralph said, would be "a notorious lie". He sent his wife to England to help the Doctor.

These were hard times, but women threw themselves into the struggle for family and home. Ralph's wife Mary arrived pregnant, gave birth to a boy while the negotiations were in progress, who did not long survive, and the Doctor had to break the news to her that the small daughter she had left behind in France had died. Of Ralph Verney's six children only two survived to adult life. The Doctor worked hard in the Verney interest, and Mary wrote to her husband in 1647 about the Doctor that "he is only a little chargeable" and that she had to try to keep him from the lawyers who "are very dear and not much use". At last, however, she and the Doctor succeeded in saving Ralph's property. Montaigne (1533-1592), at this time, suggested that "There is little less trouble in governing a private family than a whole kingdom". Before returning to France Mary Verney attended as "the chyfe guest" at the wedding of the Doctor's step-daughter, Moll Bert, to William Gape an apothecary. The Doctor's matrimonial troubles must have been considerable, he had three wives. Little is known about the first two, the third was the widow of Edmund Bert with four daughters. *The Verney Memoirs* describe her as a "loud, hearty, vulgar woman, affectionate and impulsive". The Doctor called her "Queen Katherine" and the family referred to her as "Doctor's Widow". When Mary went back to her family the Doctor wrote to his nephew

> I have with much regret (pardon my passion for her, for if she is so worthy of your love, you cannot blame me if I think her soe of mine) returned yr Jewell.

This much loved, tenacious, reliable lady died in France from consumption in 1650. Ralph wrote

> Ah, Dr., Dr., her company made every place a paradice unto me, but she being gonn, unless God be most meraculously mercifull, what good can be expected by your most afflicted and unfortunate servant.

In 1649 the King was put on trial, the Doctor said,

> It is almost every man's opinion that nothing will satisfy but his head.

After the execution he wrote

> We are now in the maddest world that ever we mortalls sawe, and have great reason to feare we doe but now begin to drinke the dreggs of our bitter cupp... The Kinge's book, with his deportment, indurance, att his tryal and on the scaffold, hath amazed the whole kingdome, to see soe much courage, Xstianity and meekness in one man.

As the Doctor wrote, the King, in death, secured the respect of the English people and the Puritan Revolution was never quite the same again. It held power by the sword, and conditions for the restoration of the monarchy began to form even as the Commonwealth set out on its eleven-year rule.

Stuck in France Ralph was unable to come home. He worried about the running of his estate and the integrity of his steward, William Roades, who received the rents and sold the produce but sent him inadequate reports. The Doctor was asked to go to Claydon and check the steward's management. He reported that all was well and that he had gone

> to as little purpose as one would wish besides eatinge and drinking... It is an ill cooke cannot like his owne fingers, but let me once finger your rents and then get me out again if you can, however, it is the best way, for y^u had better lett me have them than W^m.R.

The Doctor had now not only to manage the affairs of his own brother's orphaned children but inherited a new generation of great nephews and nieces to deal with. Then there was always the black sheep of the Verney family, brother Tom, to look after: "the fellow is in danger of hanging in Paris and of the pillory in London". In 1648 Tom was writing pious, penitent letters from prison and the Doctor commented:

> To see now his letters you would think him a St. or a preacher at least. He goes far that never turnes. God can do much. Paul persecuted till he could noe longer kick against the pricks.

Mary Verney (Molly), one of Ralph's younger sisters, became pregnant and it was the Doctor who had to pacify her indignant sisters, keep her and her secret in his house and see to it that the offending Robert Lloyd married her. This marriage, achieved with some difficulty, turned out to be a success, they lived happily together until her death in 1684.

In 1653 Ralph was allowed to return to England, the Doctor found him a house in London and he was soon back at Claydon putting things in order. The Doctor's coach was stopped by highwaymen in 1657 and he was robbed, the incident was treated as a great family joke. Lady Hobart, displaying the lack of attention to female education of the day, wrote

> When you see the doctor let him knew, I goo nowhar but I met with his news, and never any man was so lafed at, for ever body macks mearth at it: tis said he knos the thefs, and my ant Varney vows Harry Verney one.

In 1658 Cromwell died and his son Richard became Protector, the Doctor being elected a member of "Dick's Parliament" in January 1659. He wrote to Ralph: "I can tell you noe news but that I graced the Parl^t House by making a simple speech in it." When Ralph expressed surprise, the Doctor wrote to him, "Soft Sir, soft. It is not for Plebeians to know why we made our learned speech in the House".

When, in the next year, the monarchy was restored, neither Ralph nor the Doctor joined the new Cavalier Parliament. The Doctor wrote treatises on policitics with fine titles, *Horae Subsecivae: or a Treatise shewing the Original Grounds, Reasons and Provocations necessitating our Sanguinary Laws against Papists made in the days of Queen Elizabeth etc.* and *The Burnt Child Dreads the Fire* on the claims of Papists to toleration. He was becoming more and more whiggish and for the rights of the people.

Under the Merry Monarch, London life became gay again and wild. Winston Churchill, in his *History of the English Speaking People* (1956) captured the situation in his usual arresting style:

> The sense of relief from the tyranny of the Puritans spurred forward every amorous adventurer. Nature, affronted, reclaimed her rights with usury.

Rowse has written that:

> The Society that emerged from the stress of Civil War and the rule of the Saints lived its life on a lower plane: it had had too much high-mindedness: it was post-war: it was content to live. Ralph and the Doctor breathed the air of a purer, happier clime.

The Doctor wrote accounts of the goings on: of Lord Pembroke's dinner party, which broke up with swords drawn and ended in a brawl with someone thrown into the Thames; afterwards, with his Lordship on a balcony in the Haymarket, "some Blades passed by and fired at him but mist him and killed another". There were tales of kidnapping, robbery, death in a tavern and duels fought every day. Just as well they had no bombs.

Ralph's son Edmund married Mary Abell in 1662: her mother had died before her father came to East Claydon to take the property adjoining that of the Verneys. William Abell had married again but died the year before Mary's wedding, and she eventually brought his fortune and The White House at Claydon to the Verneys.

Her long story was a tragic one. Soon after her marriage she "became subject to fits of moody silence and hysterical excitement during which she was a torment to herself and all about her". She became unreasonably suspicious and the Doctor wrote, "Zelotipia (jealousy) is gott into her pericranium, and I doe not know what will get it out". She had intervals of gentle amiability, was better when she had a child to look after, but deteriorated into bouts of violence and became slovenly in her person and attire. The Doctor reported that she is "much worse, laughs more than before, speaks more boldly, descants upon by standers... few escape her". Her poor husband weighed twenty stone by the time he was thirty seven, had mounting debts and was a great worry to his father. However, his devotion to his wife was wonderful, his behaviour exemplary, he was "constant and pitiful in his attendance". Mary grew very ill. The Doctor in his usual engaging style wrote to Ralph of her manic depression: "Your daughter is noe changelinge yet; A Diabolical Agew, up and downe, one day Hosanna, the next crucifye". Many doctors were called, and eventually a woman named Clark offered to cure her in two months for twenty pounds. She went with them from London to Claydon, where "the woman Dr" gave her physic which corresponded with a marked though temporary improvement. Mary's husband died in 1688, but she lived on until 1715 with long fits of silence and intermittent hysterical attacks. The poor people of the village, whom she had loved, unaffected by the day to day anxieties of the household, cherished her memory.

In 1665, when the great plague raged in London, the Court, Parliament and the Judiciary escaped to Oxford. Smollett wrote in *A Complete History of England* (1757) that it "swept off above one hundred thousand of the inhabitants". The official remedy was "Garlic with butter and a clove or two" but, with a fine distinction, "the richer sort" were offered a more impressive but equally futile prescription by the College of Physicians: "Powder of hartshorn, pearls, coral, tormentil, hyacinth-stone, onxy-stone and East Hunicorne's horn". The great fire followed, Dr Smollett saying that it

> was supposed to be the effect of malicious design, and variously imputed to the Roman catholics and the republicans, as the stream of prejudice happened to run; though it does not appear how such a scheme could contribute to the interest of either party.

The stream of prejudice was never short of invention, suspicion and malice. The Doctor wrote that "Clothworkers Hall is now on fire but in a fair way of being stopped"; the *Verney Memoirs* reported

> Dr Denton is much exercised, the City is a desert, the physicians who practiced there are flocking westward, where they find so many more of their craft bereft of patients, that they fear they shall be reduced to bleeding one another.

One of the Doctor's interesting historical-medical comments was made when he drew a dramatic picture of the end of Henrietta Maria "La Reine Malheureuse" in 1669, at her chateau at Colombe near Paris.

> The night the Queen Mother died she called for her Will, said she did not like it, tore off the seals, said she would alter it tomorrow; she complained much of want of sleep, so an opiate

was ordained her, and her physician watched with her to give or not to give it to her, he did not like to give it her, but by impatiency extorted it from him, and she died that night.

The opiate had been prescribed by M Vallot, first physician to Louis XIV, at a great consultation of visiting doctors from Paris, despite Henrietta Maria's concern that Sir Theodore Mayerne, who had become her English physician after her mother Marie de Medicis had helped to expel him from the French court and who died in 1655, had warned her against such drugs and that a gipsy had once told her that she would never die except of a "grain". She never woke from the deep sleep and M Vallot's reputation suffered a severe blow. The Queen Mother was known to have made a will while in England in 1664 but, when no trace of one could be found on her death, a fine old wrangle took place with claims made by the Kings of France and of England and by the Prince of Orange. Charles II won but behaved handsomely over his mother's French property and valuable treasures, so that the convent she had founded at Chaillot and the members of her household all benefited. He kept some of her paintings but passed her other possessions to Henrietta-Anne his youngest sister, the beautiful and charming wife of Louis XIV's younger brother Philippe duc d'Orleans, loved by everyone except her husband.

With the advent of James II, the sometime Royalist Doctor wrote a treatise justifying the peaceful revolution and attacked the King, whose stupidity added point to his warnings. He welcomed William and Mary with his *Jus Regiminis: Being a Justification of Defensive Arms in General*, dedicated to William III, a vindication of the new King's position. He bustled about as usual and paid visits to Claydon. When he became ill, Ralph went to London and was with him when he died on May 9th, 1691.

William Denton, doctor, author and letter writer of pithy charm, was a man of affairs and importance as well as a devoted and dedicated support to his large family, always to be relied on. The dear Doctor lived for eighty-six years in the seventeenth century, caring for others and spreading humour and good cheer around him.

Adair, John *By the Sword Divided* Century Publishing, London, 1983.

Courtenay, Thomas Peregrine *Memoirs of the Life, Works and Correspondence of Sir William Temple, Bart.* Longman, Rees, Orme, Brown, Green and Longman, London 1836.

Oman, Carola *Henrietta Maria* Hodder and Stoughton, London, 1936.

Rowse, A.L. *The English Past* Macmillan & Co., London, 1951.

Slater, Miriam *Family Life in the Seventeenth Century The Verneys of Claydon House* Routledge and Kegan Paul, London, 1984.

Verney, Frances Parthenope *Memoirs of the Verney Family During the Civil War* Longmans Green, London, 1892.

Verney, Sir Harry *The Verney's of Claydon* Robert Maxwell, London 1969.

Verney, Margaret *Memoirs of the Verney Family* Longman Green, London, 1899.

JOHN LOCKE

CHAPTER TWO

The Philosopher and the Lord Chancellor

AMONG A fine variety of learned and versatile members of the medical profession a few became philosophers. A number have written on the philosophy of medicine, a subject much in vogue in recent years, but occasion discovered one English medical philosopher of international and lasting fame – a Somerset man of Puritan stock and trading class who was born in the reign of Charles I and lived into the reign of Queen Anne. It was in the turmoil of revolution that he grew up to become an outstanding figure in an age in which many of his contemporaries were rejecting the narrow world of bitter conflict of opinion and intolerant enthusiasm into which they had been born. His reputation rests chiefly on his famous *Essay Concerning Human Understanding* (1689-90) but this philosopher also wrote wide-ranging treatises on medicine, education, government, christianity and toleration. Accused of being a traitor at the time of the Monmouth insurrection, he took refuge in Holland and returned to England in 1689 as a leading intellectual influence on the "Glorious Revolution", and a champion of freedom of thought and tolerance of opinion. Gilbert Ryle and Bertrand Russell, debating the reason for the profound effect which he had had on the whole intellectual climate of mankind, agreed they had found the answer when they said he had "invented common sense".

John Locke (1632-1704) was born at Wrington in Somerset and brought up at Belluton, a Tudor farm-house at Pensford, a market-town looking over the Mendip hills. His grandfather, Nicholas Locke, had prospered in the clothing trade, dealing in that most important commodity of the time, wool – all the way from sheep to cloth. Nicholas's own grandfather, Sir William Locke, had been Mercer to Henry VIII and a Sheriff of London. Grandfather Nicholas was a highly respected member of the community, a fashionable, rich, important man, employing many people. His son John married Agnes Keene, a relation of his step-mother, the daughter of Edmund Keene a tanner of Wrington. With good solid country trading backgrounds on both sides of the family, this John, our John Locke's father, nevertheless, became a lawyer, a position which then carried less money and an inferior social position to that enjoyed by the rest of his family. Attorneys at that time were still held in scant respect, the rise in public esteem achieved by the legal profession in the early eighteenth century was some way off. More than one hundred years later, Boswell, who was admitted an advocate in 1773, recorded, with his sharp understanding of what mattered in reporting Dr Johnson's views, that "he was willing to allow a due share of merit to the various departments necessary to civilised life", but had observed of someone who had just quitted the company, that "he did not care to speak ill of any man behind his back, but he believed the gentleman as an *attorney*". However, Locke's father owned some land and had taken a wife from the local gentry so, although he was in the law, he could hold his head up in Pensford society, a point which has been embroidered by some enthusiastic Somerset historians to enhance the rather lowly standing, in their eyes, of the origins of so great a man as his son John Locke. John's brother Peter died in infancy and his other brother Thomas at 26. His cousin Anne married Jeremy King and their son Peter, born in 1669, became the first Baron King of Ockham. He it was who inherited John Locke's papers and passed them down through members of the King family to the fourth in descent from John Locke's cousin who became the first Earl of Lovelace in 1838 and married Byron's daughter Ada (1816-1852). These papers, known as "The Lovelace Collection", were housed for safety by the Bodleian in 1942 and then, having been examined by Dr Wolfgang von Leyden, were bought by the library. They comprise some 3000 letters and 1000 manuscripts which, when the war was over, were made available for study for the first time.

John Locke, as a boy, lived in troubled times greatly disturbing to his Puritan household; he was ten years old when Charles I made his famous entry into the House of Commons in an attempt to arrest five members for treason. His father was severe and taciturn and his mother, ten years older than his father, a pious, handsome woman, died when he was twenty-two. Two of John's early interests were in books and in the great prehistoric circle of stones nearby at Stenton Drew. John Aubrey (1626-1697) of *Brief Lives* (1813), who was living close by with his grandmother at the Manor House at Burnett, acquired his antiquarian interest from the same stone circle about which they were to write to each other years later. John's father became personal attorney to Alexander Popham, the wealthy, prudent, avaricious Balliol man of Littlecote, the lovely Tudor manor house in Wiltshire which has recently been sold. Popham was born in 1605. He became a colonel in the Parliamentary army and was to help John Locke to shape his life. When Parliament took over Westminster School, Colonel Popham gave his attorney's son a good start, for he was able to nominate him, aged 15, for admittance as a pupil.

When John Locke arrived at Westminster, Richard Busby (1606-1695), aged 41, was the Master; as a Royalist and an amateur actor of note he was about as unlikely a person to have been retained at the school by the Puritans as one could imagine. However, he was recognised as a great teacher and was Headmaster of Westminster for 55 years. When Locke had been at the school for two years, Charles I was beheaded close by in Whitehall and the boys were held at prayer for the King while the terrible deed was done. School life at Westminster, both at work and play, was hard but the teaching was liberal. In 1650 Locke became a King's Scholar through the system which allowed a candidate to challenge the next above him in school order, to translate, parse and give the rules of grammar for passages selected from the classics, moving up a place if the one above failed. Locke took extra tuition from Dr Busby himself. Even from his school days, however, he was criticising the current form of education with its endless Greek and Latin exercises. Latin was a necessity for an educated man at the time but Locke thought that Greek and other ancient languages should be confined to professed scholars so that there would be more time to extend the scope of education for the rest. His chief condemnation later on was for the "malpertness, tricking and violence learned in schools" which led him to favour private tutors. In 1652 Locke secured a scholarship at Christ Church and, in that October, Colonel Alexander Popham took his *protégé* to Oxford to install him in his rooms.

Some Puritans were in favour of the abolition of Universities but a compromise was reached and all staff, of whatever degree, were required to take an oath of submission to the new authority. At Christ Church seventy senior students resigned and Cromwell's own chaplain, John Owen, became Dean. Communication with tutors was in Latin and instruction was given in logic, metaphysics and classical languages with compulsory attendance at two sermons a day. Locke once again complained of the scope of the education provided and denounced the futility of the philosophy taught. Qualification for a degree was secured by disputation, maintaining a thesis before a questioning audience.

John Owen had received from Parliament in 1649 the daunting charge of examining the spiritual condition of the inhabitants of Ireland. His report, however, had the important result of setting up a committee to develop Trinity College and the adventurous appointment of some outstanding Puritan teachers who recognised the need for education reform without sudden radical change. One of those appointed was Dr John Stearne who developed Trinity Hall which awarded it first medical degrees in 1659. At Christ Church, John Owen proved to be a tolerant and gentle man who neglected to dismiss promising undergraduates just because they were not good Puritans and was prepared to issue the certificate of conformity necessary to cover their continuation at the University when needed.

The Warden of Wadham at that time was John Wilkins, Cromwell's brother-in-law, who had brought to Oxford a passion for scientific experiment. John Aubrey wrote "He was the principal reviver of experimental philosophy at Oxford, where he had weekly meetings of an experimental philosophical club, which began in 1649, and was the incunabule of the Royal Society". Many of the club members were doctors who, growing tired of the authority of classical texts, were anxious to extend their understanding by following observation and experiment. Among the members of what was to develop into The Royal Society was William Petty (1623-1667), like Locke from a clothier's family, who was an economist, anatomist, physician, industrialist and inventor – he invented a copying machine and a double-keeled boat some 350 years ago. Another club member was Thomas

Willis (1621-1673), physician and anatomist (after whom the Circle of Willis formed by arteries at the base of the brain is named) whose book on cerebral anatomy was illustrated by Christopher Wren. Willis denied that nerves were hollow tubes conveying humours but described them as solid conductors of "animal spirits". He it was who invented the word "neurology" to cover his field of study and became the first neurologist to relate clinical signs to post-mortem findings in the localisation of nervous disorder. Richard Lower (1631-1691), a friend of Locke's from Westminster was another member, the first man to give a blood transfusion from one animal to another and to propose its use in man, though he was anticipated in the performance by Dr Denys in Paris in advance of his own demonstration when he gave a blood transfusion to an "eccentric scholar" before the Royal Society in 1667. Sir Geoffrey Keynes in *The Life of William Harvey* (1966) said that Lower "came next to Harvey both in time and merit as a writer on the heart".

In the Royal Society Catalogue of Fellows 1660-1700 there are ninety-one doctors, twelve of whom are also described as writers or authors, while John Locke is described as philosopher. Robert Hooke (1635-1703), a chemist, physicist and engineer, also of Westminster and Christ Church, helped Willis with his dissections, became Robert Boyle's assistant and was the first curator of experiments of the Royal Society. There were mathematicians and astronomers but, with the exception of medicine, few representatives of other branches of science. In 1663, of the one hundred and thirty-seven Fellows of the Royal Society, twenty-six were physicians or surgeons.

Locke's notebooks reflect the great excitement caused by this surge of experimental scientific work and show how his own interest in chemical medicine was aroused by Boyle, who he first met in 1660, and who had an important influence on the development of his ideas. Locke studied botany at the Oxford Botanical Gardens and, with David Thomas, distilled, extracted, purified, analysed and made balsams, elixirs, oils, spirits and nearly every commonly used medicine of the day. He worked on the physiology of respiration before turning his attention to clinical medicine when he started in practice with David Thomas in 1666.

In 1665 Locke had been appointed secretary to Sir Walter Vane on a diplomatic mission to Brandenburg. It was his first visit to the continent and there he discovered religious tolerance: "They quietly permit one another to choose their way to heaven" he wrote to Robert Boyle. The Elector would not promise support against, or even neutrality towards, the Dutch without money which the English Government declined to pay.

Locke's lady friends wrote to him, particularly one who signed herself 'Elia', giving the gossip of Oxford and of the Court which was there to escape the plague:

> Pocock, the book-seller, came off with Honour from his last enterprise, he with a peaceful assault is now possessed of Mr West's daughter, having stole her.

On return Locke was offered another diplomatic post but after some thought chose to stay on in his chosen way of life in medicine and philosophy at Oxford.

Anthony Ashley Cooper, Lord Ashley, afterwards 1st Earl of Shaftesbury, at the beginning of his political career, was advised to go to Oxford for his health where he might drink Astrop Waters from a spring near King's Sutton. David Thomas had been asked to arrange for carriers to bring the water to him. Something went wrong with the arrangement while David Thomas was away, so Locke called on Lord Ashley to explain matters. This chance meeting with a man who was to become one of the most influential in the country turned out to be of great importance for Locke. He made a fine impression on Ashley and they got on so well that they were soon dining together; from the first they found each other's conversation agreeable and soon so interesting that they became fast friends. Their association was to be a major factor in determining Locke's future.

In 1667 Lord Ashley invited Locke to live at his house in London and become his personal physician. The plague and the fire had passed, the capital was itself again, the Royal Society was newly established in London making its vernal debut in discussion and research, Willis and Lower had already gone down, Boyle was going, the offer was tempting. So, at thirty-five, Locke left Oxford for London where he was soon to become associated with the famous Doctor Thomas Sydenham (1624-1689) who, in Mary

Beale's portrait, looks more like a captain of horse for the Parliamentarians, which indeed he had been, than one of the most renowned physicians of his age, which he had become. Locke collaborated with him in several essays which stressed the importance of clinical observation and experiment. Hermann Boerhaave (1668-1738) the Dutch physician and Professor of Medicine in Leyden, is said never to have referred to Sydenham without raising his hat. Samuel Johnson included in his *Lives of Eminent Persons* an account of Dr Boerhaave who had become the first great bedside teacher and was Professor of Botany and of Chemistry and also Rector of the University. Johnson wrote of him:

> Boerhaave lost none of his hours, but when he had attained one science, attempted another; he added physic to divinity, chymistry to the mathematics, and anatomy to botany. He examined systems for experiments, and formed experiments into systems. He neither neglected the observations of others, nor blindly submitted to celebrated names. He neither thought so highly of himself, as to imagine he could receive no light from books, nor so meanly, as to believe he could discover nothing but what was to be learned from them.

In 1668 Ashley, now Lord Shaftesbury, had an attack of abdominal discomfort, recurrent jaundice and a painful inflammation in a swelling below the right costal margin about which Locke consulted with Francis Glisson, physician to Charles II. The swelling was incised in June and a large quantity of pus and cysts evacuated but irrigation continued to produce slough for weeks afterwards so that Locke inserted a six inch long, silver drainage tube which proved effective but had to be kept in place. Sir William Osler, reviewing the diagnosis in 1900, settled on "Suppurating hydatid of the liver". Locke's treatment of Shaftesbury thus became the first clinical account of hydatid abscess of the liver successfully treated by operation.

Locke was extremely busy: he was practising medicine, through Shaftesbury he had become secretary to the Lords Proprietors and was helping to draft the constitution for the government of Carolina, he was also writing essays on toleration and a treatise on economics. He suffered from asthma and chronic bronchitis and was badly affected by the London climate, so he escaped whenever possible either to Somerset or to stay at Shaftesbury's house at Wimbourne. In 1672 Shaftesbury became Lord Chancellor and appointed Locke as Secretary of Presentations and later Secretary of the Council of Trade and Plantations, making him an almost full-time civil servant. Locke handed over most of his practice to Sydenham, though he returned to medicine for a while when Shaftesbury fell from power in 1673.

In 1675 he went on a prolonged tour of France for his health spending more than a year in Montpellier where he met Thomas Herbert, Earl of Pembroke. Together they held many discussions with the doctors and philosophers gathered there. In Paris he lodged with Moïse Charas (1618-1698) the chemistry demonstrator at the Jardin des Plantes who was working with viper's venom and published *New Experiments upon the Viper*, printed in London in 1670, "the first treatise of the Viper given to France in its Native Language". Charas wrote:

> I say nothing of my way of writing. From a person of my profession, you are not to expect the Elegancy and Purity of our Tongue. I thought it enough for me, to deliver myself clearly and intelligibly, which in my opinion, is all that could be expected of me.

Charas's experiments "on divers animals" were unorthodox and he was a Protestant – an unfortunate combination which led to his prosecution for the heinous crime of attempting to overthrow an established belief. He fled to England where he became apothecary to Charles II.

Locke's affection for women is well documented by a large number of notes and letters going back to his early Oxford days. The letters mostly refer to ladies by their initials, often reversed: for example though P.E. is a mystery, E.A. probably stood for Anne Evelegh a daughter or niece of John Evelegh of Black Hall, but there were others who not only remain anonymous but without initials. Locke once said that he found the girls of Somerset more warm-hearted than those of Oxford. His father tried to persuade him to marry a Somerset widow "young, childless, handsome with £200 per annum and £1000 in her purse", but no marriage came out of these affairs.

In 1682 Locke met Damaris Cudworth who was to become his closest friend for the rest of his life. She was then twenty-four and had been brought up in the Master's Lodge at Christ College, Cambridge. She was the daughter of Ralph Cudworth who had been Sir William Temple's tutor at Emmanuel and was the author of *The True Intellectual System of the Universe* (1678. English Edition 1743). Locke probably got his idea of man as "thinking matter" from Cudworth who argued that God could simply have added the power of thought to the substance that is man. Long before ideas of evolution took root and before the emergence of new qualities through biological organisation had been accepted, he wrote:

> the properties of a rose, a peach, or an elephant, superadded to matter, change not the properties of matter; but matter is in these things matter still.

He could not contemplate the possibility that life or understanding could rise out of inert, dead, stupid matter, but there it was, so why should God not simply have added life, motion, thought and sense to physical substance. Damaris, educated by her father, had become interested in philosophy. Locke was to write about her to his old friend Philip van Limborch in Holland eight years later saying:

> The lady herself is well read in theological and philosophical questions, and of such an original mind that very few men could equal her in the abundance of her knowledge and her ability to use it. Her judgement is excellent, and I do not know many people who can bring such clarity of thought to the study of the most difficult subjects. She has also a capacity for searching through and solving problems beyond the range not only of most women but of most men.

She and Locke had a common interest but they also developed a deep romantic attachment which lasted to the end of their lives. At first they exchanged airy, light-weight verses, she perhaps a little the better poet. Damaris offered love to Locke's friendship, but, when later he was the one to offer love, she had only friendship to give, each disdaining in turn the lesser offer. For too long they played a waiting game with one another, and, as time passed, she it was who seems to have most regretted the cooling of their attachment. She had written to him:

> The friendship once I gave retain
> But think from me no more to gain
> To whom thy passion comes too late
> That scorn a conquest given by fate.
> With this she left the trembling swain
> Half dead with grief at her disdain
> Who for his love no cure can find
> But breathes his plaints into the wind.
> Not daring Clora's eyes to see
> Since her unjust severity
> Who still insensible remains,
> His constant passion still disdains
> And laughs at all his grief and pains.

At this time Locke was getting into deep water politically: Shaftesbury was intriguing against the Stuarts; Charles II was altering town charters so as to secure them for the Tories; Parliament was not being called; the courts were being packed for the King; succession by a Papist was in the wind; plots were being hatched. Whigs were being watched and Shaftesbury's known confidant, John Locke, was making a series of suspicious trips around the country. Dryden's (1631-1700) satire was helping to turn the people against the Whigs. In *Achitophel: The Earl of Shaftesbury* (1681) he wrote:

> A name to all succeeding ages curst:
> For close designes and crooked counsels fit,
> Sagacious, bold, and turbulent of wit,
> Restless, unfixed in principles and place,
> In power unpleased, impatient of disgrace;
> A fiery soul, which, working out its way,
> Fretted the pigmy body to decay
> And o'er-informed the tenement of clay.

Shaftesbury's revolution was not going well, his associates hesitated, the public were unmoved and he felt it advisable to escape to Holland in disguise where he was taken ill and died soon afterwards in January 1683. For seventeen years he had been Locke's close friend and chief support. In June the Rye House Plot to kill King Charles and his brother James on their way back from the Newmarket races was discovered and many Whigs were arrested, though some, including the Duke of Monmouth, their candidate for the throne, escaped. Locke, though sympathetic with their cause, was unlikely to have been directly involved; he certainly maintained that he had kept aloof from the plotters, but his movements were watched, he grew fearful and decided that he had better go.

Locke liked Holland. The climate was much kinder to him than that of foggy London and though lonely at first, he got on well with the people, making many friends, one of whom was Philip van Limborch, the pastor of the Remonstrants, known all over Europe for his advocacy of full liberty of belief. When the time came for Locke to leave Holland after a stay which had lasted for over five years he was quite sad to go. While there, with some leisure at last, he applied himself to serious work on his *Essay Concerning Human Understanding*, at which he had been working for twenty years before its publication in 1690. The King ordered the Oxford authorities to deprive him of his studentship at Christ Church when he was accused of having written against the government. His extradition was demanded and a warrant for his arrest issued at the time of Monmouth's insurrection. However, there was small chance that the authorities would agree to send him home; the Dutch had little sympathy with James II's Catholic court and had received the refugees well. Nevertheless, Locke saw fit to hide even in Holland for a while and assumed the name of Dr van der Linden, and then of Dr Lynne. Later, when he was offered a pardon and invited to return, he preferred to stay in Holland so long as he was still uncertain of his reception at home. In exile he was becoming more involved in politics and with plans for the revolution. Damaris Cudworth wrote rather sad letters: one, eventually, to say that she had married a widower, Sir Francis Masham, a baronet with a country seat in Essex, eight sons and one daughter.

On a visit to Leyden, Locke was much taken with the medical teaching but did not stay to study as he was busily engaged in writing, doing articles and reviews for Leclerc's *Bibliotheque Universelle*, one of the first of the literary journals. Locke also visited Delft, and met Prince William at The Hague, probably introduced through his friend Lord Mordaunt who was actively engaged in plotting the revolution. He spent a winter in Utrecht at the house of the painter Van Gulick. The Municipal Archives of Utrecht contain records of works by him. He seems to have painted fish still-lives and to have been associated with a group of Utrecht artists such as Marcus and William Ormea, Jan de Bont and Jacob Gillig. The greatest age of Dutch painting was passing: Franz Hals died in 1666, Rembrandt in 1669 and Vermeer in 1675. Pieter de Hooch probably died about 1684 but Hobbema, after marrying the kitchen maid of an Amsterdam burgomaster; becoming a well paid wine gauger and producing few paintings of outstanding value for some years, was back and painting his most glorious work *The Avenue Middelharnis*. Locke met Anthony van Leeuwenhoek, a draper of Delft, the inventor of the microscope, "the first of the microbe hunters", who was writing amazing, rambling letters to The Royal Society in which homely chat was interspersed with wonderfully accurate descriptions of his new world of discovery. Leeuwenhoek lived to be ninety-one, to become famous and to show his marvels to Peter the Great of Russia and the Queen of England: but he kept the best of his microscopes to himself, not allowing anyone else to use it. He was also appointed trustee for the glorious, few-remaining pictures of the supreme master Vermeer, who had been born in the same year as both Locke and Leeuwenhoek. It has been suggested that Vermeer's painting *A Street in Delft* now in the Rijksmuseum in Amsterdam, that wonderful, simple view of Dutch bourgeois life at the time of Locke's visit, depicting a Lady in the alleyway with her broom, may be of Leeuwenhoek's house. It certainly fits well with the description he gave of his home.

Locke moved to Rotterdam to be more closely in touch with the movement for displacing James II from the English throne. The peaceful exchange of Kings and the return to the status quo was not much of a revolution when, in November 1688, Prince William left for England and James II fled. The Princess of Orange, soon to be Queen Mary, sailed to Greenwich and Locke, who had been left to bring Lady Mordaunt, crossed with her. He was much improved in health, had committed his greatest work to paper and had become a figure of considerable influence in the new régime. King William was later to offer him the post of

Embassy Secretary in Paris and then an alternative, neither of which he felt able to accept. He continued in London writing *Two Treatises on Government* and *A Letter Concerning Toleration*. His friends the Earl of Pembroke and Viscount Mordaunt entertained him, and an intellectual *salon* at Lord Pembroke's brought together many of the most distinguished men of the day in free discourse, amongst them Isaac Newton.

Philosophy is a curious activity, a life-time fascination for a few and a troublesome questioning of established beliefs for many. To be effective people function on the basis of accepted opinion – no one would wish his surgeon to be worried by doubts about the concepts on which his actions are based while performing in the operating theatre. Those who are getting on with their job, try to improve their practice from an established basis which is, for the moment at least, taken for granted. The business of philosophy, on the other hand, is to question fundamental concepts in order to secure progress in understanding. Some of the greatest doctors have combined effective practical action, founded on the best evidence available at the time, with a questioning mind bent on acquiring a new understanding.

Locke's philosophy grew out of his medical training and his Oxford laboratory work; they had established for him the importance of observation and experiment. He was also a man with deep religious convictions which, nevertheless, he attempted to regard with reason. There was an important body of puritan opinion which held that reformation of the Church would naturally be accompanied by a revival of learning. Locke's mind developed in an age of enlightenment in the company of men who formed The Royal Society, men who adopted as their creed a sober reasonableness in the weighing of evidence, and the rejection of partiality and prejudice in the pursuit of truth. Locke was a leader in the changing intellectual climate of his time. He advocated tolerance and insisted that evidence should be judged on its merits by each man for himself. Voltaire is said to have learned English so that he could read Locke's work, and to have introduced both him and Newton to France; he said, of Locke, in high praise, that he dared to doubt.

Many of Locke's theories were soon superseded, but he introduced new concepts, stimulated enquiry and removed long established obstacles to intellectual progress. There has in recent years been a marked revival of interest among philosophers in Locke's wide-ranging work, with re-assessment of his views and attempts to rectify past misinterpretations. His philosophy dealt with the acquisition of knowledge and with its limitations; with ideas and their complex relationships, and with the nature of matter and of mind. He placed man firmly as a part of nature, as matter which was capable of thinking as it was able to excite motion or perform other functions, a concept which seemed such a shocking form of materialism to many men of his day that he was furiously attacked, especially by theologians. Nevertheless, Locke believed in a trilogy of God, mind and matter, and held that the gift of thought was sufficient in itself to necessitate the existence of God. He was, however, much influenced by Boyle's corpuscular theory holding that a study of the minute structure of the component parts of wholes might define the entire range of connections and reactions in nature. Within modern molecular biology an extreme reductionist view has carried this mechanistic approach forward to a curious theory that all phenomena of life are ultimately explicable in terms of chemistry and physics. This simplistic concept of the animate world has provided a profitable framework for experimental biology leading to great success in the clarification of organic mechanisms, of which the elucidation of the genetic code has been the most notable example. Much may be revealed by simplicity. E.H. Gombrich claimed that one of Mondriane's paintings, all straight lines, a little square and primary colours, had explained boogie-woogie to him, but Mondriane's more extreme abstractions, such as a painting consisting of just two straight lines crossing, though certainly a relationship, left a whole kingdom of art and beauty unexpressed. To explain everything in life solely in terms of properties of ultimate units, however suggestive or revealing of detail, cannot account for such things as beauty, conceptual thought, compassion, piety, wonder or ingratitude. We should be thankful for the developing potentials which follow increased complexity in the organisation of hierarchical systems. Certainly, for a while, simplification may clear the ground, allowing a new approach to old complexities. Graham Smith in *The Novel and Society* (1984) quotes A.R. Humphreys who wrote:

By greatly simplifying the constitution of the mind by stripping off notions of inherited reverencies, prejudices, and beliefs supposedly grounded in its very Nature, by clarifying what had seemed a complex as involved as to defy analysis, Locke had enabled 'the science of man' to stand forth as an intelligible subject of knowledge.

Scientific ideas at that time were fresh and exciting; concepts such as the acceptance of doubt, of putting everything to the test of reason and experience and rejecting blind adherence to traditional doctrines, all had to be defended; they appeared to be even more important than new discoveries because they seemed themselves to be the great discovery. Locke opposed the belief in innate or implanted knowledge supplied ready-made from birth; knowledge, he said, has to be gained, knowledge is discovery. This left many questions unanswered about how knowledge might be first acquired and where the process of learning could begin.

> Tell me where is fancy bred
> Or in the heart or in the head?
> How begot, how nourished?
> Reply, reply.

Locke thought "all the materials of reason and knowledge" were due to simple ideas built up piece by piece in the mind, derived either from sensations received or through reflection on things observed. He saw no reason to suppose that we receive at birth ideas which are independent of our experience. To him the mind started as a blank sheet on which each individual could develop and display his understanding as he analysed his experiences and compared the various elements of his impressions seen in combination and in association. He saw this as no passive state but as a reaction to the involuntary force of impressions when they intruded on the mind. Hobbes (1588-1679) in *Leviathan* (1651) wrote concerning the thoughts of man:

> The original of them all is that which we call 'sense' for there is no conception in a man's mind which hath not at first, totally or by parts, been begotten upon the organ of sense. The rest are derived from that original.

Leibniz (1646-1716) had quoted the axiom "*Nihil est in intellectu quod non prius fuerit in sensu"*. Knowledge, Locke thought, was seeing connections, in agreement or in disagreement, between ideas. The blank-sheet mind might be an advance on belief in innate knowledge, but an incremental development of understanding through the simple accretion of sensations, even though subject to reflection, was always unconvincing.

Advances in understanding no doubt proceed step by step, some of which may be quite simple in themselves and appear obvious as soon as they are recognised. Doctors, however, have good reason to be deeply suspicious of simple biological explanations. They know, better than most, that no two people are the same, that actions provoke reactions, and that a single disease is never manifest in quite the same way in different patients. They expect matters of mind even more than those of body to be complicated, variable and difficult to disentangle, decipher or comprehend. George Eliot in *Middlemarch* beautifully expressed the awesome thought, of a true understanding of man's experience:

> If we had a keen vision and feeling of all ordinary human life, it would be like hearing the grass grow and the squirrel's heart beat, and we would die of the roar which lies on the other side of silence. As it is, the quickest of us walk about well wadded with stupidity.

William James (1842-1910), the outstanding American doctor-philosopher, who was also a delightful writer, was opposed to a corpuscular theory of experience, he maintained in the *Principles of Psychology* (1890) that the mind is completely unaware of single nervous impacts which initiate its activities. What we notice, he said, is a "stream of consciousness". We know nothing of the mystery of how thought, experience and nerve activity mingle in the processes whereby we make choices, reason, remember, lapse into vague confusion, are struck by beauty or perform miracles of imagination. Consciousness, James said, consists of instant, complex wholes: ideas, desires, memories, appreciations or whatever; not a host of separable units of sensation or experience but wholes which cannot be sorted into component parts (or only partially so in hindsight). Consciousness, to him, was itself a starting point rather than an accumulated

accumulated end-product, a beginning in the sense that while some constituents may be derived from it by analysis the activity itself cannot be constructed out of components. The "stream of consciousness", that extraordinary, wide ranging, momentary comprehension that comes to us, with training, in veritable pulses of revelation, allows us to drive a car, conduct a conversation, or type an incredible number of words per minute and even permits a few virtuosos to play a violin concerto. A person may not only perform such feats but, with the experience and training he has so far gained and with his present mood and immediate sensibility influencing him (all inseparable at the moment of perception when thought and feeling are one), may suddenly comprehend. In this moment he may find himself gloriously standing "Silent, upon a peak in Darien".

Locke was influenced by the revolt against Scholasticism with its calm agreement with authority, received opinion and accepted dogma. He thought that everything had to be learned, but failed to suggest how it was possible to begin to learn from experience if we are forced to do so from a completely blank start. Sir Karl Popper disposed of the blank sheet idea of the mind, the *tabula rasa*: he called it the bucket theory in which the mind is seen as an empty space in which knowledge accumulates as it is slowly filled through the senses. Knowledge is not just bits of information from which beliefs may be formed by noting repeated or even unfailing associations between such sensory elements. Popper pointed out that we learn from childhood to cope with a host of complicated, indeed, chaotic impressions by selection, ignoring some and decoding others, doing so through the benefit of a rather vague system of dispositions supported, however, by an extremely efficient method of testing by trial and error. Learning is not a question of developing innate knowledge, as Locke saw, but neither is it a question of stacking little bits of experience into a vernal basket or of adding them together on a clean slate untouched by divine hand; it is a matter of developing those inherited selecting and organising abilities (programmes) with which each individual starts out in life. In fact, we learn by cultivating, and improving on, a basic ancestral, dispositional system. Experiences or sense-impressions alone are a most insecure basis for acquiring knowledge. They have to be referred to an ordered system of maturing dispositions in order to generate knowledge which grows by modifying previous levels of understanding. The mind has to make sense of experience and the vitally necessary starting point is inherited common sense, a none too secure disposition but quite indispensable, which is influenced by experience and developed by criticism. Popper said "All science and all philosophy are enlightened common sense".

Noam Chomsky (born 1928), Professor of Linguistics, following Locke only in placing a limit on our capacity to understand and to communicate, found a good example of inherited dispositional influence in the speed and accuracy with which children can master the structure of language, and in the grammatical similarity existing between different languages. The idea that the individual is merely a lump of cells being moulded by the environment through responses to stimuli as it develops and learns was, he thought, untenable. It just cannot explain how each one could master the use of language, an extremely complicated and difficult skill, acquired so quickly, so young and without deliberate teaching. This left him in no doubt that grammar is neither taught nor learned from scratch; language must depend on an innate, inherited property which grows in the mind just as structures grow in the body, programmed to develop just as puberty is, for example. Chomsky's system of ideas has been sympathetically and clearly investigated by Fred D'Agostino (*Chomsky's System of Ideas*, 1986).

Many questions about developmental biology remain unanswered, whether structural, functional or behavioural. If those pre-formed programmes which specify aims in morphology or in behaviour patterns, the characteristics either of form or of dispositional systems, are built up piecemeal in evolution solely through mutations and selection, then their origins differ drastically from computer programmes, which must be inserted by purposeful programmers. We do not know how such complex goals are achieved either in form or in performance within developing, organismal, hierarchical systems, where new properties arise at each level which are not present in constituent parts in isolation. Here is a mystery wrapped up in that winding network of directed plans, patterns, regulations and restrictions which we call organisation.

It is not known how far inherent biological programming may go, or from whence it comes. Nevertheless, it is such ideas in developmental biology which have helped to break down artificial barriers between philosophy, linguistics, psychology and biology – an important activity because these are but names given to areas of enquiry, disciplines which can never be completely separated in any successful approach to human understanding.

Locke's objection to innate knowledge was sound, indeed everything does have to be learned, but he knew nothing of an essential, built in, contrivance in man, by which the mind, no mere blank sheet for accepting impressions, is guided by dispositions which present challenges to the impacts of the environment; select and assess relevance, and help to create a growing, rather than a merely accumulating, understanding in a comparable way perhaps to that in which morphogenic fields mould the developing and regenerating forms of living structure. Locke's common sense may not have been enough but he had the outstanding virtue of accepting doubt, of being ready to reject authority and of charting a way forward for understanding. Professor John Yolton wrote of his philosophy that:

> He held some basic hopes about man: that we can become responsible moral agents, that our faculty of reason can control our passions, that reason can work with God's laws of nature to build a stable political society.

Leslie Stephen, the father of Virginia Woolf, said that Locke had

> laid down the fundamental outlines of the creed, philosophical, religious and political, which was to dominate English thought for the next century.

Back in England Locke was again finding London bad for his health and was welcomed by Damaris on a long visit to Oates, the Masham Tudor manorhouse at High Laver where she lived with her husband and which was demolished in 1802. Damaris was by then a mother; her boy, Francis Cudworth Masham, and Sir Francis Masham's daughter, Esther, became great favourites of Locke. Sir Francis seems to have been an affable bore, a landed gentleman without the cultivated mind of his wife; he and Locke got on easily enough by hardly bothering with each other at all.

Damaris, however, was delighted to see her old friend with his stimulating conversation and the new zest to life provided by discussions with the interesting people he attracted to her home. He went back to London but was at Oates again for the winter, joined there for a time by Isaac Newton. He acquired two rooms on the first floor of the house and was there attended by Sylvanus Brownover, his valet and assistant. Ten servants looked after the family and Locke made the comfortable Oates his permanent home, though he spent much of the summer in London attending to his duties as Commissioner for Trade, his concern with the new coinage and devising a method for dealing with piracy. At this time he was also writing on economics and on *The Reasonableness of Christianity* (1695). In 1700 Locke resigned from the Board of Trade and began to put his affairs in the hands of his cousin's husband, Peter King, now a Member of Parliament as well as a barrister.

Princess Anne's last child died in 1701, and in the next year King William fell from his horse and died of his injuries; Queen Anne came to the throne and war was declared against France. John Locke with swollen legs and shortness of breath was nearing the end of his life. When the end came the faithful Damaris, Lady Masham, sat alone with him for many hours and received his last instructions.

Aaron, Richard *John Locke* Clarendon Press, Oxford, 1955. 2nd Edition.

Alexander, Peter *Ideas, Qualities and Corpuscles: Locke and Boyle on the External World* Cambridge University Press. 1985.

Barzun, Jacques *A Stroll with William James* University of Chicago Press, London, 1983.

Berlin, Isaiah *The Age of Enlightenment* Oxford University Press, 1956.

Brown, John *Horae Subsecivae. Locke and Sydenham 1866* David Douglas, Edinburgh, 1890 Edition.

Cranston, Maurice *John Locke* Longmans, London, 1959.

D'Agostino, Fred *Chomsky's System of Ideas* Oxford University Press. Oxford 1986.

Dewhurst, Kenneth *John Locke, Physician and Philosopher* Wellcome Historical Medical Library, London 1963.

Hunter, Michael *The Royal Society and its Fellows 1660-1700* The British Society for the History of Science, 1982.

James, William *The Principles of Psychology* Harvard University Press Edition, London 1981.

Locke, John *The Works of John Locke, Vols. 1 and 2 1824* Printed by C. Baldwin, London.

Osler, Sir William *John Locke as a Physician* Lancet, 1900, 2, 1116-1123.

Popper, Sir Karl *Objective Knowledge* The Clarendon Press, Oxford, 1972.

Webster, Charles *The Great Instauration* Gerald Duckworth, London, 1975.

Woolhouse, R.S. *Locke* The Harvester Press, Brighton, 1983.

Yolton, J.W. *Thinking Matter Materialism in Eighteenth Century Britain* Basil Blackwell, Oxford, 1985.

Yolton, J.W. *Locke, An Introduction* Basil Blackwell, Oxford, 1985.

JOHN ARBUTHNOT

CHAPTER THREE

The Physician and the Scriblerians

THIS STORY is set in the great age of satire and treats of the pressures and constraints imposed on authors who are dependent on patronage and politics for their support. It is concerned with an escape from such tutelage achieved by two of the great literary figures of the Augustan age, one willingly, one reluctantly, who shared a celebrated doctor-writer as friend and collaborator. The doctor was physician to a Queen, he was also a mathematician, and perhaps almost their equal as a satirist. One of them addressed him in a famous Epistle, and the other said of him, "The doctor has more wit than we all have, and his humanity is equal to his wit". James Boswell wrote:

> We talked of the geniuses in England in Queen Anne's reign. Mr Johnson said he thought Dr Arbuthnot the first man among them; as he was the most universal genius, being an excellent physician, a man of deep learning, and also great humour.

John Arbuthnot (1667-1735) was the son of a minister of the kirk, Alexander Arbuthnott, a keeper of his family records first compiled in 1583 by another Alexander who was Principal of King's College, Aberdeen. The main branch of this Jacobite family came from Arbuthnott Castle in Kincardineshire. At the time of the uprising of 1688 which brought William and Mary to the throne, John's father lost his living for refusing to conform to the Presbyterian system, being shabbily, if wisely, deposed by his relative and patron, Viscount Arbuthnott. John's younger brother, Robert, fought for James II at the battle of Killiecrankie, where the highlanders achieved a famous victory, a grand though quite unproductive success. John was not one to espouse a lost cause but Robert left for France, became a banker in Rouen and from there helped to finance the Jacobite rebellion of 1715. After John Arbuthnot's death, Lord Chesterfield, politician, Lord Lieutenant of Ireland, famous for his letters of advice to his son and, in reverse, for a renowned letter of cutting reprimand addressed to him by Samuel Johnson, was to write of Arbuthnot that he was "a Jacobite by prejudice, and a Republican by reflection and reasoning".

John Arbuthnot went to London when his father died to become a teacher of mathematics and wrote *Of the Laws of Chance* (1692), a book in which the art of gaming is described in terms of the ability to calculate on which side the best chance will lie in dubious cases. The desire to win and the hope of gain may lead to an obsession with gambling, but are, nevertheless, the foundation of our preoccupation with the laws of chance, the philosophy of coincidence and the mathematical significance of observations. In 1694 Arbuthnot entered University College, Oxford, but later transferred to St Andrews to study medicine, taking his degree there at the age of 29. He returned to London to practice, married and had ten children, only four of whom, George, Charles, Margaret and Anne, survived to adult life, and none of whom had children of their own. In 1704 he was elected a Fellow of the Royal Society during Sir Isaac Newton's presidency and served on a committee with Newton and Sir Christopher Wren which supervised the long wrangle over the publication of the work of John Flamsteed, the first Astronomer Royal. Dr Arbuthnot attended the Queen's husband Prince George, by the fortunate chance of being on the spot when he was taken ill at Epsom, and made such an impression that he was invited to become the Prince's doctor and, following this, was appointed Physician to Queen Anne. He was elected Fellow of the College of Physicians and physician to the Chelsea Hospital and was the Harveian Orator for 1727. His interest in music led to his being proposed for the Court of Directors of the Academy of Music; he was a friend of Handel and with Pope wrote the text for the masque *Haman and Mordecai* which with additions by Samuel Humphreys became *Esther*, the first of the oratorios on the path to *Messiah*.

Arbuthnot was handsome, jovial, prudent and urbane, and his intimate concern with the affairs of the Queen made him much sought after by those who wished to secure his influential support at court. In 1707 Abigail Hill became Mrs. Masham at a secret ceremony held in Arbuthnot's apartment and attended by the Queen. In 1711 Arbuthnot met Jonathan Swift (1667-1745) who had been soliciting the Whig government on behalf of the Irish church while pursuing his own ambitions. In his *Journal to Stella* Swift wrote of going for a ride with Arbuthnot at Windsor to see the country, meeting the Queen, and of supping together with Harley (Earl of Oxford, the Tory Chancellor to the new government), Abigail Masham (who had become the Queen's confidant and successor to Sarah Duchess of Marlborough) and Arbuthnot ("the Queen's favourite physician"). On a subsequent visit ("to seek my fortune") he wrote to Stella of how Arbuthnot had engaged him for dinners and how they had together played a trick on the maids of honour. Years later Swift was to write to Arbuthnot

> you who were pleased to take such generous constant care of my Health, my Interests, and my Reputation; who represented me so favourably to that blessed Queen your Mistress, as well as to her Ministers, and to all your friends.

Swift appreciated that Arbuthnot was a man of wide-ranging interests and diverse abilities as well as an eminent physician who had acquired considerable influence at court. He also recognised in him unusual literary gifts and admired his talent for satire presented in a characteristic style of mock gravity. Arbuthnot in 1697 had written *An Examination of Dr Woodward's Account of the Deluge* in which criticism and satire were cunningly combined to counteract the eccentric John Woodward's theory that the Flood was due to the interior of the Earth being filled with water which escaped to cover the World. In 1700 *An Essay on the Usefulness of Mathematical Learning* appeared in which Arbuthnot followed "the incomparable Mr Newton" in his commitment to the objective investigation of the physical world.

Until Swift persuaded him to a higher regard for his writing, Arbuthnot had looked on the satires he produced as no more than light-hearted diversions from medicine. Though his scientific work was prepared with the greatest care, his other papers were treated in such an off-hand manner that his friends had been allowed to alter his manuscripts and his children to make kites out of his drafts. Under Swift's guidance he began to take his non-medical writing more seriously and in 1712 his first published satire appeared in four pamphlets, *Law is a Bottomless-Pit, or the History of John Bull*. This allegory, republished by Pope fifteen years later, introduced John Bull, representing England, an honest, choleric, bold, short-tempered, plain-dealing man susceptible to flattery, who was to become the pattern Englishman. John Bull's first wife was the Whig government and his second the new Tory ministry; the Earl of Oxford was Sir Roger Bold, John Bull's mother the Church of England and his difficult sister Peg, Scotland. When Peg was asked if she were related to John Bull, she replied, "Yes, he has the honour to be my brother". Marlborough's war, which had dragged on in the Low Countries, was depicted as a prolonged process of litigation, and the Peace of Utrecht, just concluded by the Tories, as a conference held in the Salutation Tavern attended by Bull (English), Frog (Dutch), South (Archduke of Austria) and Baboon (King of France). Macaulay called it "the most ingenious and humorous political satire extant in our language". Daniel Defoe (1660-1731) likened the Treaty of Utrecht to a fair with French jockeys bidding for a horse which had several joint owners.

Arbuthnot then wrote *The Art of Political Lying*, defined as "the art of convincing the people of salutary falsehoods for some good end". Here he discussed the question of whether a lie is best contradicted by truth, or counteracted by another lie but, holding that there was a "great propensity to believe lies in the generality of mankind", he favoured opposing one lie with another. He gave as a medical example

> Thus, if it be spread abroad that a great person were dying of some disease, you must not say the truth, that they are in health, and never had such a disease, but that they are slowly recovering of it.

The method of topping one lie with another has been brought to a fine art in our own day. When the College of Physicians applied to parliament to prevent apothecaries dispensing without a physician's prescription, Arbuthnot represented the undertakers as urging that they would be seriously injured by the decrease in the number of deaths that would result from these precautions. This satire on the special pleading of self-interest, still being freely offered by organisations representing both sides in disputes, is a method we might use more freely in the hope of promoting good sense today.

Another of the physicians to Queen Anne, Sir David Hamilton

(1663-1721), Boswell's uncle, has become famous for his writing. Hamilton's diary (1709-1714) provides a wonderful insight into certain aspects of the last years of the Queen's reign as seen from the position of a confidential physician-in-ordinary. He was a Whig sympathiser, a trusted go-between, a shrewd observer and a perceptive recorder. His concern was always for the comfort of his patient, never did he betray a medical confidence though he discussed the Queen's terminal illness in his diary, his aim was always to see her through "a succession of Disquiets".

Medical diaries published about the great have not always been so circumspect. Hamilton's jottings throw light on the famous break between the Queen and the Duchess of Marlborough and the substitution of Abigail Masham in the Queen's favour. Sarah was badly treated but she must have been impossible to deal with. Hamilton went back and forth between her and the Queen trying both to protect his patient from disquiet and to ease Sarah's humiliation. The diary with its short, sharp entries injects a pulse of life into this slight but fascinating morsel of history. Hamilton, who had studied medicine in Leyden and Rheims, practised in London where he became fashionable and rich. He was first called to the Queen in 1708, the year he was elected Fellow of the Royal Society. In 1714 he recorded his uneasiness at coming so seldom to the Queen and how Arbuthnot proposed that they should each come one day in turn. They were both in attendance when she died.

Another doctor-writer and contemporary of Arbuthnot's was Mark Akenside (1721-1770), the son of a Newcastle butcher, who trained in Edinburgh and Leyden and practised in Northampton before coming to London. He suffered from a marked sensitivity about his humble origin, made worse by lameness caused by an accident in youth when his foot was badly injured through one of his father's cleavers falling on it. This feeling is thought to have been the main reason for his arrogant, supercilious and grand, starchy manner. A surgeon-apothecary who knew him well said, "He could not bear to see any one smile in the presence of an invalid; and, I think, he lost a good deal of business by the solemn sententiousness of his air and manner". Tobias Smollet (1721-1771), another of the great doctor-writers, satirised him as the doctor in his novel *Perigrine Pickle* (1751). Akenside wrote poetry from an early age, the best known of his poems being *Pleasures of Imagination* (1744). His verse though rather stiff, like himself, is given to grand sentiment and noble feeling. Johnson took him seriously, certainly for his critical judgement if a little doubtfully for his poetry for all his recognition of its technical excellence, smooth flow and musical pauses. Akenside edited the works of William Harvey for the College of Physicians in 1766 and gave the Croonian Lectures on "The Revival of Learning" regarded then, as Dr Ober has rather coldly expressed it, as a "topic not suited to its audience". He anticipated Keats with an "Ode to a Nightingale", not quite the "immortal Bird!" but comparison with Ruth "in tears amid the alien corn" and

> Charm'd magic casements, opening on the foam
> Of perilous seas, in faery lands forlorn.

is not easily sustained. However he wrote

> O sacred bird, let me at eve,
> Thus wandering all alone,
> Thy tender counsel oft receive,
> Bear witness to thy pensive airs,
> And pity Nature's common cares
> Till I forget my own.

Akenside never married but his poems do not suggest that he really deserved the stigma of misogamist which was perhaps the wrong epithet to apply to him. He achieved some success in medicine, was Goulstonian Lecturer, Harveian Orator, on the staff of St Thomas's Hospital and physician to George III's Queen, Charlotte-Sophia, from the time of her arrival in England.

There are some interesting stories about Akenside, one of which is the curious incident of Milton's bed. In 1761 a Mr Hollis purchased the bed in which Milton had died and gave it in homage to Dr Akenside with a note which said

> An Englishman is desirous of having the honour to present a bed, which once belonged to John Milton, and on which he died; and if Dr Akenside, believing himself obliged, and having slept on that bed, should prompt him to write an ode to the memory of John Milton, and the assertor of British liberty, that gentleman would think himself abundantly recompensed.

While in Leyden, Akenside met the wealthy Jeremiah Dyson who, from that time, became his friend for life and his main support, at one time allowing him £300 a year. They returned to London together, Dyson to the bar, Akenside to medical practice; their relationship appears in many of Akenside's poems. In 1747 they were concerned in making history when Dyson purchased the Clerkship of the House of Commons for the fine sum of £6000. This gave him the right to appoint the Clerk Assistant; both he and the "Clerks without doors" would expect to pay for the privilege. This was the usual form of recompense for the original outlay from which some profit might be expected on all sides in the days when the sale of offices formed part of a widespread net of patronage and sinecures. Dyson, however, appointed his deputy and clerks as vacancies occurred, without seeking any remuneration from them. The deputy, John Hatsell (Clerk from 1768 to 1820) was introduced to him by Akenside, and decided, in his turn, not to resume the practise of selling appointments in the House of Commons so "honorably abolished". He was the one who wrote Hatsell's *Precedents of Proceedings in the House of Commons* (1781), the standard work on parliamentary procedure before *Erskine May*. It was early in the nineteenth century before the sale of such offices was outlawed by Act of Parliament; however, the last lingering pockets of patronage were not eliminated until the Commission of 1912-15. Dyson held the Clerkship until he became a Member of Parliament. Mr. Justice Hardinge wrote that he never saw anything like the friendship of Mr Dyson and Dr Akenside

> and yet nothing could be more dissimilar than they were. Mr Dyson was quite a man of business, of order, of parliamentary forms, and of political argument. He had neither fancy nor eloquence; and though he had strong prejudices, he veiled them in obliging manners.

A great change in the medical profession was taking place in the time of Drs Akenside, Arbuthnot and Hamilton. The legal profession was already larger, with many wealthy and successful members having university degrees and a mounting status in society. In 1700 there were some 3000 qualified physicians in the country backed by a motley collection of semi-professional craftsmen, apothecaries and surgeons. In the decade 1730-40 a fusion took place of physicians, surgeons and apothecaries into one profession, with a consequent rise in the standing of the doctor in society. Surgeons, without anaesthesia, were struggling, but, by learning anatomy, developing dexterity and speed, treating syphilis with mercury and taking students, were moving towards affluence and the best were prominent in leading the profession towards a new respect. Physicians with little effective treatment at their command were chiefly valuable for understanding and the offer of comfort, diagnosis and prognosis; knowing which patient was likely to survive, and which not, was an important skill. Lists of those associated with the Royal College of Physicians had been compiled since 1694 but there was no medical register before 1779. A good deal of establishment superiority amongst the senior physicians was backed by a genuine feeling for education. Dr Thomas Withers, of the York County Hospital established in 1740, wrote *A Treatise on the Errors and Defects of Medical Education* about the year 1774, in which he said, "The character of a physician ought to be that of a gentleman, which cannot be maintained with dignity but by a man of literature", meaning that a doctor ought to have a liberal education. Samuel Garth (1661-1719) Harveian Orator in 1697, still another of the doctor-writers of the time, born in Durham and, like Mark Akenside, trained in Leyden, was highly scornful about his colleagues in *The Dispensary* (1699), but, with honesty, if no encouragement, said of his own patients that

> It was no matter whether he saw them that night or next morning, for nine had such bad constitutions that no physician could save them, and the other six had such good ones that all the physicians in the world could not kill them.

Sir Samuel Garth had a flourishing practice with many prominent patients. He was generous, witty, good natured, and renowned for his writing of poems, lectures and orations. He was much influenced by Dryden and, on hearing that he had been buried in Soho obtained permission for his body to be exhumed, to lie in state in the College of Physicians and to be reburied in Poet's Corner in Westminster Abbey.

Much of what the doctors did in the way of therapeutics was

harmful; bleeding, vomiting and purging were usually detrimental, they mostly relied for treatment on herbal medicines. Defoe in his *A Tour Through the Whole Island of Great Britain* (1724) wrote a revealing note about this aspect of practice on his visit to Ipswich,

> Dr Beeston, an eminent physician, began, a few years ago, a physic garden adjoining to this house in this town; and as he is particularly curious, and as I was told exquisitely skill'd in botanic knowledge, so he has been not only very diligent, but successful too, in making a collection of rare and exotic plants, such as one scarce to be equall'd in England.

It was in 1714, for a brief but memorable period, that a famous group of satirists came together calling themselves The Martinus Scriblerus Club. They exerted a considerable social influence and acquired a lasting literary fame. At that time the social, literary and political life of London revolved around the coffee houses and taverns with a natural tendency for each to develop into a meeting place for men of like mind. There they assembled for discussion, carried out business transactions, and even conducted medical consultations. Thomas Dover saw his patients at the Jerusalem Coffeehouse off the Strand, Sir William Blizard (1743-1835) his at Batson's Coffeehouse in Cornhill. Samuel Johnson attracted such an outstanding group around him at the Turk's Head in Gerrard Street that they became known simply as "The Club". Similarly those with the same political leanings tended to gather for their own purposes, Tories at the Cocoa Tree Chocolate House and Whigs at the St James's Coffee House. Samuel Garth was a member of the Kit Cat Club where he occupied a position with the Whigs comparable to that of Arbuthnot with the Tories. Edward Lloyd had his coffee house in Lombard Street where merchants met for business and to obtain the latest information especially about shipping.

The Scriblerians were a remarkable group: Arbuthnot, Gay, Oxford, Parnell, Pope and Swift. The association started in 1713 when Pope proposed to Swift that they should collaborate in producing a monthly burlesque satirising a sententious journal called *The History of the Works of the Learned*, theirs was to be called *An Account of the Works of the Unlearned*. The purpose was clear, to prick the bubble of pomposity and introduce some reasonableness and more sense into literary discussion. The idea came to nothing but led directly to the formation of the Scriblerians when Swift persuaded Arbuthnot to join them and he became the prime mover in the new scheme. Besides its regular members, there were a few occasional associates like William Congreve (1670-1729), who had been at Trinity College Dublin with Swift, dramatist, poet and novelist, by then nearly blind; also Francis Atterbury (1163-1732) with Jacobite leanings who became Bishop of Rochester (Pope's "mitred Rochester") in 1713 and, refusing to sign the declaration of fidelity in 1722, was committed to the Tower and then banished to die in Paris. Joseph Addison (1672-1719), who had known Swift since he was in Ireland as secretary to the Lord Lieutenant, Lord Wharton, was approached, liked the idea of the club, but, being a Whig, found it difficult to join such a Tory-slanted group. In 1715 he treated Pope most shabbily over a rival translation of the *Iliad* which for a time threatened Pope's attempt to secure his financial freedom.

Doctor Arbuthnot was responsible for the biography of the Club's invented "hero", Martinus Scriblerus (the name being derived from Dryden's Sir Martin Mar-All and a latinised form of scribbler) and was host at many of their meetings held in the chambers at St James's Palace which he occupied by virtue of his attendance on the Queen. Robert Harley (1661-1724) the Lord Treasurer, became the first Lord Oxford, he and Henry St John, first Viscount Bolingbroke, having taken over the government when the Whig ministers were dismissed in 1710. John Gay (1685-1732) born in Barnstaple, secretary to the Duchess of Monmouth and then to Lord Clarendon, had already published his first poems and a pamphlet on *The Present State of Wit*. Thomas Parnell (1679-1718), an Englishman whose family had settled in Ireland where he took holy orders, was a poet and eloquent conversationalist. Alexander Pope (1688-1744) and Jonathan Swift (1667-1745) completed this wonderfully gifted group. They used their talents to ridicule pretentious moralising, to deride complacent assertions based on inadequate evidence, and to satirise dull generalisation, pedantry and bad writing. One member would undertake a project either on his own or assisted by others and the result would be reviewed by them all so that authorship was often uncertain and always confused. They produced a number of works, the best known of which was *Memoirs of the Extraordinary Life Works and Discoveries of Martinus Scriblerus* which started:

> In the reign of Queen Anne (which, notwithstanding those happy times which succeeded, every Englishman may remember) thou mayst possibly, gentle reader, have seen a certain venerable person who frequented the outside of the Palace of St James's, and who, by the gravity of his deportment and habit, was generally taken for a decayed gentleman of Spain. His stature was tall, his visage long, his complexion olive, his brows were black and even, his eyes hollow yet piercing, his nose inclined to aquiline, his beard neglected and mixed with grey; all this contributed to spread a solemn melancholy over his countenance.

There were other such writings as *God's Revenge Against Punning* and *Peri Bathous, or the Art of Sinking in Poetry*. However, much of the best work inspired by the association of Scriblerians appeared after the group had been dissolved. The sudden, premature demise of the club was brought about by a combination of concurrent events at a time of national crisis. While Swift was away in Ireland being installed as Dean of St Patrick's, a conflict broke out between two of his close associates, Oxford and Bolingbroke, the leaders of the Tory ministry for which Swift had become the main writer and propagandist. Oxford and Bolingbroke, faced with the Queen's illness and the inevitability of the Hanoverian accession if they failed to make terms with the Queen's half-brother James, the Old Pretender, quarrelled as time ran out and had to choose between flight and imprisonment. Oxford and Bolingbroke were politicians at a time when morality in politics was little known. Oxford, an able man of devious mind, had left the Whigs for the Tories for personal advantage; Bolingbroke also pursued political ambition without restraint of principle, but he was a gifted man who wrote with style and spoke with eloquence. Swift, working for them, had helped to turn public opinion in favour of the Tories and towards a desire for peace with France. He was employed to use his considerable literary skill to vindicate the party and denigrate its opponent, being "the master of poisonous compliments", according to David Nokes (*Jonathan*

Swift 1984). By these efforts Swift almost secured for himself a bishopric, but had to be content with a deanery.

A vast number of words in many volumes have been written about many aspects of Swift's life and works; there has been much myth and speculation as well as scholarships; salacious stories as well as accounts of his essential spirituality with assessments of his personality, varying from mental instability to well adjusted wisdom.

As Queen Anne's reign was coming to its end, Swift became increasingly disillusioned and more of a radical; reluctantly acknowledging the approach of the end of Tory dominance, he saw his own position at the seat of power slipping away. He decided to leave London and escaped to the peace of Letcombe, a village under the Berkshire downs.

The Queen died in 1714 and Arbuthnot lost his influential post as Royal Physician. Gay found himself without a patron, though he was soon fortunate in finding the best of his several supporters in the Duke and Duchess of Queensberry. Parnell, not long after, went back to Ireland, where he took to drink after his wife's death and was soon to die himself. A selection of his poems was published by Pope after his death. Pope was busy producing the enlarged edition of *The Rape of the Lock* (1712) and translating the *Iliad* into English verse. So the meetings of the club came to an end, but its members remained in touch and continued to collaborate. Swift in the parsonage at Letcombe, staying with Mr. Geree and his wife for a guinea a week, was writing *Free Thoughts on the Present State of Affairs*, his letters to Stella and composing a memorable and sad farewell to Oxford. He received an embarrassing, passionate visit from Vanessa (Esther Vanhomrigh) the daughter of a wealthy Dutch merchant who had been his pupil and who had transferred her love of learning to her love for Swift and died in 1723 after his rejection of her. He refused invitations to return to political affairs and had news from Arbuthnot about the battles and fate of "the Dragon" (Oxford) and "the Squire" (Bolingbroke). Pope and Parnell came to see him as "Scriblerus Envoys" and described their visit in a fanciful newsletter in the style of the friendly gaiety of the Scriblerian association, for example:

They were received at the back-door, and having paid the usual compliments on their part, and received the usual chidings on that of the Dean, were introduced to his landlady, and entertained with a pint of Lord Bolingbroke's Florence.

They spoke of Martin Scriblerus as though he were alive, Parnell wrote to Arbuthnot in 1714

the immortal Scriblerus smiled upon our endeavours, who now hangs his head in an obscure corner, pining for his friends that are scattered over the face of the earth.

Swift went back to Ireland at the end of that summer and thereafter only returned to London for two visits one in 1726 and another in 1727. When he came in 1726 the remaining Scriblerians helped him to plan the, at first anonymous, publication of *Gulliver's Travels* (1726), those fantastic adventures of a ship's doctor, a satire on those men and their affairs he had come to despise, in which some of the scientific fun of the third voyage had been sketched out for him by Arbuthnot. Swift was responsible for persuading Gay to write *The Beggars Opera* (1728) which was a roaring success from the first. Writers who identified references to themselves in Scriblerian works turned on Pope, "the wasp of Twickenham", and when *The Dunciad* appeared in 1728 they besieged the bookshop, threatened to use the law and tried to prevent the sale. Dedicated to Swift, *The Dunciad* set about the great empire of dullness in literature, especially in poetry, with highly personal attacks and lines like "Prose swelled to verse, verse loitering into prose", and "Less human genius than God gives an ape". *The Art of Sinking in Poetry* came out in 1729 causing more discomfort. The later Book IV of *The Dunciad* was less Scriblerian, different from the first parts, more general and with its teeth into educationists and scientists.

The Scriblerians with wit, intellect, imagination, and brilliant attacks on all that was spurious, sententious and second-rate, not only brought satire to its peak but produced a lasting effect on English literature. Their partnership realised more than they could each have achieved alone, helping to create allegorical works of fine quality.

In some ways Pope was the most interesting member of the group. He had met Samuel Garth when a child, and he gave him much encouragement with his writing. They remained friends until Garth's death. Pope wrote a dedication to Garth in one of his Pastorals which said:

> Accept, O Garth, the muse's early lays,
> That adds this wreath of ivy to thy bays;
> Hear what from love unpractised hearts endure,
> From love, the sole disease thou canst not cure.

When Pope was twenty-one his father had recommended the study of physic to him but he started with terrible disadvantages of body to limit his activity, offset by the brilliance and sensitivity of his mind. A cripple from about the age of twelve, not more than 4'6" high, his spine was bent and deformed by Pott's disease, long known but accurately described by Percival Pott (1714-1788), and suggested to be due to tuberculosis by Jean-Pierre David (1737-1784), but the tubercle bacillus was not discovered by Robert Koch (1843-1910) until 1882, more than a hundred years after Pott's death. Pope had to be strapped into a canvas jacket and was unable to get dressed or to go to bed without help. Plagued by headaches, he required a special chair at table to raise him to the level of his companions. He was a Roman Catholic 100 years before the passing of the Act of Parliament for Catholic emancipation. Sir Joshua Reynolds said that he was "very hump-backed and deformed" and Bonamy Dobrée (1891-1974), a lieutenant-colonel who became Professor of English at Leeds, called him "a little diminutive hero desperately battling against ogres". Pope's physical problems had their mental effect, he suffered from nervous irritability which, though it seldom led him into unprovoked attacks, lent a ferocious and devastating aspect to his ripostes, a fierceness of defence which was perhaps a condition of his survival. He was severely goaded by his enemies and meanly provoked by some who even stooped to vicious references to his physical deformity. Though he could be petty and spiteful, to his friends in sympathetic company he was warm-hearted, gentle and loyal; he was also generous and thoughtful, often helping in the publication of works by his friends. It is interesting to wonder what difference an upright healthy body might have made to this man with such outstanding gifts. His dependence on others for his normal day-to-day existence no doubt sharpened his hatred of dependence on patronage and galvanised him into escape from a purely politico-literary strife, achieved when financial success followed his translation of the *Iliad* and later the *Odyssey*, as he wrote:

> "But (thanks to Homer) since I live and thrive
> Indebted to no prince or peer alive....."

Dobrée said he "transformed the social position of the man of letters" and claimed that he was "the first author to live by his profession without adulation or fawning or parasitism". Sadly authors may still be subject to restraints and persuaded into parading opinions other than their own for "the public good" or "the benefit of the state", not only to obtain a living and the opportunity to practice their craft, but for their very right to life and liberty. Pope's retreat at Twickenham, the house where he went with his mother and the garden he created there, gave him peace and a fine place to entertain his friends. The house being separated from the garden by the road from Hampton Court, a passage was dug under the road from the front of the house to emerge in a small temple in the garden. Dr Johnson, in his grand manner, wrote of it "he extracted an ornament from an inconvenience, and vanity produced a grotto where necessity enforced a passage".

Pope wrote a series of Epistles, such as the one to Lord Burlington *On Taste*, another to Lord Bathurst *On the use of Riches*, some of which were published as *Moral Essays*. The greatest of these was the *Epistle to Arbuthnot* or the *Prologue to the Satires* which contained many famous lines such as: "Damn with faint praise", "Not fortune's worshipper nor fashion's fool". Partly autobiographical and an apology for his own life this Epistle contains these lines:

> Why did I write? What sin to use unknown
> Dipt me in Ink, my Parent's, or my own?
> As yet a Child, nor yet a Fool to Fame,
> I lisp'd in Numbers, for the Numbers came.
> I left no Calling for this idle trade,
> No Duty broke, no Father dis-obey'd.
> The Muse but serv'd to ease some Friend, not Wife,
> To help me thro' this long Disease, my life,

> To second, Arbuthnot! thy Art and Care,
> And teach, the Being you preserv'd, to bear.

Partly a tribute to his old friend in his last days, for Arbuthnot died a few months after this Epistle was published, it was put in the form of a dialogue, though Arbuthnot was not given many lines even if he was allowed "Who breaks a butterfly upon a wheel?", but he did secure the last word. In Scriblerian days Arbuthnot had been the controlling influence on personal attacks, he was as sharp to expose shallow, false profundity as any of them but more anxious not to give offence, so Pope allowed him to intervene on the side of restraint in his Epistle. After a reference to the asses ears King Midas grew (first seen by the Queen) for awarding a musical prize to Pan, Arbuthnot says:

> *A.* Good friend forbear! You deal in dangerous things,
> I'd never name queens, ministers or kings;
> Keep close to ears, and those let asses prick;
> 'Tis nothing – *P.* Nothing? let the secret pass,
> That secret to each fool, that he's an ass:
> The truth once told (and wherefore should we lie?)
> The Queen of Midas slept, and so may I.
> You think this cruel? take it for a rule,
> No creature smarts so little as a fool.

and later with a reference to his own small stature,

> *A.* Hold! for God's sake – you'll offend,
> No names! – be calm! – learn prudence from a friend!
> I too could write and I am twice as tall;

Arbuthnot died on February 27th 1735 and was buried in St James's Church, Piccadilly where a notable collection of doctors are interred: Thomas Sydenham (1624-1689), Mark Akenside (1721-1770), William Hunter (1718-1783), Sir Richard Croft (1762-1818), Richard Bright (1789-1858) and Sir William Bowman (1816-1892). Pope was with Arbuthnot the evening before his death. What doctor ever received so memorable a tribute as this Epistle or so famous a word of thanks?

> Friend to my life (which did not you prolong,
> The World had wanted many an idle song).

Aitken, G.A. *The Life and Works of John Arbuthnot* Clarendon Press, Oxford, 1892.

Beattie, Lester M. *John Arbuthnot, Mathematician and Satirist* Harvard University Press, 1935.

Bucke, Charles *On the Life, Writings and Genius of Akenside* James Cochrane, London, 1832.

Dobrée, Bonamy *Alexander Pope* Sylvan Press, London, 1951.

Holmes, Geoffrey *Augustan England* George Allen and Unwin, London, 1982.

Nicolson, Marjorie and Rousseau, G.S. *This Long Disease my Life* Princeton University Press, Princeton, 1968.

Nokes, David *Jonathan Swift: A Hypocrite Revered A Critical Biography.* Oxford University Press, 1984.

Ober, William B. *John Arbuthnot, M.D., F.R.S., F.R.C.P.* N.Y. ST. J. MED. 1966, 66, 276-281.

Ober, William B. *Mark Akenside, M.D.* N.Y. ST. J. MED. 1968, 68, 3166-3180.

Roberts, Philip (Editor) *The Diary of Sir David Hamilton 1709-1714* Clarendon Press, Oxford, 1975.

TOBIAS SMOLLETT

CHAPTER FOUR

The Historian and the Surgeon

SOME OF the company of medical authors have led adventurous lives, either physical or intellectual. Tobias George Smollett (1721-1771) was one of those who indulged in both. He sailed to the Caribbean as surgeon's mate, was present at the attack on Carthagena in 1741, married a creole beauty, fought a law suit over land and slaves in Jamaica, translated *Don Quixote*, produced *A Compendium of Voyages* in seven volumes, was imprisoned in the Marshalsea for libel, launched violent satires on men and Government, wrote adventure-novels exposing folly and wickedness while campaigning for social reform, and became involved in a vicious battle with his senior contemporary novelist, Fielding.

Smollett, when he was seriously ill, retired to Italy where he finished his novel *Humphrey Clinker* (1771) published just before he died. In this, his final work, a delightful passage occurs in a letter written by Matt Bramble in Bath to Dr Lewis, where he justifies the use of his doctor for catharsis by a rare parade of excuse, demand, compliment and extenuating circumstances:-

> If I did not know that the exercise of your profession has habituated you to the hearing of complaints, I should make a conscience of troubling you with my correspondence, which may be truly called *The Lamentations of Matthew Bramble*. Yet I cannot help thinking I have some right to discharge the over-flowing of my spleen upon you, whose province it is to remove those disorders that occasioned it; and let me tell you, it is no small alleviation of my grievances, that I have a sensible friend, to whom I can communicate my crusty humours, which, by retention, would grow intolerably acrimonious.

We all need a doctor who is also a sensible friend.

Smollett was a Scotsman who wanted to change society, he mixed violent antipathies with unbounded generosity and combined passionate quarrels with warm-hearted friendships. He was a force in the literature of his day and gained a lasting reputation. A good Smollett story was told by his friend Alexander Carlyle. They were sitting in a coffee house in Cockspur Street when the news of the utter defeat of Bonny Prince Charlie at Culloden arrived and created a great stir in London. They set off for home through a riotous mob celebrating the victory and letting off squibs, and, careful not to speak in case their accents should betray them as Scots, put their wigs in their pockets, drew their swords and walked forward with them in their hands going by narrow lanes from the Haymarket. It is through small personal reactions such as this, with two doctors, wigs in pocket, swords in hand, that a picture of the time is brought suddenly to light. It was after this that Smollett wrote the best of his undistinguished verse, "The Tears of Scotland", though no Jacobite he was horrified at the atrocities committed by "Butcher" Cumberland's troops after their victory.

> Yet, when the rage of battle ceas'd
> The victor's soul was not appeas'd
> The naked and forlorn must feel
> Devouring flames, and murd'ring steel!

The first sketch of the poem was written in a tavern while his companions were playing cards before supper. When he read it to them they suggested that the final stanza was too strong and would be certain to give offence. So, without reply, responding to mild counsel which was tinder to his indignation, he at once added a new and even more vigorous concluding stanza.

> While the warm blood bedews my veins,
> And unimpair'd remembrance reigns,
> Resentment of my country's fate,
> Within my filial breast shall beat;
> And, spite of her insulting foe,
> My sympathizing verse shall flow:
> 'Mourne, hapless Calendonia, mourne
> Thy banish'd peace, thy laurels torn,

Amongst Smollett's vast literary output was included *A Complete History of England* published in 1757, stretching from "The Descent of Julius Caesar to the Treaty of Aix La Chapelle, 1748". Many doctors have written on the history of medicine and a few have undertaken general historical studies. Robert Brady (d. 1700) and James Wellwood (1652-1727) both wrote English histories and James Drake (1667-1707) wrote, *Historia Anglo-Scotica: or an Impartial History from William the Conqueror to Queen Elizabeth* (1703). Nathaniel Johnston (1627-1705) published five hundred folio pages on *The Excellency of Monarchical Government* and some foreign doctors have chosen historical subjects, for example, Engelbrecht Kaempfer (1651-1716) wrote a *History of Japan* (1727), Friedrich Schiller (1759-1805), the great historical dramatist and friend of Goethe, wrote an account of the liberation of the Netherlands from Spain and a history of the Thirty Years' War. Smollett's history, even after a great deal of reading in preparation, still contained too many inaccuracies and confusions to please historians but was, in its day, a great success with the public. An ode of fulsome acclaim, *To Dr Smollett*, signed "K" appeared in *Lloyd's Evening Post and British Chronicle* in 1760, exalting the virtues of his novel *Ferdinand, Count Fathom* (1753) and the *Complete History*, which contained:

> But in thy Hist'ry, all thy Genius blooms,
> Old England's battles o'er again we wage,
> Tread Cresci's plain, and follow Edward's plumes,
> And glow with Conquest, Liberty and Rage.

There was some rivalry because David Hume (1711-1776), engaged on a similar project, had published two volumes of Stuart history and was working backwards to Roman times. Hume's history which came out in six volumes, emphasised once more the common problem of how historians are to avoid bias. Smollett was certainly not alone in purveying historical inaccuracies, the great Macaulay (1800-1859) was accused not only of political bias but of sacrificing truth for the sake of epigram.

Smollett dedicated his history to William Pitt, later Earl of Chatham, without his permission but with a fine flourish, including sentiments which still apply today:

> Power and office are adventitious and transitory. They are often vested in the wicked and the worthless. They perpetually fluctuate between accident and caprice. Today, you stand conspicuous at the helm of state: tomorrow, you may repose yourself in the shade of private virtue. My veneration is

attached to permanent qualities: qualities that exist independent of favour or of faction: qualities which you can neither forfeit nor resign.

His *Continuation of the Complete History of England* was published from 1761 to 1765 and the work was re-issued in a large number of small parts which sold so well that Smollett made some £2000 from this venture, a large sum of money at that time. There is a curious edition of Hume's *History of England* of 1776, published by William Ball in 1840, of which I have a copy, and which combines the old rivalries by attaching part of Smollett's work, cramming so much into one volume in such small print as to be almost unreadable. This was entitled *The History of England from the invasion of Julius Caesar, to the Revolution of 1688 by David Hume, Esq., continued to the Death of George the Second by T. Smollett, M.D.*

Tobias Smollett was born at Dalquhurn in Dunbartonshire in March 1721 the grandson of Sir James Smollett a judge who brought him up after his father Archibald Smollett had died when the boy was only two years old. Sir James (1648-1731), like John Locke, had been a supporter of the peaceful revolution which succeeded in replacing James II where Monmouth's forces had failed, he was knighted by William III in 1698. He was a member of the commission which framed the articles for the union of Scotland and England and was the first representative of Dunbartonshire Boroughs in the British parliament. Tobias was sent to Dunbarton Grammar School and Glasgow University where he was a student with William Hunter. There he studied medicine, he had hoped to go into the army but had been forestalled in application by his elder brother. Tobias was apprenticed to Dr John Gordon, who became a well known and respected Glasgow physician and of whom he wrote "Had he lived in ancient Rome he would have been honoured with a statue at the public expense". His friend Dr John Moore (1729-1802) was also assistant to John Gordon and was later to become Smollett's biographer and editor. Moore was another of those doctors who became a man of letters. This John Moore was the father of Lieutenant-General Sir John Moore who was mortally wounded at the battle of Corunna in 1809. Smollett's friend served as an army surgeon, travelled with the Duke of Hamilton, practised in

Clarges Street in London, and had his first novel *Zeluco* published in 1786.

Smollett went off to try his fortune in London taking with him a tragedy, *The Regicide*, written in an unfulfilled hope of having it performed. He set up in practice but was never a very successful doctor; he found the going difficult and looking round for a living decided to take the examination for a naval surgeon. We have an entertaining account of that examination which took place in December 1739, derived from the records of the Barber-Surgeons, recalled by Jessie Dobson in her article *Smollett the Surgeon* (1957) and from Smollett's own version in his *Adventures of Roderick Random* (1748). The examiners were important people in the medical profession of their day: William Petty, Master of the Barber-Surgeons and surgeon to the London Hospital; Claudius Amyard surgeon to St Georges and James Ferne and William Cheselden, surgeons to St Thomas's. Cheselden, the eminent anatomist, was noted for his work on bones – *Osteographia*, published in 1733, with fine illustrations beautifully etched, was the most accurate account of the subject available at the time – and for removing stones from the bladder through the perineum by lithotomy, normally in two minutes flat but sometimes in less than one, a speed highly prized by patients in the days before anaesthetics. He was one of the founders of the Company of Surgeons which separated from the Barbers in 1745 and of which he was Master in 1746; it was to become the Royal College of Surgeons of England in 1800.

The account of this examination designed to determine medical competence and suitability for naval service contains situations some of which are familiar even today: the crowd of young men waiting to go in, besieging a pale, tremulous, wild-eyed youth as he came out, to hear what he had been asked and how he had answered, and Smollett's entry, in terror on first confronting the examiners, not helped by being attacked by William Petty who asked him how he dared to be so presumptuous as to present himself before them for assessment with so little experience. However, conditions improved when Cheselden tried to put him at his ease and find out what he knew. Then there was the facetious, unidentified humorist who asked him how he would treat a man who had had his head shot off; but here our Tobias scored by humbly replying that he had no knowledge of any cure being proposed for such a condition. After this the examiners fell into an argument amongst themselves about the proper treatment to follow with wounds of the intestines. This examination was little more than a masquerade because the demand for naval medical officers at the time was so urgent that there was small chance that any candidate would fail.

Before long Smollett was sailing to the West Indies as Surgeon's Mate on the *Chichester*, sent under Sir Charles Ogle to reinforce Admiral Vernon's fleet in the Caribbean by Sir Robert Walpole in an attempt to re-establish the country's position after the treaty of Utrecht and to maintain her maritime supremacy. Smollett gave a fanciful account of the attack on Carthagena in 1741 in *Roderick Random* but described the action with greater accuracy in his *History of England*. Admiral Vernon refused to bring his ships in close enough to bombard the fort of Saint-Lazar and General Wentworth mismanaged the attack, his troops losing their way so that, without proper direction, they stormed the strongest point carrying scaling ladders which were too short.

Smollett wrote of the need for unified command:

> The Admiral and General had contracted a hearty contempt for each other, and took all opportunities of expressing their mutual dislike: far from acting vigorously in concert, for the advantage of the community, they maintained a mutual reserve, and separate cabals; and each proved more eager for the disgrace of his rival, than zealous for the honour of the nation... The conductors of this unfortunate expedition agreed in nothing but the expediency of a speedy retreat from this scene of misery and disgrace.

They had to withdraw to Jamaica leaving many dead.

In *Roderick Random*, the hero, suffers bitter attacks and false accusations made by the surgeon Macshane, because Random saves Jack Rattlin from the unnecessary amputation proposed by his senior when his leg is broken by a fall from the main-yard. There is a horrifying account of the cramped, insanitary conditions suffered by British sailors and the terrible effects of the resulting disease. On the Carthagena expedition half of the 16,000 soldiers and sailors who died did not do so in battle but from Yellow Fever. The story aroused public indignation and the resentment of the Naval authorities but did have some influence in persuading the Admiralty to an improvement in hygiene and diet. Thomas Carlyle in his *History of Frederick II of Prussia (1858-1865)* spoke in his wry manner of "Excellent Tobias" and his "Mission to take Portraiture of English Seamanhood with due grimness, due fidelity; and convey the same to remote generations before it vanish". The task of improving conditions for sailors in the navy was promoted more successfully by Dr James Lind (1716-1794) who published *A Treatise on Scurvy* in 1753, instituted the first controlled clinical trials and became famous for his service as a Naval Medical Officer. However, Dickens was still thundering against the plight of sick soldiers shipped back from India in 1860 in *The Great Tasmania's Cargo*.

In Jamaica Smollett met his future wife, Nancy Lascelles, the daughter of an English planter. Thus advantages, other than his roughly-bought experience, came to him from this naval excursion for not only did his wife's money keep him for some years while his practice declined and his writing began to prosper, but she bore him a much-loved daughter and remained with him to the end through all the ups and downs of his varied life. When her father died they had great trouble with a law suit and only recovered a fraction of her £3000 dowry invested in land and slaves in Jamaica.

Smollett had settled to practice in Downing Street, Westminster, and obtained his degree of M.D. Aberdeen in 1750. He moved to Monmouth House, once called Great House, an Elizabethan mansion in Lawrence Lane, Chelsea, demolished in 1835, which was less expensive than Downing Street. Here he was writing in earnest with an astonishing output. His only contribution to medical literature was published in 1752 after several visits to Bath where his idea of setting up in practice was scotched by his censorious appraisal. This was entitled *An Essay on the External use of Water, Particular Remarks upon the present Method of using the Mineral Waters at Bath in Somersetshire, and a Plan for rendering them more safe, agreeable and efficacious* by T. Smollett, M.D. As usual he had become indignant about unhygienic inefficiency, complaining that diseased persons of all ages, sexes and conditions were promiscuously admitted into an open bath affording little or no shelter from the inclemencies of the weather. His denunciations of conditions in Bath appeared again through the fine fury of Matthew Bramble in *Humphrey Clinker*. Smollett wanted to protect the bathers both from prying eyes and the danger of infection, with good practical sense though with poor scientific argument. He still believed in such oddities as cures achieved by the laying on of the hands of a person who had been hanged. He was not a great success as a doctor, though he practised for thirteen years and campaigned well for improvements in public health, he was, however, to give up the practice of medicine for literature, to his advantage as well as ours. Perhaps his comment on a doctor in *Peregrine Pickle* was a rueful reference to himself.

> It has been supposed, that his want of success in a profession where merit cannot always insure fame and affluence, was owing to his failing to render himself agreeable to the fair sex, whose favour is certainly of consequence to all candidates for eminence whether in physic or divinity.

The novels contain many references to medical matters which have been summarised by Dr Underwood in *Medicine and Science in the Writings of Smollett* (1937). There is much talk of people being deprived of their senses, of dropsy, fever and bleeding, at which Rory Random was an expert, but most of this is light-hearted comment on the medicine of his day rather than, a serious appreciation of its problems. The treatment recommended by Smollett was rather confused since he believed in improving muscle tone and purifying body fluids by cold baths, exercise, purging and bleeding followed by helping natural filtration by increasing fluid intake to build up what had been removed. Smollett was a reformer long before he was a scientist. In *Humphrey Clinker* Mr Burdock, after a quarrel in a public house with an excise-man ending in a bout of single-stick, is brought home tongue-tied with shame and terribly belaboured about the pate. A country apothecary called Grieve (who for some curious reason turns out to be a reformed Count Fathom) is called and prescribes blood letting, a poultice and patience. However, Burdock's mother calls in a York surgeon who prepares to trepan on the grounds that he can't tell if there is a fracture until he takes off the scalp and that either way the operation could be of service in giving vent to any blood that might be extravasated above or below the *dura mater*. With his periwig off and a nightcap on, he is about to begin when the patient suddenly finds his voice, grasps the assistants, bellows "I ha'n't lived so long in Yorkshire to be trepanned by such vermin as you" and leaps to the floor. The surgeon, with his advice spurned, is now sure that the patient's brain must be injured, but Burdock has the last word with "A man's scull is not to be bored every time his head his broken".

In *Roderick Random*, Smollett described Crab the surgeon with all his bizarre, freakish and exaggerated detail in a most amusingly grotesque portrait.

> This member of the faculty was aged fifty, about five feet high, and ten round the belly, his face was capacious as a full moon and much of the complexion of a mulberry; his nose, resembling a powder-horn, was swelled to an enormous size, and studded all over with carbuncles; and his little grey eyes reflected the rays in such an oblique manner that, while he looked a person full in the face, one would have imagined he was admiring the buckle of his shoe.

In his *Continuation of the Complete History of England*, Smollett sums up the medical achievements of the reign of George II with some complacency:

> Tho' few discoveries of importance were made in medicine, yet that art was well understood in all its different branches; and many of its professors distinguished themselves in other provinces of literature. Besides the medical essays of London and Edinburgh, the physician's library was enriched with many useful modern productions; with the works of the classical Friend, the elegant Mead, the accurate Huxham, and the philosophical Pringle. The Art of Midwifery was elucidated by science, reduced to fixed principles, and almost wholly consigned into the hands of men practitioners. The researches of anatomy were prosecuted to some curious discoveries by the ingenuity and dexterity of a Hunter and a Monro. The numerous hospitals in London contributed to the improvements of surgery, which was brought to perfection under the auspices of a Cheselden and a Sharpe.

The Smollett's home became a meeting place for Scottish

medical men in London: John Armstrong (1709-1779). another doctor-writer, John Clephane, William Hunter, George Macaulay, Archibald Pitcairne, who was a professor in Leyden a Jacobite and founder of the medical faculty at Edinburgh, and Sir William Smellie who sought Smollett's help in revising his *Treatise on Midwifery* (1751). Scottish trained doctors were beginning to dominate English medicine. Celebrities such as Garrick, Goldsmith, Sterne and Wilkes were also visitors at Monmouth House. Usually in financial difficulty, Smollett spent what he earned and then was short of money until the next payment. In 1754, like William Denton, he was robbed while travelling on a coach between Chelsea and London, which now seems to be such an unlikely setting for a wild excursion on which one might be likely to be held up at some lonely spot. William Hunter remained his friend until his death and five letters from Smollett to Hunter are in the Hunter-Baillie Collection, one, written from Nice, refers to his poor health and the advice received there from

> Dr Fitzmorrice an honest physician of the Place; and I consulted Dr Fizes the Boerhaave of Montpellier, who is an old Sordid Scoundrel, and an old woman into the Bargain... he prescribed Bouillons of Land Tortoise for a fortnight, opiates at night and then a course of Goats milk, but not a word of Exercise – I found he had a Set of Phrases and Prescriptions which he applied in all Cases indiscriminately for when I arrived at Nice Mr Mayne an English Gentleman (now dead) showed me a Paper of Directions written by Fizes in exactly the same words which he had used to me.

The novels continued to appear: *Roderick Random* was followed by *Peregrine Pickle* in 1751, *Ferdinand Count Fathom* came out in 1753 and *Lancelot Greaves* in 1760. As well as novels, translations, *A Compendium of Voyages* in seven volumes, a massive Universal History of which he was planner and part author, magazines, accounts of travels and satires poured out laced with controversy and attacks, one even on an old friend, Wilkes, who, however, got the better of the exchange. The novels are of their day, full of fabulous characters, actual as well as fictitious, serious and ludicrous, with lively descriptions of towns such as Bath, London, Harrogate, Scarborough, Edinburgh and Glasgow, the whole interspersed with comment, reforming anger and notes on such varied matters as free speech, the British Museum and the University of Edinburgh. The stories gloriously evocative of laughter, are thronged with people and places of the eighteenth century. That lovely character, Matthew Bramble, is a classic figure to rank with the great men of fiction but is surely Smollett's own reflection, irascible, generous and adventurous with a weakness for unfortunate rogues. Thackeray said that *Humphrey Clinker* "is I do think, the most laughable story that has ever been written since the goodly art of novel-writing began". He also wrote of Smollett:

> His brain had been busied with a hundred different schemes; he had been reviewer and historian, critic, medical writer, poet, pamphleteer. He had fought endless literary battles; and braved and wielded for years the cudgels of controversy. It was a hard and savage fight in those days, and a niggard pay. He was oppressed by illness, age, narrow fortune; but his spirit was still resolute, and his courage steady; the battle over, he could do justice to the enemy with whom he had been so finely engaged, and give a not unfriendly grasp to the hand that had mauled him.

Grahame Smith in *The Novel and Society* (1984) quotes John Barth as saying,

> Smollett may lack breadth of vision, but width he had aplenty, in all directions, more than Richardson or Fielding combined. Sailors, soldiers, fine gentlemen and ladies, whores, homosexuals, cardsharpers, fortune hunters, tradesmen of all description, clerics, fops, scholars, lunatics, highwaymen, peasants and poets both male and female – they crowd on a stage that extends from Glasgow to Guinea, from Paris to Paraguay, and among themselves perpetuate battles, debaucheries, swindles, shanghais, duels, seductions, rescues, pranks, poems, shipwrecks, heroisms, murders and marriages.

Smollett had a considerable influence on Dickens, who records in *Pictures from Italy* (1846) how when travelling with Kate they went from Pisa to Leghorn which was, he comments, "made illustrious by Smollett's grave". Edgar Johnson in his *Charles Dickens* (1952) says,

Of classical literature he knew little and showed hardly the slightest influence. But he knew the entire range of English prose fiction, from Bunyan and Defoe through Swift, Fielding, Richardson, Smollett, Sterne and Goldsmith, to Cooper, and Scott.

When Dickens was weaving his own childhood into that of his creation David Copperfield, David, almost stupefied by the harshness of the Murdstones, was saved by one circumstance:

> My father had left a small collection of books in a little room upstairs, to which I had access (for it adjoined my own) and which nobody else in our house ever troubled. From that blessed little room, Roderick Random, Peregrine Pickle, Humphrey Clinker, Tom Jones, the Vicar of Wakefield, Don Quixote, Gil Blas and Robinson Crusoe, came out, a glorious host, to keep me company. They kept alive my fancy, and my hope of something beyond that place and time... I have seen Tom Pipes go climbing up the church-steeple; I have watched Strap, with the knapsack on his back, stopping to rest himself upon the wicket-gate; and I *know* that the Commodore Trunnion held that club with Mr Pickle, in the parlour of our little village alehouse.

The earlier Dickens works adopted Smollett's special episodic pattern in which we follow the adventures of the leading characters. They were told in just as robust but in a slightly more decorous manner to suit his superficially more dainty public. These characters created by Smollett and Dickens meet on their way a fantastic and sometimes grotesque series both of rogues and of staunch lovable comrades while they are developing their mettle and acquiring some authority and self-reliance. There is a Scotsman in *Humphrey Clinker* who keeps his medicine bottle on the breakfast table to take his unsuspected tipple in the style of Sairey Gamp's "something cold out of a teapot". Another similarity is that the vicissitudes of a hero's journey are often shared with a devoted companion such as Hugh Strap and Tom Pipes or Sam Weller and poor Smike. *John Bull* reviewing *Pickwick* wrote

Smollett never did anything better.

Edgar Johnson said

The very scenes of Pickwick though free from Smollett's astringency and coarseness, are steeped in his knowledge of the shadier sides of existence; and the invigorating air that streams through them has blown over the same highroads and coppices and downs that Fielding knew.

Dickens lifted some incidents and a few characters almost direct from Smollett but made them memorable by refurbishing them with his own fine brand of understanding.

Smollett's health began to fail in 1763. His daughter Elizabeth died aged 15, a terrible blow, he and his wife were "overwhelmed with unutterable sorrow". His health broke and he knew that his only hope lay in living abroad in a better climate. So Smollett and his wife went off to France and Italy for two years in 1763. His account of this expedition, *Travels through France and Italy* (1766) contains some of his most engaging writing with particular descriptions of the town, territory and climate of Nice, and some harsh comments on foreign medicine, French "politeness" and poor accommodation – "stewed a week in a paltry inn". On their way to the city of Nice, "This night we passed at Cannes, a little fishing town, agreeably situate on the beach of the sea". He returned in better health for a while, wandered around Britain and was soon in trouble again. David Hume tried to help him to obtain a diplomatic post abroad, without success. In 1768 the Smolletts left England again for Pisa and Florence, settling in Leghorn in 1770 where he was attended by Dr Giovanni Gentili and where he finished his last novel *Humphrey Clinker* (1771), published just before his death. It is said that his last words were a courageous, thoughtful reassurance to his devoted and long suffering wife: "All is well, my dear".

Bouce, Paul-Gabriel *The Novels of Tobias Smollett* Longman, London 1976.

Carlyle, A. *The Autobiography of Dr Alexander Carlyle of Inveresk* Edited by John Hill Burton, Edinburgh, 1910.

Dobson, J. *Smollett the Surgeon* Ann. Roy. Coll. Surg. Eng., 1957, 20, 260-264.

Drinker, C.E. *Doctor Smollett* Ann. Med. Hist. 1925, 7, 31-47.

Giddings, Robert *The Tradition of Smollett* Methuen & Co., London, 1967.

Johnson, E. *Charles Dickens* Hamish Hamilton, London, 1952.

Jones, C.E. *Tobias Smollett - The Doctor as Man of Letters* J. Hist. Med. 1957, 12, 337-348.

Knapp, L.M. *Tobias Smollett Doctor of Man and Manners* Princeton University Press, 1949.

Musher, D.M. *The Medical Views of Dr Tobias Smollett* Bull. Hist. Med. 1967, 41, 455-462.

Smith, Grahame *The Novel and Society. Defoe to George Eliot* Batsford Academic and Educational, London, 1984.

Smollett, T. *Letter to William Hunter* Annals of the Roy. Coll. of Surg. of Eng. 1980, 62, 146-149.

Underwood, E.A. *Medicine and Science in the Writings of Smollett* Proc. Roy. Soc. Med. 1937, 30, 961-974.

OLIVER GOLDSMITH

CHAPTER FIVE

The Notable Man and the Lexicographer

"A GENTLENESS, delicacy, and purity of feeling distinguishes whatever he wrote, and bears a correspondence to the generosity of a disposition which knew no bounds but his last guinea." So wrote Sir Walter Scott of Oliver Goldsmith (1730-1774); Thackeray added, "To be the most beloved of English writers, what a title that is for a man"; and Oliver Gogarty called him "the gentle Irish Virgil". Yet, as well as a great literary artist, he was wild and reserved by turns and a gambler, nearly always in debt, often retrieved by family or friends. When James Northcote told Sir Joshua Reynolds that he was anxious to meet Goldsmith, Sir Joshua invited them both to dine but, as they met, embarrassed Northcote by suddenly asking why he had wished to know Goldsmith. He answered hurriedly and in some confusion that it was because he was a notable man. This seemed so contrary to his character and conduct that Sir Joshua announced with a hearty laugh that in future Goldsmith should always be called "the Notable Man" and John Ginger took this as the title of his excellent book about him (1977).

Oliver Goldsmith has a special appeal both as man and writer. Foolish, of course, irresponsible, over anxious to shine in company, attempting to protect his vulnerability by boasting and trying to counteract his ugliness by wearing highly coloured clothes. Extravagant and impulsive but wonderfully kind, he was immensely talented and had a delightfully sharp insight into both the virtues and the vices of his friends. Neither Hester Thrale nor James Boswell understood or valued him as Samuel Johnson did; they were too easily biased against those favoured by Johnson, including each other. At their first meeting Boswell wrote "Mr Goldsmith, a curious, odd, pedantic fellow with some genius". There are many good stories about Goldsmith but one of the most affecting, revealing and woefully funny was his reaction on being

103

told that the new comedy by Hugh Kelly was doing better business at the theatre than his own play; looking closely at himself in a mirror he was heard to say, "A handsomer Fellow than Kelly however".

Oliver Goldsmith was Irish; it would be hard to imagine him as anything else; however, his mother was called Anne Jones, and James Prior in his *Life of Goldsmith* (1837) says that the family is supposed to have come from Crayford in Kent. The Goldsmiths of County Roscommon were nevertheless descended from a Roman Catholic priest who became a Protestant minister. It was this minister's great-grandson, the impecunious Rev Charles Goldsmith, who married Anne Jones, the daughter of a schoolmaster whose parents thought that she had made a bad match. To help her out, they secured a curacy for her husband in Pallasmore under a Mr Green and leased forty acres, in her name, to provide something extra in the way of farm income. Their children, Margery, Catherine, Henry and Jane were followed by Oliver. Two years after Oliver was born his father succeeded to the living on Mr Green's death and the family moved to a good house in Lissoy, with stables, a dairy, an orchard, farm buildings and seventy acres rented at eight shillings an acre. Here Oliver grew up and three more brothers were born, Maurice, Charles and John.

Oliver was a tough, sturdy child but suffered a severe setback from smallpox at 8 years of age which left him scarred for life. His father was resolved to see that his sons had a good education; his mother was convinced, on what must have seemed to others most slender grounds, that Oliver was a prodigy and that a university education must be secured for him. In this she had the support of her husband's brother-in-law the Rev Thomas Contarine who, with his wife Jane, had taken a special interest in Oliver. He was welcome at their house where he found books and music. Jane played the harpsichord and Oliver taught himself to play the flute. He owed a great deal to his tolerant uncle, a man with a most exotic background for he was the grandson of a Venetian aristocrat who had run away from Italy with a nun, married her and settled in Ireland. Uncle Contarine saw to it that Oliver became a student at Trinity College in Dublin in 1745 where he had to help pay his way by waiting at high table and doing other jobs at college.

Student life in Dublin was a rowdy affair, and Oliver was often in the thick of it, putting a bailiff under a pump and being arrested when a mob stormed the Black Dog prison gates. He got out of these scrapes and was awarded an exhibition but promptly spent the money on a party for his friends at which there was a lot of noise and more trouble. At that time he started writing ballads some of which he managed to sell for five shillings each.

His father died in 1747 while Oliver was still a student, and his mother had to move from the comfortable house in Lissoy to a Ballymahon cottage with the younger children. Meanwhile Oliver continued to give trouble of his own peculiar kind. Wandering round in Dublin he encountered a family in such poor circumstances that he took the blankets from his own bed to give to them and, splitting the remaining bedding, slept among the feathers. He decided to emigrate, sold his meagre belongings and set out for Cork where he gave his last two half-crowns to a woman with eight small children and had to be fetched back and returned to Dublin by his brother Henry. He later repaid the debt in his own best manner, conferring immortality on his brother by a delightful dedication to him of his first great poem *The Traveller, or a Prospect of Society* (1764). Uncle Contarine, hoping that Oliver might succeed to his living, tried to persuade him into the ministry, but he turned up at his interview in scarlet breeches and, aware of his moral misgivings, talked himself out of any such prospect. A short spell as a tutor to the Flinn family in Roscommon, then another emigratory trip to Cork where, inevitably, he lost his money and missed the boat, led to a blistering attack from his mother on his return home, where she was struggling to bring up three sons between the ages of 11 and 15. Given £50 by his uncle, he set out for London to study law at the Temple, but lost it all gambling, having gotten no further than Dublin. As at last chance and through his own preference, he was sent off to Edinburgh in 1752 to study medicine.

Life was hard in Edinburgh but he took some interest in medicine. In his old style, however, he managed to escape to tour the highlands on a pony, was more assiduous in attending the Edinburgh Musical Society than his lectures and had to be rescued from debt once more by some fellow Irish students. He invented stories which he hoped would account for his troubles in ways which his uncle might accept. His Irish tales, flute playing, love of literature and general good company, secured him visits to the Duke of Hamilton and a touch of luxury which, however, was not altogether to his liking. Nevertheless, there was much of interest for him in Edinburgh at what was one of the finest medical teaching schools; members of the faculty had studied in Leyden under the great Doctor Boerhaave and excellent ward rounds at the Royal Infirmary were conducted by Professor John Rutherford. Tobias Smollett, who was nine years older than Goldsmith and died three years before him, wrote in *Humphrey Clinker*:

> The University of Edinburgh is supplied with excellent professors in all the sciences; and the medical school, in particular, is famous all over Europe. The students of this art have the best opportunity of learning it to perfection, in all its branches, and there are different courses for the *theory of medicine*, and the *practice of medicine*; for *anatomy, chemistry, botany* and the *materia medica*, over and above those of *mathematics* and *experimental philosophy*; and all these are given by men of distinguished talents. What renders this part of education still more complete is the advantage of attending the infirmary, which is the best instituted charitable foundation that I ever knew.

Money from the family, chiefly from his uncle, kept Goldsmith going, but his nature asserted itself and he soon grew restless; without qualifying, he set off for Holland, having drawn twice the agreed amount of his allowance. He spent a year in Leyden but it is uncertain how much studying he did there, and he left after winning money gambling but soon lost it again. In 1755-6 he toured through Flanders, France, Germany, Switzerland and Italy where he stayed six months in Padua. He put up at monasteries whenever he could, and may have acted as a tutor for a while in Geneva. These experiences were to play their part – elaborated and furbished for the occasion, combining the autobiographical with a burlesque of the Smollett-picaresque type of fiction in which the hero experiences a series of episodic adventures – in the account of his travels given by the Vicar's eldest son George in *The Vicar of Wakefield* (1766). George left home after his engagement to Arabella Wilmot had been dissolved when his father lost his money. First he tried writing, dressing up three paradoxes with some ingenuity but no success, then merely writing for bread, though unable to suppress his lurking passion for applause and he

> consumed that time in efforts after excellence which takes up little room, when it should have been more advantageously employed in the diffusive productions of fruitful mediocrity. George then learned the art of living off subscriptions raised for books which are never written but was too proud to stoop to such indignities. Abandoning literature George was employed by a nobleman to perform a number of curious services for him, attending at auctions, carrying his corkscrew, standing godfather to his butler's children, and even fighting a duel on his employer's behalf. Next he tried to teach English to the Dutch, without any knowledge of their language, and Greek at the University of Louvain, where they wanted no such instruction. He sang songs for the peasants in Flanders, tried the art of picture-buying in Paris, became a tutor, then a philosophical disputant and, back in England, an actor with a travelling company.

When Oliver Goldsmith returned from his own adventurous tour of Europe in 1756, he found that his uncle had died, his allowance had ceased, and only £10 had been left to him in his uncle's will.

In London, where he was to find fame, Goldsmith first tried to practice medicine almost certainly without a qualification, though he put it about that he had obtained a degree in Padua, and his friends long believed that he had a degree from Dublin. He was forced at first to serve as an apothecary's assistant, then ran a medical practice for the poor on Bankside, to the south of London Bridge, but his medical efforts were no great success. Johnson's friend Topham Beauclerc advised Goldsmith to give up medicine on the grounds that if he were resolved to kill he should concentrate on his enemies. For a while Goldsmith became a schoolmaster at the Rev John Milner's boys school at Peckham at £20 a year and to help matters out, took what proved to be a fateful step by becoming a proof reader at Samuel Richardson's printing house. While abroad, he had written part of a poem from which *The Traveller*, his first serious claim to literary attention, was to be developed. He had looked down on Europe in a pensive mood "placed on high above the storm's career" seeing "Creation's charms".

"Yet oft a sigh prevails, and sorrows fall,
To see the hoard of human bliss so small".

He had seen much scenic beauty and some solid human worth but mostly man seemed base. Goldsmith wrote of Italy: "Could Nature's bounty satisfy the breast, The sons of Italy were surely blest", but added: "Man seems the only growth that dwindles here" where they are "even in penance planning sins anew". His Traveller in a weary search for that "bliss which only centres in the mind" found that "His first best country ever is at home".

"There all around the gentlest breezes stray,
There gentle music melts on every spray;
Creation's mildest charms are there combin'd,
Extremes are only in the master's mind;
Stern o'er each bosom reason holds her state,
With daring aims, irregularly great,
Pride in their port, defiance in their eye,
I see the lords of human kind pass by
Intent on high designs, a thoughtful band,
By forms unfashion'd, fresh from Nature's hand;
Fierce in their native hardiness of soul,
True to imagin'd right above controul,
While even the peasant boast these rights to scan,
And learns to venerate himself as man."

Ralph Griffiths, who started the *Monthly Review*, met Goldsmith, who was beginning to move in literary circles, was impressed by the lively conversation of this travelled young man with a love of literature, and took him on the staff at the lavish salary of £100 a year plus board and lodging. One of his colleagues on the *Monthly Review* was James Grainger (1721-1766), another doctor-writer, who went to the West Indies in 1759 to practice medicine and there wrote *Sugar Cane*, a poem running into four books. On the *Monthly Review* Goldsmith met many well known literary figures who introduced him to a new world. Here he was kept busy doing reviews in which he managed at times to express ideas of his own and to make forays against hypocrisy. At last he had a secure income, good hours of work and a chance to settle down to an occupation well suited to his talents. But, typically, he thought that Griffiths was exploiting him, wondered whether he should go to India, started a book on no less a subject than

European learning and literature from classical times, and gave up his steady job. Fortunately for him the Indian venture fell through, and a new journal the *Critical Review*, edited by Tobias Smollett, accepted two of his articles. Griffiths was not one to allow a writer to defect to a rival journal without protest, and he immediately threatened legal action over a tailor's bill which Goldsmith had asked him to endorse, and over books he had been given to review and had pawned. Goldsmith was reduced to humble apologies, very much against the grain, in order to avoid going to goal. The *Critical Review* was owned by Alexander Hamilton, a man sympathetic to Goldsmith, who became yet another of those prepared to bail him out. Now, however, Goldsmith was only paid for his copy, his guaranteed salary had ceased. However, things were looking up, Dr Goldsmith had come to work for Dr Smollett.

Goldsmith's circumstances were still precarious despite his work for the *Critical Review* so he had to take cheap lodgings in an over-crowded block in Green Arbour Court near the Old Bailey. Here his landlady, Mrs Butler, became famous through Hogarth's portrait, "Goldsmith's Hostess, Mrs Butler". Goldsmith had the habit of inviting the Butler children and their friends to his room to dance to his flute and, when their father was arrested for debt, pawned his much loved fine clothes to help the family.

In 1759 *Goldsmith's Enquiry into the Present State of Polite Learning* was published and, predictably, was attacked with gusto in the *Monthly Review*. In 1760 he was writing for John Newbery in the *Public Ledger*, producing creative work twice-weekly as journalist and philosopher, for which he was paid £100 a year. Now, at last, at the age of 30, he was an established writer, sending contributions to several new magazines. He moved into better quarters in Wine Office Court off Fleet Street where *The Vicar of Wakefield* was written with its charm, country scenes, domesticity, innocent unsuspecting Vicar gloriously unaware of his own eccentricities, and those shrewd comments on human nature which have held the affection of so many people for so long.

It was at this point, just at the start of the reign of George III that Goldsmith became a personage in the literary world of London. He already knew many of the famous people of his day such as Hogarth, 31 years older than he, and his contemporaries,

David Garrick and Joshua Reynolds. In 1761 he met Samuel
Johnson, who was then 52. He and Johnson had a mutual friend
in the Rev. Thomas Percy and Goldsmith invited them both to a
supper party at Wine Office Court. Percy took Johnson on this
first visit, and

> As they went together, the former (Percy) was much struck with
> the studied neatness of Johnson's dress. He had on a new suit
> of cloaths, a new wig nicely powdered, and everything about
> him so perfectly dissimilar from his usual appearance that his
> companion could not help inquiring the cause of this singular
> transformation. "Why, sir" said Johnson, "I hear that
> Goldsmith, who is a very great sloven, justifies his disregard of
> cleanliness and decency by quoting my practice, and I am
> desirous this night to show him a better example."

He had been badly misinformed, Goldsmith was a lover of fine
clothes and bright colours which kept him regularly in debt to his
tailor.

Johnson and Goldsmith were very different people who had
much in common. Each had had a shaky start writing hack work for
magazines, living in poverty, schoolmastering when things were bad,
and failing to acquire a feeling that they were themselves of any real
consequence until they were 30 years of age. In addition they shared
a great fund of instant sympathy with the unfortunate. Their
differences, however, were marked. Goldsmith's type of easy,
light-hearted anecdote which, with his flute playing, had gone down
favourably in other company, was not well suited to the more serious
intellectual climate of the Johnson circle. His desire to be noticed and
admired and his lack of sound opinion, combined with attempts to
be too bright, led him to foolish excess at times. Goldsmith had to
write to be fully appreciated, Johnson, who understood this,
remained a supporter and his friend until he died. He once came to
Goldsmith's assistance in what has become known as "The Bottle of
Madeira Story". The best version of which, whether quite true or
not, is inevitably Boswell's given in Johnson's "own exact narration"
and put forward with typical economy of narrative and clarity of
expression:

> I received one morning a message from poor Goldsmith that
> he was in great distress, and as it was not in his power to come

to me, begging that I should come to him as soon as possible. I sent him a guinea, and promised to come to him directly. I accordingly went as soon as I was drest, and found that his landlady had arrested him for his rent, at which he was in a violent passion. I perceived that he had already changed my guinea, and had got a bottle of Madeira and a glass before him. I put the cork in the bottle, desired he would be calm, and began to talk to him of the means by which he might be extricated. He then told me that he had a novel ready for the press, which he produced to me. I looked into it, and saw its merits; told the landlady I should soon return, and having gone to a bookseller, sold it for sixty pounds. I brought Goldsmith the money, and he discharged his rent, not without rating his landlady in a high tone for having used him so ill.

It is natural that this delightful and revealing tale should have become known as "The Bottle of Madeira Story", but it is memorable at a different level for it is also the story of how it was Samuel Johnson who chanced to be the first person to read and to appreciate *The Vicar of Wakefield*.

Newberry, in an attempt to keep his leading writer working and out of trouble, persuaded Goldsmith to move to Islington where he appointed the landlady, Miss Elizabeth Fleming, to be his guardian and banker. Newbery was to be repaid for Goldsmith's expenses by off-setting them against his literary earnings and Miss Fleming was to manage his affairs with care but with some liberality. It was hoped, by these means, both to contain his debts and to hold onto the services of so valuable and gifted a writer. The system worked fairly well for a while, disaster was avoided and literary output secured though debts were never quite eliminated. It was clearly impossible to change Goldsmith's habits. Johnson later said to Boswell that Goldsmith had squandered money "by every artifice of acquisition and folly of expense. But let not his failings be remembered; he was a very great man".

In 1764 Joshua Reynolds was the prime mover in organising a discussion group to form a sounding board for Samuel Johnson, which was to meet at the Turk's Head in Gerrard Street. The members represented many interests, there were, for example, Samuel Dyer F.R.S., Edmund Burke, David Garrick, the lawyers

John Hawkins and Robert Chambers, Anthony Chamier a civil servant, two young Oxford friends of Johnson, Topham Beauclerk and Bennet Langton, and for medicine Dr Christopher Nugent, Burke's father-in-law. First thought of as "The Literary Club" it soon became known simply, and with justifiable authority, as "The Club". Goldsmith was a founder member and he was the one taking the chair when James Boswell was proposed for membership.

In 1774 one of those added to "The Club" was Dr Fordyce, of whom a good story is retold in a footnote in the Birkbeck Hill edition of *Boswell's Life of Johnson* (1887):

> Rogers (*Table-Talk* p.23) tells how Dr Fordyce, who sometimes drank a great deal, was summoned to a lady patient when he was conscious that he had had too much wine. Feeling her pulse, and finding himself unable to count its beats, he muttered, "Drunk, by G–". Next morning a letter from her was put into his hand. "She too well knew", she wrote, "that he had discovered the unfortunate condition in which she had been, and she entreated him to keep the matter secret in consideration of the enclosed (a hundred-pound bank-note)".

Another doctor appeared in the Johnson circle, though in a more humble, dependent position. This was Robert Levett (1705-1782), born in Hull, who became a servant to Lord Cadogan, saved some money for travel and worked as a waiter in a Paris coffee-house. There he met some surgeons who made it possible for him to be admitted to lectures in anatomy and pharmacy. Returning to London he took lodgings near Charing Cross and set up as "a practitioner of physic". He was a surly, uncouth man, often drunk, a condition supported by his poor patients who tended to pay him, if at all, in drink. Johnson met this grotesque man of no learning and found him to be conscientious, or, as Goldsmith said to Boswell, "he is poor and honest which is enough to Johnson" and with typical reaction, took him under his wing to join the collection of misfits he had living in his house and wrote a poem about him.

Johnson's own medical history is of special interest since it accounts for so much of his odd behaviour and for his struggles with his compulsive temperament. It is worth a digression because it also raises questions of fundamental importance in the

112

understanding of human behaviour and particularly of the individual's speed of reaction.

Johnson's mother had brought him up to believe in hell-fire and to fear retribution, and instilled in him an excessive anxiety about health. He had to put up with many ills from the age of 2½ years. He was touched for the King's Evil (scrofula) by Queen Anne at St James's Palace in 1712, and the scars which resulted in his neck from what were presumably tuberculous abscesses (this was 170 years before the tubercle bacillus was identified) were visible for the rest of his life. He was short sighted but, more importantly, the loss of sight in his left eye may have been caused by tuberculous keratitis. Later on he developed bronchitis and emphysema, had high blood pressure and dyspepsia, recovered from a stroke in 1783, had dropsy, some degree of deafness and a hydrocele and died with renal and heart disease aged 75. He dabbled in medicine, criticised doctors' treatment, wrote articles for Robert James's *Medical Dictionary*, sent his own prescriptions to his acquaintance, even recommending treatment to his old friend Thomas Lawrence, the President of the Royal College of Physicians, when he advised that his swollen hand would be helped by "electricity if it were frequently and diligently supplied". He knew William Heberden (1710-1801) who distinguished chickenpox from smallpox and described *angina pectoris*, and Percival Pott (1714-1788) of Pott's fracture and Pott's disease of the spine, was attended by Sir Lucas Pepys and by his godfather Samuel Swynfen early in life and by Richard Brocklesby, Dr Thomas Young's uncle, at the end. A necropsy was performed by James Wilson with Heberden present.

Much has been written about this long catalogue of ailments, to which Johnson himself often referred, but though they must have had an effect on his behaviour and his temper, far more interesting and likely to have had a greater effect on his literary work, conversation and relations with other people, were his morbid fears and his involuntary movements of which he rarely spoke. The disease which gave rise to Johnson's particular form of excitement, and the reverse disease which suppresses those very regions of the brain involved, are better understood than they were and have initiated a study of quite fascinating interest. Johnson was given to compulsive acts, touching posts, stepping over paving joints, performing a series of gestures before entering or leaving a room, he was also subject to involuntary jerky movements, he made noises, let out whistles and blowing sounds and repeated words, phrases or prayers again and again (echolalia). His tics, sounds and gesticulations were quite alarming to those who met him for the first time. Johnson was twice rejected when applying for posts as a schoolmaster on the grounds that he would be an object of ridicule to the pupils. He did, however, start a school with David Garrick but was indeed the subject of too much merriment for it to continue. Those laughing boys missed an opportunity of being taught by one of the greatest literary men of the age. Boswell said that all Johnson's peculiarities were forgotten the moment he started to talk.

Johnson's tics, compulsive acts and involuntary noises have been accounted for by Professor T.J. Murray (1972, 1982) as being typical of the symptom-complex known as Tourette's syndrome. The story of this disorder goes back to 1825 when Dr J.M.G. Itard described the case of a French noblewoman who suffered from involuntary movements from the age of 7, and then developed a habit of uncontrollable, obscene utterances. Her later life was described by the neurologist Gilles de la Tourette (1885), together with a series of similar cases he had collected; the swearing (coprolalia) was rare, the involuntary tics and vocalisations common. Tourette's syndrome shows itself early in life, it may be partly hidden by those affected who can manage to convert their sudden involuntary movements into less conspicuous purposeful ones, and obtain added help through periods of remission. Oliver Sacks (1981) wrote that the disease was

> characterised by an excess of nervous energy and a great production and extravagance of strange motions and notions: tics, jerks, mannerisms, grimaces, noises, curses, involuntary imitations and compulsions of all sorts, with an odd elfin humour and a tendency to antic and outlandish kinds of play.

The twitchings are increased by anxiety and stress, diminished by concentration and disappear during sleep. The severity varies from the mild and benign to the grotesque and violent, so it is not surprising that some of the sufferers were thought to be possessed. McHenry (1967) classified the range of Johnson's tics and gesticulations and was the first to mention Tourette's syndrome as a partial explanation for them. However, in 1985 he thought that Johnson did not have Tourette's on the grounds that he had some control over his movements and did not have coprolalia, neither of which would seem to rule out this diagnosis. Most authors had attributed all Johnson's odd behaviour to a neurotic, depressive state occurring in an eccentric genius, whereas the probability is that, whatever his childhood neuroses, he also suffered from an abnormal sensitivity of nervous transmission in the grey matter of the brain through structures known as dopamine receptors. This condition can be treated today with haloperidol, a drug which partly blocks the activity of these receptors.

The very opposite effect to that produced by oversensitivity of the dopamine receptors can occur through disorders which lead to their depression. Serious damage to their functions occur in encephalitis lethargica (sleepy-sickness) with heart-breaking stories of young people who are frozen into a state of "sleep", timeless for many years, or are transformed in moral character and have violent outbursts. Oliver Sacks, in a wonderful book *Awakenings* (1973), about the survivors of the great sleepy-sickness epidemic of fifty years ago, tells of their dramatic response to laevo-dihydroxyphenylalanine (L-Dopa). Some of these post-encephalitic Parkinsonism patients were maintained on the drug for over twelve years after "awakening" from their trance-like state of absolute passivity. In one of the most extraordinary stories of medicine, Sacks illustrates these effects through biographies of patients, some of whom were almost literally brought back to life. It is an account presented with such an intimate, compassionate, sensitivity and understanding of people that it rekindles faith in the fundamentals of the profession of medicine.

Dr Johnson suffered much embarrassment from his compulsions, he seldom spoke of them and his friends avoided all mention of his oddities of behaviour, but Boswell once heard a small child ask, in that lovely simple, direct way of children, "Pray, Dr Johnson, why do you make such strange gestures?" to which he replied "From habit. Do you, my dear, take care to guard against bad habits". However, the overactivity of his dopamine receptors may have provided some stimulant to his intellectual ferment and been the basis for his extraordinary ability to produce those instant, particular responses, which, through the excellent Boswell, secured his renown as the acme of vigorous eloquence.

These remarkable effects of changes in the ease of transmission of nervous impulses through an important subcortical area of the brain, evoke conjectures about human nature and, more particularly, about the speed and intensity of reaction permitted to each individual by the sub-cortex of his brain. We may speculate on how far our quickness of intellect and the testiness of our reactions, if not our underlying abilities or disposition to passion, may be determined by an inherited or an acquired irritability of certain receptor organs at the base of the brain. There is, of course, a complicated higher level of nervous control over such activity, so obviously we are not entirely subject to "the blind force of the subcortex". Dr Johnson's tics subsided when he was most eagerly engaged in controversy, and some patients with post-encephalitic Parkinsonism, otherwise immobile, can walk when someone takes their arm and goes with them. One such said: "I do not walk, I am walked". Oliver Sacks wrote:

> The motionless Parkinsonian can sing and dance and when he does so is completely free from Parkinsonism; and when the galvanised Touretter sings, plays and acts, he in turn is completely liberated from his Tourette's. Here the 'I' vanquishes and reigns over the 'It'.

Tourette's syndrome on the one hand, and some of the effects of encephalitis lethargica on the other, provide a most interesting stimulus to thought about behaviour patterns in man.

Goldsmith could not be long confined. In 1768 he returned to the Temple, his favourite abode, and lodged in Brick Court. He contracted to write *An History of the Earth and Animated Nature*, produced his *History of England from the Earliest Times to the Death of George II*, as well as compilations of ancient Greek and Roman history at a time of insistent demand for such wide-ranging works. He engaged in a furious output which for a while shouldered out his genius as a poet, playwright and essayist. Nevertheless, *The Deserted Village* was published in 1770. Another voluminous doctor-writer, Dr John Aikin (1747-1822), wrote a *Critical Dissertation* on Goldsmith's poetry.

Goldsmith furnished his rooms in Brick Court in an extravagant manner with advances from friends and booksellers, and these, added to his tailor's bills, involved him in debts once more which he never managed to discharge. The rooms opposite to his were occupied by Edmund Bott, a barrister friend, who on Goldsmith's death was his chief creditor and became the owner of his papers. Some Irish hangers-on visited the celebrity at Brick Court and sponged on him, notably Paul Hifferman, who had practised as a doctor in Dublin but transferred to London where he operated as a part-time theatrical agent and journalist and was given to use of the newspaper columns for discreet blackmail. Goldsmith's extravagant behaviour, despite the support of Edmund Bott, couldn't last. He retired to a more simple life at a farmer's house in the country at Hyde, west of the Edgeware Road. This was six miles away from the spongers but not too far for visits from such old friends as Sir Joshua Reynolds and Sir William Chambers. Here he wrote his famous play *She Stoops to Conquer*, dedicated to Samuel Johnson, with its improbabilities, lasting appeal, perfect pace and wonderful evocation of laughter. Tom Davis wrote of Tony Lumpkin in *She Stoops to Conquer*, in an introduction to Dent's edition of Oliver Goldsmith's *Poems and Plays* (1975), that

> Like Goldsmith he is both child-like and mature; he is provincial, like Goldsmith, and this is both a strength and an absurdity. He is a gentleman, and a buffoon, happiest, as Goldsmith was, when singing comic songs at an inn. He sums up the paradox of Goldsmith's character; he is a fool, a booby, and yet has the sharp satiric intelligence that penetrates the shams and snobberies of the other characters.

Goldsmith died, predictably still in debt. After his death his poem *Retaliation* appeared, written about his friends, not intended for publication, in which he mixed praise with blame and, with gentle irony, revealed love and understanding with an ease which concealed the hard-won quality of a work that confronts such giants as Burke, Garrick, Reynolds and Cumberland. At a feast each guest enters with a dish which is himself, and so there comes "Magnanimous Goldsmith, a gooseberry fool", and other friends in turn, for example, Burke who is "tongue, with a garnish of brains", and here, after much wine, as they sink under the table he ponders on the dead. His praise is nicely balanced by a telling insight into their foibles. His Edmund Burke "Too nice for a statesman, too proud for a wit"; his David Garrick "On the stage he was natural, simple, affecting 'Twas only that, when he was off he was acting". It ends with Joshua Reynolds:

> Here Reynolds is laid, and to tell you my mind,
> He has not left a better or wiser behind;
> His pencil was striking, resistless and grand,
> His manners were gentle, complying and bland;
> Still born to improve us in every part,
> His pencil our faces, his manners our heart;
> To coxcombs averse, yet most civilly staring,
> When they judged without skill he was still hard of hearing;
> When they talk'd of their Raphaels, Correggios and stuff,
> He shifted his trumpet, and only took snuff.

Boswell, James   *The Life of Samuel Johnson*   Ed. G. Birkbeck Hill. 1887.

Davis, Tom   *Introduction to Oliver Goldsmith's Poems and Plays*   Dent, London, 1975.

Ginger, John   *The Notable Man*   Hamish Hamilton, London, 1977.

Irwin, George   *Samuel Johnson: a Personality in Conflict*   Auckland University Press, 1971.

Itard, J.M.G.   *Mémoire sur Quelques Fonctions Involontaries des Appereils de la Locomotion de la Préhension et de la Voix*   Arch. Gen. Med. 1825, 8, 385-407.

McHenry, L.C. Jr.   *Samuel Johnson's Tics and Gesticulations*   J. Hist. Med. 1967, 22, 152-168.

McHenry, L.C. Jr.   *Neurological Disorders of Dr Samuel Johnson*   J. Roy. Soc. Med. 1985, 78. 485-491.

McHenry, L.C., Jr. and MacKeith, R.   *Samuel Johnson's Childhood Illnesses and the King's Evil*   Med. Hist. 1966, 10, 386-399.

Murray, T.J.   *Dr Samuel Johnson's Movement Disorder*   Brit. Med. J. 1972, 1, 1610-1614.

Murray, T.J.   *Doctor Samuel Johnson's Abnormal Movements*   Adv. Neurol. 1982, 35, 25-30.

Prior, James   *The Life of Oliver Goldsmith*   John Murray, London, 1837.

Rolleston, Sir Humphrey   *Samuel Johnson's Medical Experiences*   Ann. Med. Hist. 1929, New Series 1, 540.

Sacks, Oliver   *Awakenings*   Gerald Duckworth, London, 1973. Pan Books, London, 1982.

Sacks, Oliver   *Witty Ticcy*   Ray London Review of Books 1981, Vol. 3, No. 5, P3.

Swarbrick, Andrew Ed.   *The Art of Oliver Goldsmith*   Vision Press, London, 1984.

Thackeray, William Makepeace   *The English Humourists Vol. 23 of The Works*,   Smith Elder, London, 1892.

Tourette, Gilles de la   *Etude sur une Affection Nerveuse Characterisée par de L'incoordination motrice Accompagnée d'Echolalie et de Coprolalic*   Arch. Neurol. Paris, 1885, 9, 19-42, 185-200.

THOMAS YOUNG

CHAPTER SIX

The Genius and Egyptian Hieroglyphics

THIS IS a story about a singular boy, the very thaumaturge of a lad, who grew up to be a phenomenal man of varied and exceptional achievements. It is about his exciting adventures which, though he studied horsemanship and dancing, were those of the mind rather than the body. Thomas Young (1773-1829) had a head start for he was able to read at the age of two, at four he had read through the Bible, at six he began to study Latin and by fourteen he had acquired a good knowledge of several other languages. He became a doctor, was the founder of physiological optics, established the wave theory of light, and was the first person to recognise the phonetic principle of Egyptian hieroglyphs. His versatility so dissipated his endeavours, that, though an innovator and indeed a master in many fields of study, he never settled to making any one discipline entirely his own. He believed that "What one man can do, another may".

Genius, that strange capacity for exceptional application, imaginative creation, uncommon thought and original invention, is a rare attribute indeed. Attempts have been made to place genius as a product of psychiatric disturbances. The latest of those is put forward by Hershman and Lieb (*The Key to Genius*, 1988) who went so far as to say "Manic depression is almost indispensable to genius"; mania providing creative energy and depression the necessary self criticism. They offer Newton, Beethoven, Dickens and Van Gough as examples to support their thesis. It is not obvious that Thomas Young fits into such an idea nor is it clear that they have established their theory in their chosen examples let alone as a general proposition.

It was believed at one time that a spirit, or genius, was assigned to each one of us at birth to preside over our destiny. If so these spirits display a shockingly wide variation both in efficiency of guidance provided, and attention paid to the work in hand, even if they may, with justification, claim to be able to do little about the basic quality of the creatures assigned to them. It is difficult for them to avoid censure for their too frequent failures to see that their charges make the best of a bad job through sustained effort.

Wonders have been wrought by hard work with the most unpromising materials, it is, however, pointless to blame some imagined genie for failure to realise potential, the fault, we have been told, lies "not in our stars but in ourselves". Given our inheritance, over which we have no control, for it is certain that we are not all created equal, and with what help we are fortunate enough to receive from teachers or through example, we develop ourselves into the people we become. We achieve this self-creation by the choices we make, the habits we acquire, the opportunities we grasp and the attention, diligence and directed effort we see fit to put into the tasks before us. Today failure of character is too often attributed either to the external pressures of modern society or to some essential internal element which lurks within the self. Some modern novelists have enveloped their characters in such a variety of psychoanalytic excuses as would have made Charlotte Brönte, George Eliot or Anthony Trollope despair of reality. The myth that there is an essence which makes things what they are and nothing else, has been applied to an animistic view of life and at times infected biology all the way from man to cell. It should long ago have been laid to rest. People with inherited disabilities may indeed have a diminished chance of success and a greater need for intelligent help than others, but the spur can be greater too and the results astonishing; the finest inheritance is not much good without application. The genius, even when such bounty has been bestowed, is no less his or her own creation than is the case with lesser folk. Mental development is just as certainly a continuous creation as is the physical. Life may begin with the fertilisation of an ovum but each person is being continuously formed from birth. It is impossible to say when an individual acquires a persona for we are becoming ourselves throughout our lives.

Genius is thrown up from time to time by the chance of mixed genetic inheritance, sometimes in unexpected places or from a none too remarkable lineage. What the dictionary calls "native intellectual power of exalted type", however, is given to very few. Thomas Young qualified for the title without question and on all counts, and was a most handsome man into the gloriously unfair bargain. He had an abundance of exalted intellectual power and developed a mighty degree of dedicated application, or, if you will, as Carlyle put it, "a transcendent capacity of taking trouble" to go with it. It is of interest that Young had little faith in any peculiar gift of genius, he supposed the differences in potential between people to be far less than was commonly believed and thought that what one could achieve others might accomplish with sufficient application.

Thomas Young was the eldest in a family of ten all born in The Old Bank House in Milverton in Somerset. His father was a cloth merchant and local banker, both he and his wife Sarah, neé Davis, were Quakers. From an early age Thomas kept a journal mostly in Latin and made notes about the books he read. For the greater part of his first seven years Young stayed with his maternal grandfather, Robert Davis, in Minehead. He attended the village school but was fortunate in being taught at home by his Aunt, Mary Davis, and encouraged by his grandfather who was fond of classical studies; together they helped him to form his habits of learning. When he was six he had learned all four hundred and fifty lines of Goldsmith's *Deserted Village* by heart. He was always reading, one of his first books being *Gulliver's Travels*.

In 1780 when nearly seven years old, Young was sent to "a miserable boarding-school" for a year and a half where the master was "morose and severe" and he made little progress. We still fail our exceptional children far too often by providing inadequate means for the development of their talents, but fortunately for us many teach themselves. No country can afford to underestimate its good fortune in possessing gifted children or to neglect their special needs by failing to recognise and support unusual ability. Young continued to read with unquenchable fervour tackling at this time, before he was eight, *Robinson Crusoe*, *Stories on Shakespeare*, *Tom Telescope's Newtonian Philosophy* and much else. For the first six months after escaping from this school he was at home. He found friends who had a new library for him to explore and here he read a *Dictionary of Arts and Sciences* in three folio volumes with great delight.

At nine he went to a new school at Compton in Dorset and was there for four years. Mr. Thompson was an understanding master who allowed this unusual boy a good deal of freedom. Young discovered that by getting up in the morning an hour before the other boys or going to bed an hour later he could do the necessary school work, leaving most of the day free for self-education. Mr Thompson had a library with a good collection of classical literature and Young's list of books read while there included the works of Horace and Virgil, selections from Cicero, Greek and Latin Testaments, the first seven books of the *Iliad* and books on mathematics. He was fortunate to make friends with the most unusual school usher, Josiah Jeffrey, who lent him Ryland's *Introduction to the Newtonian Philosophy* and Benjamin Marten's *Lectures on Natural Philosophy* which started his interest in optics. Jeffrey also taught him such practical things as how to use a lathe, make a telescope, do drawings and bind books. When Jeffrey left, Young acquired the usher's perquisites selling paper, copy-books, and colours to the other boys and, with the money he made, bought books, one of his first purchases being a Hebrew Bible. At thirteen he had studied Chaldee, French, Greek, Hebrew, Italian (with the help of one of the other pupils), Latin, Persian and Syriac, and was later to add Arabic, Ethiopic, German, Samaritan, Spanish and Turkish, surpassing Robert Boyle (1627-1691), the great doctor-chemist who had learned Chaldee, Greek, Hebrew and Syriac so as to be able to read original texts.

The next step in his development was taken when David Barclay heard of Thomas Young. He, a Quaker, of Barclay and Perkins brewery and a partner in the banking house, wished to arrange for the education of his grandson, Hudson Gurney, by appointing a tutor and securing a companion, Hudson Gurney was 12½, Thomas Young was 14, and they joined forces at Barclay's country house near Ware. The tutor who had been engaged decided to take a post elsewhere so, in the meantime, Thomas took over Gurney's teaching. When the new tutor, John Hodgkin, a classical scholar arrived he soon found that he was able to pursue his own studies while Thomas Young continued to direct those of Hudson Gurney; Hodgkin needed only to provide some general supervision. Indeed George Peacock, *Life of Thomas Young* (1855), relates how Hodgkin himself found that he derived much valuable assistance and advice in his studies from Young, the extraordinary youth whose stability of conduct and intensity of application seemed to place any desirable object of literary or scientific pursuit within the reach of his astonishing mental powers.

Young, attending to his own education, extended his reading to the English classics, mathematics, astronomy and botany, he read Newton's *Principia* and *Optics*, Linnaeus on botany, Lavoisier on chemistry, Boerhaave on medicine and much else. The astonishing list of books he read and on which he made notes between 1787 and 1790 fills a whole page of Peacock's biography. Young spent five years at David Barclay's home during which time he was almost entirely self taught while educating Hudson Gurney, who inherited a large fortune, and remained his friend for life. Gurney became an antiquary, writer and politician; had an estate at Keswick Hall in Norfolk, was High Sheriff for the county and was elected Fellow of the Royal Society in 1818.

At sixteen Young was taken seriously ill in London while staying at David Barclay's town house and an uncle on his mother's side, Dr Richard Brocklesby, author, Fellow of the Royal Society and distinguished physician, was called in to see him. He brought with him Dr Thomas Dimsdale, who had been made a Baron by the Empress, Catherine the Great of Russia. She had sent for him in 1768 in consequence of his reputation for inoculation for smallpox in the hope of stemming the epidemics sweeping her country. He taught the technique and inoculated the Empress and her son together with 140 other Russians without mishap being awarded £10,000, with £2000 for expenses and an annuity of £500. Young was thought to have pulmonary tuberculosis so he was bled and kept for two years on a diet of milk, eggs, vegetables and weak broth. He still made a good recovery. His uncle became entranced with this extraordinary patient. He asked him to translate some English classics into Greek for him and showed the results to Edmund Burke, an old friend with whom he had been at school. Burke was astonished by the boy's erudition and he and Brocklesby introduced Young into a most distinguished circle of their friends which included the statesmen William Windham and Lord North, Sir George Baker, nine times president of the College of Physicians and a writer of elegant Latin prose, Sir Joshua Reynolds and Charles Burney the musician and father of Fanny. They found Young's learning, modesty, beautiful penmanship, ready conversation on equal terms with distinguished scholars, his Quaker garb, artless simplicity, ignorance of popular literature and absence of any of the usual habits of thought of others of his age and social origins, all most appealing.

Dr Brocklesby was largely responsible for persuading Young to study medicine, and in 1792 at the age of 19 he began work at the Hunterian School of Anatomy and St Bartholomew's Hospital. His lecture notes, often in Latin or Greek, were interspersed with mathematical calculations presumably made to keep his mind occupied while waiting for classes to begin or during dull intervals. He continued his studies of languages and took up his old interest in optics. While still a student he was the first to explain ocular accommodation by proving that adaptation for variable distance vision was due to changes in the curvature of the lens. In 1793 he read a paper entitled *Observations on Vision* before the Royal Society to which he was elected a Fellow at the age of 21. For the first time he had to suffer criticism and quite virulent attacks from people who could not readily abandon old beliefs on new evidence, and began to doubt his own conclusions, but in 1800, in another paper of his *On the Mechanism of the Eye*, he was able to confirm his original observations.

Young decided to continue his education in Edinburgh with its great reputation as a teaching school of medicine, but first toured the north of England on horseback. One of the people he met on this journey was Erasmus Darwin; a detailed critique of Darwin's *Zoonomia, or the Laws of Organic Life* (1794-96) was found in Young's journal. Darwin wrote to a friend of his in Edinburgh to announce Young's arrival adding, "He unites the scholar with the philosopher, and the cultivation of modern arts with the simplicity of ancient manners". Young arrived in Edinburgh in October 1794. His notes on the professors were not all complimentary, but to Dr James Gregory, Professor of the Practice of Medicine, who had studied in Leyden and was a Latin scholar and famous lecturer, he gave qualified approval, "Gregory is a very agreeable and well informed man; he seems to have vigorous and rapid thought". Two of his fellow students were from Germany and helped him with his study of their language, strengthening his resolve to visit Göttingen. While in Edinburgh he was able to widen his already extensive acquaintance with classical scholars and it was here that he began to break with Quaker observances and the restrictions of Quaker dress. He went to the theatre, where he saw Mrs Siddons, and took lessons in dancing and in playing the flute. With a good strong horse he explored the highlands and when he left Edinburgh he toured the lakes and North Wales, staying with Edmund Burke at Beaconsfield on his way home.

In 1795 he set out for Göttingen where the fame of the medical school had secured the attendance of some one hundred students at that time. He took rooms within a hundred yards of what he described as "the second library in Europe", saying "I can have any book I wish to consult on sending for it; this is the chief reason for my desiring to graduate here". As well as medicine he studied history, including the history of art, drawing, dancing, horsemanship and playing the clavichord. His graduation thesis was followed by a presentation for dispute for which he chose the subject of the human voice, the sounds of which it is capable, and the physical and mathematical analysis of sound both as a theory and as applied to different languages. In Göttingen he began to enlarge the range of his reading, tackling for the first time works by Fielding and Goldsmith, revealing to him a new vigour in literature as well as a coarseness in human nature. He also read Kant's *Critique of Pure Reason* (1781) of which he wrote in his notes "His language is unpardonably obscure". He planned a European tour and did carry out much of it even though some restriction resulted from Napoleon's campaign in which he took Piedmont and went on to the victory of Lodi.

On returning to England Young decided to obtain a Cambridge degree and went to Emmanuel to secure some of the undoubted medical privileges which graduates of Oxford and Cambridge enjoyed at that time. The College of Physicians was almost entirely run by such graduates not without many complaints about discrimination. Later when money was no longer one of the chief factors in determining entry, discrimination turned in favour of those considered less fortunate, with some bias developing against privilege both of home and schooling. However, clamour for redress of past inequalities on the one hand and an agitated defensiveness by those responsible for entry on the other, are not necessarily the best means of securing full educational opportunity for merit. Young found Cambridge more civilised and more refined than the foreign universities he had visited.

In December 1797, while at Cambridge, Young paid a visit to London and dined with Dr Brocklesby who appeared to be in good health and spirits but who died suddenly that night soon after retiring to bed. He had been intimate with most of the distinguished men of his day, had offered Dr Johnson an annuity and apartments in his own house and had given Burke £1000 during his life; he left to Young his house and furniture in Norfolk Street, Park Lane, his library and his valuable collection of paintings most of which had been chosen with the help of Sir Joshua Reynolds. Young was now free to pursue his own inclinations without concern for husbanding his slight resources. He went back to Cambridge to complete his studies, visited many of his rather grand acquaintances, such as the Duke of Richmond at Goodwood, Mr John Ellis, Lord Seaford's rich brother, and a large circle of distinguished friends. In London he read papers before the Royal Society on sound and light. Bitter attacks were made once more on the new ideas he introduced in the age-old manner of those who find it disturbing to be asked to change established beliefs. John Locke had written,

> The imputation of novelty is a terrible charge amongst those who judge of men's heads, as they do of their perukes, by the fashion; and can allow none to be right but the received doctrines.

Young's counter to the attacks on his description of the undulatory propagation of light, and his further papers on physical optics which followed, soon established his lasting reputation in this field.

Young set up in medical practice at 48 Welbeck Street where he stayed for 25 years. Alongside his practice he continued to produce theoretical papers in many branches of science. In 1801 he was appointed Professor of Natural Philosophy at the Royal Institution, not long established by an extraordinary American,

Sir Benjamin Thompson (1753-1814), a soldier, who left his wife and daughter came to England, supplied confidential information about America and was appointed to the Colonial Office. He entered the service of Bavaria where he reformed the army, drained marshes, started a cannon factory, established a military academy, created a poor-law system, lectured on nutrition and domestic economy, improved the breed of horses and cattle and, in his spare time, laid out the English Garden in Munich. For these varied efforts he was made a Count of the Holy Roman Empire and took the title of Count Rumford. Back in England he set about improving this country, writing at enormous length on his own peculiar mixture of household hints, humanity and civilisation. Well intentioned, scientifically inclined, inventive and both useful and impractical by turns, he became a household name, people had their homes "Rumfordised". He invented a smoke-free fireplace. An air of solemn ridicule had developed around him in Jane Austen's day. When Catharine Morland arrived at Northanger Abbey, expecting "massy walls of grey stone" and mystery with a dash of horror, Colonel Tilney's modernisations seemed out of place. In the drawing-room

> The fire-place, where she had expected the ample width and ponderous carving of former times, was contracted to a Rumford, with slabs of plain though handsome marble, and ornaments over it of the prettiest English china.

Count Rumford left for Paris, married Lavoisier's widow, and no doubt set about improving France. One of his lasting English successes came from his treatise of 1799 *Proposals for Establishing the Royal Institution.*

Young was appointed Director of the Royal Institution and gave 31 lectures in his first year and probably 60 in the next, they were on Natural Philosophy and the Mechanical Arts. He spoke on mechanics, hydrostatics, hydrodynamics, acoustics, optics, astronomy, tides, electricity, magnetism, theory of heat and climatology; all published four years later in a great work unique both for its scope and originality. The matter was masterly but his style of delivery was "compressed and laconic", he presumed on intellectual capacities which most of his audience did not have. In 1802 he took the Duke of Richmond's two sons to stay in Rouen for the summer under his tuition. In that year Young was appointed Foreign Secretary of the Royal Society and served in this post for the rest of his life. He attended a meeting in Paris of the National Institute of France and met Napoleon, then First Consul, a post he had secured "for life" making him, temporarily, an absolute monarch in all but name. At the Royal Institution Young failed to get his plans for the library expansion and other improvements agreed and resigned in 1803 to attend more fully to his medical practice. In 1804 he married Eliza Maxwell of the ancient seat of John de Tubbenden at Farnborough, Kent, which she had inherited through her mother, the wife of James Maxwell and daughter of John Hammond.

The range of Young's interests and brilliance of his mind earned for him the sobriquet of "Phenomenon Young". When the *Encyclopaedia Britannica* first appeared he had written the articles on Annuities, Baths, Bridges, Carpentry, Chromatics, Cohesion, Egypt, Herculanean Language, Hydraulics, Integrals, Life-preservers, Road Making, Steam Engines, Tides, Weights and Measures as well as 45 of the biographical essays.

In August 1799, one of the most famous archaeological treasures now in the British Museum, The Rosetta Stone, was discovered by French soldiers repairing fortifications in the Nile Delta, this is a large fragment with characters engraved in three difference styles, Greek, hieroglyphic and Egyptian running script. Two of these languages could not be deciphered as all knowledge of Egyptian hieroglyphics had been lost since the fourth century A.D. so, assuming that the three inscriptions were the same, an opportunity to read them occurred since the Greek might serve to interpret the other two. As the stone was broken part of the inscription had been lost, mostly from the hieroglyphic section where no line was complete and about half was missing; fourteen of the thirty-two lines of the next section were incomplete, and, of the Greek, which had fifty-four lines, twenty-six were damaged at their ends. Impressions were made and sent to scholars all over Europe.

When the French surrendered Egypt in 1801, after Cairo had been captured by Abercrombie, and Alexandria had capitulated, the Rosetta Stone and other treasures already packed to go to Paris were shipped to England instead. The Greek was translated by Du Theil in Paris and by the Rev Stephen Weston in England and then by a number of others in Europe, with conjecture added for the missing portions. In this way the Greek section of the Rosetta Stone was revealed as carrying an edict of an assembly of priests at Memphis in honour of the boy King Ptolemy V, who had already reigned for six years. The stone was dated 196 B.C., and recorded the King's good deeds in restoring both law and order and the privileges and revenues of the priests, and decreed the honours due to him. A copy of this edict in three languages, Greek, "Writing of the speech of the God" and "Writing of the books", was cut on basalt slabs and set up in each of the temples of first, second and third orders. Thus finding the Rosetta Stone presented scholars for the first time with an opportunity to read Egyptian literature and history if they could interpret the picture-writing of the earliest dynasties and so be able to uncover an ancient civilisation.

So it was that a hunt began for a valuable prize, inspired by a search for knowledge, but also impelled by the chance of fame, to be won through priority in deciphering the inscription by solving the puzzle. The pursuit had all the true ingredients of intellectual adventure: joy in the doing, reward in knowing and, if successful, the rousing of envy in the hearts of contemporaries and assuring the recognition of posterity. A Frenchman, Silvestre de Sacy, got off to a good start by identifying the names of Ptolemy, Alexander and Alexandria but failed to establish an alphabet. A Swedish diplomat and Coptic scholar, J.D. Åkerblad, was next, he located sixteen other names but failed to apply his discoveries to the rest of the text.

Young first heard of the Rosetta Stone through Åkerblad's writing in 1806 but it was not until Sir W. Rouse Boughton bought a papyrus in Luxor in 1814, written in running Egyptian characters and asked for help in its interpretation, that Young began to take a real interest. The papyrus was badly damaged and Young had never before made a study of such script, however, he soon made sufficient progress to read a paper on the subject, *Remarks on the Ancient Egyptian Manuscripts*, in May 1814. The Rosetta Stone had been in England for 12 years but Young had never considered it. With a new language interest aroused he took a transcript and the reports of de Sacy and Åkerblad away with him on holiday and joined the hunt. He found that a small group of characters occurred so often that they must represent some termination or link such as *and*. The next most frequent group was more interesting, this occurred 29 or 30 times in the second inscription which he called Enchorial (of the country), since it could be made to correspond to the word *King* in the Greek. Another assemblage of characters was found 14 times in Enchorial seeming to agree with *Ptolemy* which was found 11 times in the Greek. Next he was able to identify *Egypt*, once he had seen that it was sometimes omitted from the Greek text or had *country* substituted for it. He then cut up the Greek text placing each suspected equivalent over the Enchorial to match the words he thought he had already fixed to try and get the whole to correspond as far as possible. He did the same with the hieroglyphic version, but the result was incomplete and he realised that most of his transactions had been guesswork.

Young was so fascinated by the challenge of this puzzle that he continued to study it on his return home. However, his progress was disappointingly slow although he had already got further than others who had been working on the script for 12 years. He told Hudson Gurney, over-enthusiastically, that he had ascertained the greater part with "tolerable certainty, and some of the most interesting without the shadow of a doubt". Young then read the greater part of the Gospels in the Coptic Testament to enlarge his acquaintance with a language which had a close affinity with the Enchorial. Young then decided to get in touch with other workers and wrote to de Sacy to find out how he and Åkerblad had been getting on. He heard that they had made little progress, and that Åkerblad's system and search for an alphabet were so much in doubt that he had become unwilling to communicate more of his work.

Now Young learned of Jean François Campollion (1790-1832), a professional and most accomplished Egyptologist who, as a brilliant boy, had been admitted to the School of Oriental Languages in Paris at the age of 15 and after meeting de Sacy had begun his study of the Rosetta Stone in the same year. In 1812 Campollion was appointed Professor of Ancient History at Grenoble and in 1814 published an extensive work on Egypt under the Pharaohs in which he claimed to have deciphered several passages of the Rosetta Stone's Egyptian text. These interpretations were, however, not in advance of those already made by de Sacy and Åkerblad. Young, who by that time had been working on the Rosetta Stone for only six months, received a copy of the book as Foreign Secretary of the Royal Society when it was presented to them by Campollion. Young wrote to him in acknowledgement, asked about the accuracy of his transcription of the markings on the stone and told him what he had himself so far achieved. He also learned that de Sacy had sent Campollion a copy of his conjectural translation of the Enchorial (or Demotic) text and his explanation of the last lines of the hieroglyphics.

At this point Young decided that the Enchorial had probably been derived from the hieroglyphic, though he seems never to have realised that the inscription may have originally been written in Greek in an abbreviated form and that the other versions were paraphrases not literal translations. He then found a correspondence between the words *God, Immortal Vulcan, Priests* and *Diadem* though it was puzzling that none of them could be reconciled to any imaginable alphabet. Through the Egyptian consulate he was supplied with every fragment of inscription they could find which might be helpful. Funeral rolls proved to be the most valuable for they contained drawings of incidents in the lives of the deceased with many sections in common. Young wrote of his findings to Archduke John of Austria in 1816 and later to Åkerblad, these letters were printed and circulated to other workers and published in 1821. Now Young turned his attention to the hieroglyphic script where no real progress had been made over 15 years. Groups of characters surrounded by an oval ring were identified as proper names, this led to the idea, derived from his work on sound as applied to different languages, that if a picture language was to be used to form the strange names of foreign conquerors then it would have to make use of the phonetic values of established pictorial characters in order to create an appropriate name picture. The same idea had also occurred to Barthélemy and Zoega without Young's knowledge and the Chinese had long given a sound-significance to characters for this purpose, and indeed still do so. Using this theory, Young identified the hieroglyph for *Ptolemy* and then the one for *Queen Berenice*. From this good start more soon followed in the first success in deciphering any Egyptian hieroglyph correctly.

In 1818 Young produced his famous supplement to the fourth edition of *Encyclopaedia Britannica*, giving a full account in English of an analysis of the triple inscription on the Rosetta Stone and pointing out for the first time the phonetic character of hieroglyphs contained within cartouches. The supplement also contained a list of publications on the subject, much relevant information with 218 Enchorial words and 200 interpreted hieroglyphs. This was a *tour de force* which, characteristically, Young attributed to industry rather than to intellect. The Edinburgh Review called it "the greatest effort of scholarship and ingenuity of which modern literature can boast". Starting twelve years behind he had left the others standing. His discovery of the phonetic principle of hieroglyphics was described by Sir E.A. Wallis Budge in 1929 as "practically the foundation of the science of Egyptology". His fame crept into fiction when George Eliot in *Middlemarch*, commenting that Mr Casaubon's rather chilling rhetoric did not make it certain that there was no good work or fine feeling in him, wrote, "Did not an immortal physicist and interpreter of hieroglyphs write detestable verses?"

We must surely have some sympathy with Campollion, who was confronted with that terrible thing the gifted amateur, out-doing him, the brilliant professional, at his own game to which he had devoted a full-time study and on which he had been engaged for so much longer. Indeed it proved too much for him. In 1821 Campollion published his great work *De L'Ecriture Hieratique des Anciens Egyptiens*, but in this he denigrated the phonetic principle and, two years after Young's report of the Enchorial derivation from the hieroglyphic, announced the same conclusion without acknowledgement. He later adopted the phonetic principle and greatly advanced the subject by many further interpretations, starting with the names of several other Greek and Roman rulers of Egypt. Experts took sides and a great international battle ensued, not about the sensational discoveries which had opened an ancient literature to the world, but about who had done what first. Young behaved impeccably, maintaining his position and dating his discoveries while giving generous praise to Campollion's brilliant scholarship and acknowledging that he could not possibly rival him as an Egyptologist.

Campollion's pride and pre-eminence in this field of study did not allow him to acknowledge Young's priority but he went on to lay the foundation on which the present knowledge of the language of the ancient Egyptians is based. Young decided to confine his Egyptian studies to Enchorial and leave pure hieroglyphics to the better equipped Campollion. Sir E.A. Wallis Budge said of Young that "He opened the door of a chamber of philological mystery, and indicated the path to be followed by those who entered the chamber". However, just as no one person invented the infinitesimal calculus (a cooperative product of a group containing Newton and Leibniz), so no one person really discovered how to read Egyptian scripts. Success came from the interplay of ideas derived from several sources.

The desire to be first and to be seen to be first in making great advances in knowledge is human enough, even if it does diminish the stature of those who too eagerly pursue such claims without generosity or understanding. In this matter Darwin and Wallace in their presentation of evolution set an example to the whole scientific world. In the days when it was customary not to publish until it was thought that an exhaustive study had left little more to be said, scientists working on the same subject might easily come to the same conclusion at about the same time without knowing of one another's work. Today each new idea in a series of investigations is put out as soon as, or sooner than, it is ready, and reviews of the subject as a whole are often needed in editorials to hold a developing story together. When personal ambition runs ahead of scholarship priority battles seem unimportant to those not directly engaged, but the establishment of such claims can still be sought as energetically as ever by the contestants.

Young indulged in many other activities and left his mark on each one of them. He worked on standards of measurement at a time when the French metre was defined as the forty-millionth part of the meridian through Paris, and the British unit of length as that of a pendulum which would beat in seconds. The inaccuracies and difficulties of measurement which such standards introduced were obvious. Standard bars at defined temperatures, and a new pendulum invented by Henry Kater, led to improvements. Young, working with a committee, laid down methods of obtaining the most accurate values for observations, and the standards then agreed were passed into law in 1824. A standard yard was placed in the custody of the Clerk of the House of Commons. Young continued with studies of weights and measures. He was asked to report to the Admiralty on claims made by Robert Seppings for a new principle of construction for ships which was said to add strength and durability and also to save timber. Young's calculations supported most of Sepping's claims but were set out in a manner so learned that it baffled Seppings himself let alone the Board of Admiralty. However his report was sound, and many of Sepping's ideas were eventually incorporated into ship building. Young did outstanding work on the Nautical Almanac and was Secretary of the Board of Longitude.

Thomas Young and his wife lived in London part of the year and in Worthing for part. He didn't like being long away from London and became fidgety when on holiday without some new study to occupy him. In 1821, however, he took his wife on an extensive tour of Europe and visited many of his friends. On their return Hudson Gurney had arranged for him to have his portrait painted by Sir Thomas Lawrence (1769-1830) who was the son of a Bristol innkeeper and then at the height of his fame and brilliance. Young was elected one of the few Foreign Members of the Academy of Science in Paris. He produced his *Dictionary of the Ancient Egyptian Language in the Enchorial Character* and on his death-bed he was propped up still writing. He was buried in Farnborough, Kent on May 16th 1829 in the Maxwell family vault.

Herman von Helmholtz, the great German physiologist, physicist and mathematician, equally distinguished in many fields, known for the invention of the ophthalmoscope (which however had been made independently, and with priority, by Charles Babbage in England), was born 8 years before Young died. Helmholtz wrote of him

> He was one of the most clear-sighted men who ever lived, but he had the misfortune to be too greatly superior in sagacity to his contemporaries. They gazed at him with astonishment, but could not always follow the bold flights of his intellect, and thus a multitude of his most important ideas lay buried and forgotten in the great tomes of the Royal Society of London, till a later generation, in tardy advance, remade his discoveries and convinced itself of the accuracy and force of his inferences.

Andrews, Carol *The Rosetta Stone* British Museum Publications, London, 1981.

Budge, Sir E.A. Wallis *The Rosetta Stone in the British Museum* The Religious Tract Society, London, 1929.

Gurney, Hudson *Memoir of the Life of Thomas Young 1831.*

Hershman, D.J. and Lieb, J. *The Key to Genius* Prometheus Books, New York, 1988.

Peacock, George *Life of Thomas Young* John Murray, London 1855.

Potts, D.M. *Phenomenon Young* Camb. Univ. Med. Soc. Mag. 1957, 34, 19.

Richardson, *Sir Benjamin Ward* *Thomas Young, Disciples of Aescalapius 1900,* Vol. 2., p 808-827.

Wood, Alexander *Thomas Young Natural Philosopher* Cambridge University Press, 1954.

JOHN KEATS

CHAPTER SEVEN

The Medical Poet

JOHN KEATS (1795-1821) was a magical person, always in extremes, tough, shy, embarrassed, pugnacious, small, with reddish hair, of surpassing imagination, richly creative, sensitive and sensuous; a poet of the greatest brilliance. Professor Christopher Ricks, in an acclaimed study of his poetry (1974), could even add to his eulogy that Keats was "the man whose letters are to many of us the greatest letters we have ever read". Yet Keats was never more than a youth, who crammed into his brief adult existence over five years of medical study and one of desperate illness, as well as all the development and achievement of his literary life. He knew himself to be a great artist in a hurry and feared that he might have too little time to establish his fame.

Biographers, since Richard Monckton Miles began it all in 1848, have poured out their accounts of his life and work, others have written the stories of his family and friends which, with numerous lectures and introductions to editions of his poetry and letters, form a sufficient body of analysis to daunt, if not to deter, even the experts from attempting further commentary. However, Keats was a member of the medical profession the members of which in common with most artists understand compassion and exercise a critical discernment about intensely personal concerns. Doctors and artists are also required to cultivate a public image and submit perforce to a plebeian accountability. Keats saw and practised the so often horrifying medicine of his day; such an experience could not fail to influence his art.

Keats' father, Thomas, was born in 1773 or 4 and there is much confusion about the origins of his family with, however, some interesting possibilities of a medical connection. Keats's sister Fanny said that she remembered as a child hearing that her father came from Cornwall, but her memories were not always accurate and Robert Gittings (1970) could find no baptismal record for a Thomas Keats of 1773/4 in any Cornish parish. Then Keats's friend, Charles Brown, said he had heard that his father was a native of Devonshire, but neither does any Devon parish show the baptism of a Thomas Keats at that time. Practically the only firm fact we have about Thomas Keats's family is that he had a relative called Elizabeth Keats who stepped in to care for his children in a crisis. The possible medical connection comes through Dr William Keate born in 1708 or 1709 who practised in Wells in Somerset and retired to Reading where he died in 1790. No strict distinction was drawn between the family names with or without the 's', one changed readily into the other through carelessness or the addition of the possessive. William Keate's son Thomas became a house surgeon at St Georges Hospital in 1767, was surgeon to George IV, Surgeon General to the Army and three times Master of the Company of Surgeons in 1802, 1809 and 1818. He is described as small, quick tempered, with reddish hair, a long straight nose and a long upper lip – a description which might be that of John Keats himself. Thomas Keate's nephew, Robert Keate (1777-1857) was also a distinguished surgeon, and President of The Royal College of Surgeons in 1831 and 1839, "a square compact little man", quick tempered, and the brother of John Keate (1773-1852), the diminutive Headmaster of Eton, who had reddish hair, was born at Wells and once flogged 80 boys at a session. The Reading connection provides the interest, for there was a Thomas Keats, son of Thomas and Elizabeth, baptised at St Mary's Reading in 1773, and Gittings says, "He is the only Thomas Keats to be born in the right year and to have the closest possible female relation named Elizabeth". This family came from Mortimer, near Strathfieldsaye, a few miles from Reading. We have, then, a strong temperamental and physical resemblance between John Keats, his father Thomas, and a doctor's family of Keate from Somerset who came to Reading, and a record of a Thomas Keats born near Reading at the right time to be John Keats's father. If indeed this was the poet's father, Thomas, he may have gone to relatives in the West Country before coming to London, and perhaps his son's resemblance and possible relationship to famous surgeons may have had something to do with John Keats's choice of profession and the special way he was treated on arrival as a medical student at Guy's.

Whatever his background, Thomas Keats came to London as a young man and in 1795 married Frances, the daughter of John

Jennings, who had a flourishing business in property, catering and livery stables. Jennings rented the Swan and Hoop on London Wall, a valuable property with stabling for thirty-six horses. Frances, Keats's mother, was well educated and had been brought up in reasonable affluence. Not much else is really known about her. She was nineteen when she married Thomas Keats on October 9th 1794 at St George's, Hanover Square; there is no record of any relative of the bride or bridegroom having witnessed the marriage. Frances had the reputation of being "a lively woman" very ready to show off her considerable charms. Their eldest son, John, was born in October 1795.

It is not known what Thomas Keats did before 1802 but his father-in-law, who had been Master of the Innholders Company in 1797/8, retired in 1802 to Enfield, leaving Thomas to manage the Swan and Hoop, the stables and some property for him. He and Frances moved in with their children, John, George and Tom, Edward had already died as an infant and Frances (Fanny) was born at the Swan and Hoop in 1803.

The boys went to school in Enfield in a fine Georgian house kept by John Clarke, an excellent master with a good library and a taste in literature, who ran a school for the sons of the prosperous middle class. His own son, Charles Cowden Clarke, inspired with a love of books and music, was to have a great influence on Keats; he became a tutor, cricketer, publisher, literary lecturer, and lasting friend to the poet. At first as a school boy, however, the small, tough, belligerent Keats was more interested in fighting than in books. He would fight anyone of any size, though his daring and generosity made him a favourite with all.

A tragedy struck the Keats family in 1804, throwing the household into confusion. Thomas Keats was killed early one Sunday morning in April, thrown from his horse. It appears that his wife Frances left home shortly afterwards and Elizabeth Keats, perhaps an aunt or a sister of Thomas's, came to the Swan and Hoop to care for the children. Just over two months after her husband's death Frances was married again to William Rawlings despite her mother's disapproval. Thomas had died intestate leaving rather less than £2000, and it took a year for Frances to obtain administration of his estate. When her father died in 1805 he left the fine sum in those days of £13,000, half to his wife, a third to his son Lieutenant Jennings, a trust for his grandchildren but only £50 a year to his daughter, who was not made an executor. William Rawlings had no assets, Frances's brother was soon demanding rent for the Swan and Hoop and she was not only short of money but resentful of her treatment. She brought an unsuccessful action against her mother and brother, contesting the will and trying to improve her position. The widowed Mrs Jennings moved house to Edmonton in 1805 and took the Keats children to live with her. The family had lost its head, the children were separated from their mother, they had been moved to their grandmother's house, there was a quarrel over the will and an upset due to the second marriage. Not surprisingly the children became deeply committed to each other. They quarrelled and fought but bound themselves into a tightly loyal community for the rest of their lives. Clarke's School was a second home to Keats and Charles Cowden Clarke became his chief companion, confidant and teacher.

The law-suit dragged on for more than a year, fees took their toll and Frances lost her case. She was separated from William Rawlings in 1806 and he may have died a few years later. She had little money and it has been suggested that Frances went to live with another man, certainly she was separated from her family for four years and Keats, despite his great devotion to her, never made a reference to his mother in any of his writings. From the age of eleven he took on a position of special care and responsibility for his sister Fanny. In 1808, when Lieutenant Jennings died of the family disease of pulmonary tuberculosis, a reconciliation took place between Frances and her mother and she returned to live with her family; just when the law-suit was over and the financial future of her children had been secured by her mother's will, Frances became ill and died in March 1810. Keats, when home for the Christmas holidays, had attended his mother, giving her the medicines himself, cooking for her and sitting up much of the night reading to her. He was overcome by grief at school when the news of her death was broken to him.

Mrs Jennings left over £8000 to the Keats children and their father's legacy and mother's annuity were added to this. Their affairs were put into a Trust in 1810 to be managed by friends of the family – John Sandell, a merchant, and Richard Abbey, a

142

coffee warehouseman. Although deprived of parents and sometimes in difficulties the children had a solid financial background for a good start in life. When Keats left school his trustees realised some of his share of the money to start him on his chosen career in medicine. Keats was apprenticed to Thomas Hammond a surgeon-apothecary in Edmonton, who lived in a fine house called Wilston in the same street as Keats's grandmother's property and within two miles across the fields to the school where his friend Charles Cowden Clarke lived. Hammond employed two apprentices, he charged them £210 each for instruction with board and lodgings and taught them well. Keats lived in a cottage in the grounds over the surgery, made up pills and medicines, pulled out teeth, vaccinated and sometimes bled the patients. Vaccination had been introduced by Jenner one year before Keats was born.

The five years which Keats spent assisting Thomas Hammond were described by Clarke as "the most placid period of his painful life". He was engaged in the profession he had chosen but found plenty of free time for his new poetic interest. Most evenings he spent with Clarke and from the age of 15 to 20 laid the foundations of his literary life. Clarke not only introduced him to much poetry but also aroused his interest in radical politics. They read Leigh Hunt's *The Examiner* to which Keats subscribed for the rest of his life. Most importantly they read Spenser's *The Faerie Queene*. Clarke wrote of Keats's reaction to *The Faerie Queene*: "he ramped through... like a young horse turned into a Spring meadow". Keats's first poem was written at the age of 18, an *Imitation of Spenser*, which started appropriately with the sunrise:

> Now morning from her orient chamber came,
> And her first footsteps touch'd a verdant hill;
> Crowning its lawny chest with amber flame,
> Silv'ring the untainted gushes of its rill;

Keats and Clarke were rediscovering an old world with new enthusiasm, in that so common cycle taken by taste and fashion. Guided by Leigh Hunt and William Hazlitt, they turned back from the Augustan age, and more particularly from Pope, to Elizabethan and Jacobean poetry which seemed to them to have a nobler quality. Hazlitt was the forceful expression of the reactionary climate of his day, to be rejoiced in by Keats who once said that "he is your only good damner, and if ever I am damn'd – damn me if I shouldn't like him to damn me". As Keats at 18 was writing his first poem, Shelley was 21, Byron 35, Southey 39, Coleridge 41, Wordsworth 43 and Blake 56, but Keats was to die before them all.

After his apprenticeship, a necessary experience before proceeding to hospital, Keats was accepted for training at Guy's. The new Apothecaries Act was introduced in 1815 to prevent unqualified practice, all had now to pass the new Court of Examiners after 5 years apprenticeship and a minimum of six months hospital training. The Guy's Medical School Office record, shows Keats's entry on October 1st 1815 and notes his appointment, in 1861, as dresser "March 3rd John Keats under Mr Lucas". A thief has cut the Keats signature from the book in which the students signed their names on entry to the Medical School. Keats started with some obvious advantages since the famous surgeon Astley Cooper put him under his own dresser George Cooper who, with Frederick Tyrrell a surgeons apprentice, took Keats to live with them in their rooms in St Thomas's Street, where they all shared a sitting-room.

The next name to that of Keats in the students' book at Guy's was John White Webster. Two years older than Keats he came from Boston where his father was a prosperous pharmacist. Webster returned to take his degree at Harvard, where he became Professor of Chemistry and worked at the Massachusetts Medical College. The name of Webster was to ring around America in 1850 when, in a highly sensational affair, he was convicted and hanged for the murder of the College benefactor. Over 5000 people visited the College in a single day to view the site of the murder and a great crowd assembled at the trial. Webster was convicted of killing George Parkman, a fellow Bostonian who had obtained an M.D. at Aberdeen and inherited wealth which he had used to build the Medical College and there to endow a Parkman Professorship of Anatomy and Physiology, held at that time by Oliver Wendell Holmes. Webster was being pressed by a number of people for the payment of his debts, most of which were owing to Parkman, whom, in the hope of being relieved of his financial difficulties, he murdered in his College rooms, dismembered and tried unsuccessfully to dispose of down a shaft washed by the waters of a tidal dock. Webster was hanged in the jail yard at Boston on August 30th 1850. Oliver Wendell Holmes examined the remains of Parkman's body and gave evidence calling attention to the teeth by which the already acknowledged identity of the deceased was firmly established.

Guy's and St Thomas's Hospitals at that time adjoined one another and were combined for teaching, being known as the United Hospitals. The anatomical department of St Thomas's had just been rebuilt with a museum, dissecting-room and lecture-hall, where Keats attended. There the students dissected corpses snatched from recent graves in London, a practice which continued until 1832. The dressers' duties were arduous and unpleasant; wounds became quickly infected, festering sores abounded, and frequent changes of foul dressings were necessary with but a few untrained women to help before trained nurses appeared. Keats had also to attend operations done without benefit of anaesthetic which students pressed around to get a view. The patients' lot was not a happy one. The belligerent boy who became a sensitive poet was a much tougher representative of his age than many are apt to imagine.

The chief lecturer in anatomy and physiology when Keats arrived was Sir Astley Cooper (1768-1841), handsome, humane, a kind person with a great gift for remembering those from the hospital years after they had left. He was so much liked as man and teacher that the students crowded round the doors of the lecture theatre to rush in as they were opened to secure a seat, the latecomers having to sit in the passages and on the steps. Sometimes as many as 300 attended. We know more than we otherwise might of these medical lectures because of searches made and records examined by Keats scholars. The most important find was Keats's own anatomy and physiology lecture notes written between January 1st and June 1st 1816, now in the Keats Museum at Hampstead, which were left to the Hampstead Public Library by Sir Charles Dilke. These were transcribed and published by Maurice Buxton Forman in 1934 and a facsimile is in the library of the Royal Society of Medicine. The arrangement of the notes is confused, the lectures are not in proper order, part is writ large, neat and clear, presumably done later as Astley

Cooper advised, and part small, close and at times running vertically and horizontally onto the margins and adjoining pages, presumably made during the lectures. A further step in this investigation was taken by George Winston, the Guy's Hospital librarian, when in 1943 he compared Keats's notes with those made by Joshua Waddington, another student who attended the same lectures, and whose notes had been presented to Guy's by his son. Waddington's notes were carefully written and numbered and showed that Forman's attempt to rearrange Keats's jumble had been inaccurate. Sir William Hale-White's (1938) high opinion of Keats's lecture notes is not supported by the Waddington comparison, which suggests rather that Keats's early enthusiasm waned and his interest, not surprisingly, declined as poetry began to take over as the main interest of his life. However, we have Sir Astley Cooper's lectures as recorded by Keats with a rather curious selection of his sayings. For example: of the fracture of the neck of the femur in old people,

> Mr C. says that in this case no union ever takes place. Mr Abernethy is, however, of a contrary opinion... injuries to the spine are considered hopeless cases... In disease Medical Men guess, if they cannot ascertain a disease they call it nervous... Those who have been much addicted to Study, from keeping up a continued determination of Blood to the Brain have often the Vessels of that part ossified.

Keats moved from St Thomas's Street to Dean Street, still in the poor area around the two hospitals. From here he escaped to meet Clarke whenever he could, cultivated aspiring poets such as George Felton Matthew, and shared rooms with Henry Stephens (later of Stephens' Ink) who had literary tastes. With little time for writing he, nevertheless, sent a sonnet to Leigh Hunt, *To Solitude*, on how he dwelt amongst a "jumbled heap of murky buildings" and longed for the country, his "soul's pleasure". Leigh Hunt published it in *The Examiner* in May 1816. It was Keats's first published work.

There are not many direct medical references in Keats's poetry. People have made lists of those few that do exist, accurate if but briefly illustrative: "my globed-brain", "the heavy pulse-painful, cloying and stagnate", "palsy-twitched" and "dew at ooze from living blood". There is, however, one delightful passage in *I Stood Tip-Toe upon a Little Hill*, written in the year he qualified in medicine about his thoughts while walking on Hampstead Heath seeing a happy view of recovery in hospital as part of his enjoyment.

> The breezes were ethereal, and pure,
> And crept through half-closed lattices to cure
> The languid sick, it cool'd their fever'd sleep,
> And soothed them into slumbers full and deep,
> Soon they awoke clear eyed: nor burnt with thirsting,
> Nor with hot fingers, nor with temples bursting:
> And springing up, they met with wond'ring sight
> Of their dear friends, nigh foolish with delight;
> Who feel their arms, and breasts, and kiss and stare,
> And on their placid foreheads part the hair.

On one of Keats's visits to Clarke, who was then living in Camberwell, he found that he had borrowed a 1610 folio edition of Chapman's translation of Homer, and they stayed up all night reading it to one another. Keats walked home in the early morning hours to the Southwark slum where he lived and wrote the sonnet *On First Looking into Chapman's Homer*, tired but still overcome with excitement and joy from his evening's discovery. He dispatched it by postal messenger and when Clarke came down to breakfast at 10 o'clock that morning there it was, ending with those magical words describing for all time the dumb-struck joy of discovery.

> Then felt I like some watcher of the skies
> When a new planet swims into his ken;
> Or like stout Cortez when with eagle eyes
> He star'd at the Pacific – and all his men
> Look'd at each other with a wild surmise –
> Silent, upon a peak in Darien.

Back at work as a dresser, with his thoughts now wandering, he had to watch the terrible "Billy" Lucas at work in the operating theatre, a man of whom it was said that he had never studied anatomy in the dissecting-room and whose career of butchery was recalled with horror by Astley Cooper. This experience added weight to Keats's growing rejection of life in medicine, for a terrible fear came over him that he might make mistakes which could endanger life. In July 1816 he passed the examination of the Court of Apothecaries and was licensed to practice. Henry Stephens, who failed the examination a few weeks later, wrote:

> He surprised many of us by passing at the examination as he had appeared to pay so little attention to his profession, but he was very quick in acquiring any thing and his knowledge of the Classics helped him a good deal in that examination, for it was the examination in Latin which the students most feared.

It was to be the end of his medical career however, and Keats wrote,

> My last operation was the opening of a man's temporal artery. I did it with the utmost nicety, but reflecting what had passed through my mind at the time, my dexterity seemed a miracle, and I never took up the lancet again.

The temporal artery was commonly used for bleeding patients.

Leigh Hunt, the model for Harold Skimpole, the wonderful talker and scrounger in Dickens's *Bleak House*, now became a guiding influence in Keats's life. He provided the companionship of an established literary man who, though he lived in continual disorder surrounded by pictures, busts, flowers, music and a growing band of children, managed to survive debt, imprisonment and a nervous breakdown. He gave Keats a sense of optimism and happiness, and provided the literary talk he so badly needed to share. He introduced Keats to Benjamin Robert Haydon, the extrovert artist who struggled for eight years to see that the Elgin Marbles were acquired for the nation. Haydon developed his art of historical painting and produced over the years his largest work, *Christ's Entry into Jerusalem*, in which, amongst his cloud of witnesses, he included portraits of some famous men, such as Hazlitt, Newton, Voltaire and Wordsworth, squeezing in a profile of Keats between two pillars on the right. Haydon took Keats to the British Museum in March 1817 to see the Elgin Marbles and received in return two sonnets from him. At Haydon's studio and at Leigh Hunt's house, Keats was meeting the artistic elite of his day: William Hazlitt, Charles Lamb, Percy Bysshe Shelley and John Hamilton Reynolds. He was becoming acquainted "with Men who in their admiration of poetry do not jumble together Shakespeare and Darwin" – this was Erasmus

148

Darwin, Charles was then but seven years old. Through his brother George, Keats made other friends: a young solicitor, William Haslam, and, more importantly, Joseph Severn, an aspiring painter, then apprenticed to an engraver.

Keats's first book of poems was published in March 1817 and dedicated to Leigh Hunt. His friends thought that it would cause a sensation. Haydon wrote: "it is a flash of lightening that will rouse men from their occupations and keep them trembling for the crash of thunder that *will* follow". It did nothing of the sort; few were roused, no work stopped because of it, and some copies were even returned. However, Keats's publisher John Taylor was convinced of his genius from the start and introduced him to Richard Woodhouse, a distinguished solicitor and literary adviser, who copied out Keats's poems, got Hilton to paint his portrait and Giometti to sculpt a medallion, promoted his work during his life and helped to establish his fame after his death.

Keats, retired from medicine, went to live with his two brothers in Cheapside and marked the turning point in his life by starting a much longer poem than he had attempted before. This was *Endymion. A Poetic Romance* (1818) much influenced by Wordsworth and combining sorrow and joy, sadness and rejoicing, the sensual and the spiritual. The famous first line is said to have started out as "A thing of beauty is a constant joy", according to his remaining medical-student friend, Henry Stephens, who said later that Keats was sitting by a window looking up Cheapside to St Pauls in the twilight as he read the line to him and asked what he thought of it. Stephens replied "It has the true ring, but is wanting in something" to which Keats instantly offered the alternative of "A thing of beauty is a joy for ever". Expressions of the coexistence, opposition and eventual harmonisation of living and dying were to remain with Keats as a theme for the rest of his short life, most exquisitely and enigmatically expressed in *La Belle Dame sans Merci*. When introducing *Endymion* Keats wrote of his adolescence "there is a space of life between, in which the soil is in ferment, the character undecided, the way of life uncertain, the ambition thick-sighted". Christopher Ricks (1974) suggests that Keats's expressions of regret at his inadequacies and inexperience, immaturity and presumption in the preface to *Endymion* should not be taken at face value. His aspirations were great, he aimed high, he could not quite achieve what he intended, but he always believed in his calling. Ricks writes: "a particular strength of Keats is the implication that the youthful, the luxuriant, the immature can be, not just excusable errors, but vantage points".

At 21 Keats acquired control of what was left of his legacy. Abbey, his remaining trustee, who strongly disapproved of his relinquishing medicine and abandoning the training which had absorbed so much of his fortune, no longer had any say in the administration of his affairs. Keats and his brothers moved to Hampstead and there he met Charles Wentworth Dilke who worked in the Navy Pay Office, a literary man who had published a six-volume collection of *Old English Plays*. Dilke and his wife Maria brought natural good sense and an orderliness of affairs into Keats's life in strong contrast to the extravagances and chaotic disorder of Leigh Hunt's abode. The Dilkes, who lived at Wentworth Place, which they built and shared with Charles Brown, became lasting friends.

Keats was making slow progress with *Endymion* and, on the Dilkes's recommendation, went off to the Isle of Wight on the first expedition he had ever undertaken alone to look for the peace necessary for his work. The trip cannot have been a great success, for although some writing was done, he became restless, and left for Margate, where he was joined by Tom. From there he went to Hastings where he met Mrs Isabella Jones to whom he wrote a love poem. He went back to London to look into his money problems, then to Hampstead for the second book of *Endymion* and then to Oxford. Here he stayed for a month to write the third book, living with Benjamin Bailey in Magdalen Hall; Bailey was another important influence, for he introduced Keats to new poets particularly Dante.

In Oxford Keats acquired an illness for which he took small doses of mercury. Much has been made of this episode with diagnoses proposed on no firmer evidence than that of the medication. Syphilis, as usual, was suggested, but Robert Gittings considers that though the weight of contemporary evidence indicates that Keats probably did have a venereal infection, it was more likely to have been gonorrhea, then thought to be an early stage of syphilis, since no one would have used "a little Mercury" had syphilis been diagnosed. Keats said "The little Mercury I have taken has corrected the Poison and improved my Health", though he was still "confined" for the next fortnight. Doctor Solomon Sawrey, who attended Keats, distinguished gonorrhea from syphilis and when he wrote *An Inquiry into the Effects of the Venereal Poison,* believed that mercury should only be used for such infections and never in large doses unless syphilis was suspected. A year later when Keats had recurrent sore throats, Sawrey did give him larger doses, with some reluctance, probably suspecting that his throat ulceration might be syphilitic. There is no evidence whatever for this, Keats was we know liable to throat infections, which became more frequent as his general health deteriorated.

Endymion was finished at last, the fourth book being written at the Fox and Hounds at Burford Bridge near Box Hill. Back in London Keats met Wordsworth for the first time and was with him and Charles Lamb at a hilarious celebration dinner with Haydon. Brother George came into his inheritance, undepleted by any training fees and at a time when government stocks were better valued. He got married and went to America, Keats sadly seeing him off at Liverpool before he and Charles Brown set out on a walking tour. They covered six hundred and forty two miles in forty two days through the lakes, into Northern Ireland and up the West coast of Scotland and across to Inverness. Upon his return Maria Dilke wrote: "he was as brown and shabby as you can imagine; scarcely any shoes left, his jacket all torn at the back, a fur cap, a great plaid, and his knapsack. I cannot tell what he looked like." We can tell that he must have been strong, fit and well at this moment just when infection was about to strike.

It was as he came back from this tour that the news of Tom's decline was broken to him and he hurried off to be with him. There followed a hopeless, harrowing time, Keats, exposed to tuberculosis once more, hardly left his brother for weeks before his death at 19 in December 1818. Here he contracted the infection which was to prove fatal just over two years later – one year for his most outstanding writing and one year for desperate illness.

While they were in Scotland, Brown had rented his part of Wentworth Place to the Brawne family: Fanny, Margaret, Samuel and their widowed mother. They lived in Hampstead, and Keats, who came to live at Wentworth Place with Brown, soon met them.

Fanny was graceful, small, vivacious, good at languages, fond of clothes, dancing and reading, and a bright light of social society. She was most happy to meet a poet, and Keats soon fell in love with this attractive new acquaintance. He wrote to George in America:

> Mrs Brawne... is a very nice woman – and her daughter senior is I think beautiful and elegant, graceful, silly, fashionable and strange. We have a little tiff now and then – and she behaves a little better, or I must have sheered off.

He had however met Isabella Jones again, written a sprightly poem on an amorous encounter for her and, at her suggestion, started *The Eve of St Agnes* written, however, with Fanny Brawne in his mind.

The Dilkes went to London to be near their son Charlie at Westminster School and the Brawnes moved back to their part of Wentworth Place where Keats saw them every day. In Mrs Brawne's eyes he was a failed medical student who ought to return to his profession and not at all the best person for her daughter. Even his poetry was attacked and similar advice harshly given – as, for example, when an infamous review in *Blackwood's* said

> It is a better and wiser thing to be a starved apothecary than a starved poet; so back to the shop, Mr John, back to the 'plasters, pills, and ointment boxes', etc. But, for Heaven's sake, young Sangrado, be a little more sparing of extenuatives and soporifics in your practice than you have been in your poetry.

Keats tried vainly to improve his prospects but his energy was flagging. He and Fanny became betrothed during a period of poetic intensity and great achievement. 1819 saw many of his finest works including *La Belle Dames Sans Merci, The Eve of St Agnes* and the *Odes to Psyche, a Nightingale a Grecian Urn and Autumn*. It seems that an intense application to creative work can triumph for a while over physical decline, supported by the joint effects of a raised metabolic rate and a growing certainty that a brief limit has already been set to life and opportunity. Keats experienced alternate bursts of creation and attacks of weariness as the pressures to seek fame and fulfilment were first stoked and then slowly extinguished by disease. He went again to the Isle of Wight, tried briefly to "get employment in some of our elegant Periodical

Works" in London and returned to Hampstead to find the vivacious, social Fanny having a good time. The Dilkes gave a dance at which Fanny shone and Keats was bitter. His health deteriorated, a year of betrothal with no prospect of marriage was becoming intolerable, he took laudanum to cheer his spirit until restrained by Brown. Things were getting worse. By February 1820 Keats was flushed, feverish and coughed up a little blood followed by a severe haemoptysis. His training and his family experience left him in no doubt that he must soon die. He said to Brown "That drop of blood is my death warrant". Fanny and her mother nursed him devotedly but in September it was decided that he must go to Italy to snatch at a last forlorn chance of recovery.

Keats could not undertake such a journey alone. He found a companion in Joseph Severn, the painter, who with great sacrifice, though he probably was not aware of what he was letting himself in for, agreed to accompany him. Severn had only just received the Gold Medal at the Royal Academy and was on the threshold of a successful career. They left on September 17th from Gravesend in the *Maria Crowther*, a cargo sailing-brig of 130 tons. It was a terrible voyage – cramped quarters, two weeks of storm in the Channel, and to cap it all a Miss Cotterell as fellow passenger, also with pulmonary tuberculosis, who was so ill that they must help to nurse her. Keats had a fever and further loss of blood. They arrived in Naples on October 21st and to add to their troubles had to spend ten days in quarantine because there was an outbreak of typhus in London. They proceeded to Rome to a house at the bottom of the Spanish Steps where accommodation had been arranged for them by Dr James Clark, who was later to return to England and become physician to Queen Victoria. Here – "Where youth grows pale, and spectre-thin and dies" – Keats became steadily worse. He could no longer write verse, but said in a letter to Fanny Brawne: "If my health would bear it, I could write a Poem which I have in my head, which would be a consolation for people in such a situation as mine".

On February 23rd, 1821, Keats died in Rome. Diagnosis and treatment of chest diseases were poorly developed, the stethoscope had been used in 1819 but it was not until after Keats's death that its value was generally appreciated, he died 61 years before the discovery of the tubercle bacillus and 74 years before the discovery of x-rays. Rest and a good diet (let alone streptomycin) were not for him, in fact the treatment prescribed was a restricted diet, bleeding and, when he could manage it, horse riding, all of which only made matters worse. Dr James Clark was kind and attentive but no real help; in view of the famous mistake he was to make at Queen Victoria's Court later on, perhaps we may hope that his statement on Keats's arrival – "If I can put his mind at ease I think he'll do well" – were words of encouragement rather than a serious attempt at prognosis.

Joseph Severn deserves great praise. As Lord Brock (1973) pointed out, he was Keats's constant, unflinching support.

He wrote

> Not a moment I can be from him... I sit by his bed and read all day, and at night I humour him in all his wanderings. He has just fallen asleep, the first sleep for eight nights, and now from mere exhaustion.

And on the day before his death:

> I have nothing to break this dreadful solitude but letters. Day after day, night after night, here I am by our poor dying friend. My spirits, my intellect and my health are breaking down. I can get no one to change with me – no one to relieve me. All run away, and even if they did not Keats would not do without me.

Joseph Severn drew a sketch of him as he was dying and wrote on it "drawn to keep me awake", his unfailing devotion was the poet's only comfort. Leigh Hunt wrote to Severn showing the understanding heart beneath his profligate disorder; "Tell him he is only before us on the road, as he was in everything else".

Severn lived to be 86, being more fortunate than Keats in his resistance to tuberculous infection. He returned to Rome after 40 years to serve as British Consul and it was there that he died. So it happened that in the Old Protestant Cemetery Severn's body was laid beside that of Keats to whom he had been devoted friend and death-bed companion so many years before.

Bate, Walter Jackson *John Keats* Oxford University Press, 1964.

Brock, Lord Russell *John Keats and Joseph Severn: The Tragedy of the Last Illness* Keats-Shelley Memorial Association, 1973.

Colvin, Sidney *John Keats, His Life and Poetry, His Friends, Critics and After-Fame* Macmillan & Co., London, 1917.

Gittings, Robert *John Keats* Heinemann, London, 1968.

Gittings, Robert *Letters of John Keats. A Selection* Oxford University Press, 1970.

Hale-White, Sir William *John White Webster* Guy's Hosp. Rep. 1932, 80, 4-17.

Hale-White, Sir William *Keats as Doctor and Patient* Oxford University Press, 1938.

Hilton, Timothy *Keats and His World* Thames and Hudston, London, 1971.

Keats, John *The Poetical Works of John Keats* Edited by H. Buxton Forman. Oxford University Press, 1920.

Richardson, Joanna *The Life and Letters of John Keats* The Folio Society, London, 1981.

Ricks, Christopher *Keats and Embarrassment* Oxford University Press, 1974.

Ward, Aileen *John Keats. The Making of a Poet* Secker and Warbug, London, 1964.

Winston, George *John Keats and Joshua Waddington, Contemporary Students at Guy's Hospital* Guy's Hos. Rep. 1943, 92, 101.

JOSEPH HOOKER

CHAPTER EIGHT

The Travelling Botanist

THIS FAMOUS botanist-doctor-writer started on his travels as a young naval surgeon going to the Antarctic, confirmed his vocation and established his reputation in India, and became the greatest authority on the world distribution of plant life. Joseph Dalton Hooker (1817-1911) was one of a remarkable band of surgeon-naturalists who were also famous as explorers, ranging from Mungo Park (1771-1806), who wrote his *Travels in the Interior of Africa* (1799) and was a friend of Sir Walter Scott, through Sir John Richardson (1787-1865), who went to the Arctic with both Sir William Parry and Sir John Franklin, to Edward Wilson (1872-1912), who reached the South Pole with Captain Scott and died with him on the return journey. Our botanist followed his father as Director of Kew Gardens, which they managed between them from 1841 to 1885. Father and son made Kew what it is, a great scientific establishment retaining the amenities of a glorious public park. Son was a prolific writer of scientific papers, an uninhibited letter writer, and, in his one work of wide appeal, displayed a marvellous gift for describing strange, unfamiliar people and remote, unexplored places. For nearly fifteen years he was Charles Darwin's chief confidant while he was struggling with his theory of evolution and withholding publication. Hooker became President of the Royal Society, and has been called the last of the great Victorian scientists. He outlived all the main protagonists at the presentation of evolutionary theory and at the age of ninety-one gave the address at the fifty-year celebration of its announcement.

Joseph Hooker was born to botany: his father and both his grandfathers engaged in the study of plant life, and Joseph was once to describe himself as "the puppet of Natural Selection". His father, William Jackson Hooker (1785-1865), came from Norwich and his grandfather, Joseph Hooker, from Exeter. His mother's father, Dawson Turner of Yarmouth, was a banker and amateur naturalist from a most accomplished family of Dawsons,

Palgraves, Cotmans and Thirkettles, with an outstanding scholastic, artistic and literary heritage. Amongst them were an eminent surgeon, a Senior Wrangler and a female classical scholar as well as artists and authors. Francis Turner Palgrave (1824-1897), his first cousin, the eldest son of Sir Francis (born Meyer Cohen) the historian, was Professor of Poetry at Oxford and the editor of the *Golden Treasury of English Lyrics* (1861).

In 1820 the Hooker family moved from Halesworth in Suffolk, where Joseph was born; to Glasgow, when William Hooker was appointed Professor of Botany at the University. Joseph attended Glasgow High School and at thirteen was extending his education on plant-hunting expeditions with his father in the Western Highlands. He entered the University of Glasgow in 1832 to study Latin, Greek, logic, natural philosophy and mathematics. Here he came in contact with medical students attending his father's lectures as part of their work on *materia medica*, at a time when plant recognition was a most important study for a doctor with such a wide variety in use in medicine. Joseph's own decision to study medicine had little to do with this association, however, for his was a more direct botanical reason. He had the opportunity to become a member of a party to explore the Antarctic, which was being planned by a friend of his father's, Captain James Clark Ross (1800-1862), who was willing to take him but who made the offer dependent on Hooker obtaining a medical qualification. Preparations for the expedition were expected to take more than two years and Hooker, who had done some preliminary medical work, had to qualify in 1839. Owing to delays he was able to spend a few months in training after qualification at the naval hospital at Haslar near Portsmouth before they set off. Some difficulties did arise over the terms of his appointment because Dr McCormick, his senior, who had already been to the Arctic with Parry, was sailing as Naturalist. However, McCormick turned out to be so helpful and accommodating that Joseph received the official title of Assistant Surgeon and Botanist.

Such an expedition was a wonderful opportunity for an ambitious young man of science, just as it had been for Charles Darwin (1809-1882) on his voyage to South American waters from 1832 to 1836 on board H.M.S. *Beagle*, and would be for Thomas Huxley (1825-1895), who sailed as a naval surgeon in H.M.S.

Rattlesnake to Australia and the Barrier Reef with Captain Owen Stanley from 1846 to 1850. Ross had two ships, H.M.S. *Erebus* of 378 tons and H.M.S. *Terror* of 340 tons, each with a crew of sixty-four. They sailed from the Medway in September 1839 and were away from England for four years.

Ross's expedition made three trips to the Great Ice Barrier where he found that the Antarctic was a continent and not the great ocean he had expected. They explored further south than any previous expedition had done or than any other would do for over fifty years. This voyage set the scene for the great overland journeys to reach the Pole, so nearly achieved by Shackleton in 1909, and successfully accomplished by Amundsen in 1911, followed by Scott a month later in 1912. Ross's party visited many places, going and coming, providing Hooker with grand opportunities for plant collecting. They spent three months in Tasmania where they were welcomed by the Governor, Sir John Franklin (1786-1847), an old Arctic explorer who was to take over the *Erebus* and *Terror* from Ross on his return to England to set off on his last voyage to discover the North West Passage, a voyage on which he was lost with his entire company after being stuck in the ice for eighteen months. Ross's party visited Sydney, where Hooker learned that his father had been appointed Director of Kew Gardens. They stayed three months in New Zealand and six months in the Falkland Islands.

Hooker's preparations for his first voyage had not been ideal; he found himself forced to store many of his specimens in pickle jars and to use rum as a preservative. However, many living plants were preserved, and one example of his father's pleasure in receiving them was expressed over those sent from Hermite Island – of which he wrote in 1843:

> So valuable a consignment has not been received at the Garden since we came here. The two new kinds of Beech, and these the most Southern trees in the world, are invaluable, and the Winter's Bark Tree (of the latter only one specimen was in the kingdom before) are growing beautifully.

Hooker was assiduous in collecting specimens on sea and land and meticulous in making detailed notes and drawings. He wrote many letters home and his mother showed them to everyone –

writing, to his great embarrassment, to tell him that "they are known far and wide". She was guilty of breaking official secrecy by making disclosures about the voyage without Captain Ross's knowledge and before his report had been made to the Admiralty. Fortunately all was forgotten or forgiven in the publicity surrounding the command visit they made to Buckingham Palace on their return. The Queen and Prince Albert had taken a great interest in the expedition and it transpired that Ross himself had been writing to the Prince Consort with advance information about the voyage.

Hooker wrote the botanical notes for Ross's official report and published accounts of his own researches in many books and papers. *The Botany of the Antarctic, Voyage of H.M. Discovery Ships Erebus and Terror in the Years 1839-1843, Flora Antarctica* (1844-1847), and others. These works were reissued in 1961 in six volumes at £83. The voyage had left the young botanist stronger in body, more independent in character, developed in mind and strengthened in profession. It also established an added bond between himself, Darwin and Huxley – "all salted in early life".

Mrs Lyell of Kinnord had given Hooker a set of proofs of Darwin's *Journal of Researches during the Voyage of the Beagle* (1839) to read while he was preparing for the expedition, and Charles Lyell (1797-1875), who was knighted in 1848 and whose *Principles of Geology* (1830-1833) had a profound influence on nineteenth-century science, himself presented Hooker with a published copy to take on the voyage. This was to be an inspiration to him; he wrote that "all Darwin's remarks are so true and so graphic wherever we go".

At St Helena, on the way home, Hooker wrote to his father about his future. There had been little medical work for him on the voyage, he had concentrated on botany and he had no wish to stay in the regular naval service as a surgeon. Many years later, in 1910, he wrote of his appointment to Ross's expedition:

> I had no idea of going as a medical man, but Ross would not take me in any other official capacity, and I had to gallop through a medical degree at the last hour: happily for the crew we had no sickness and hardly an accident to either ship throughout the voyage and we had three other Medical Officers, hence my time was devoted throughout to my natural history studies.

Ross proposed him for promotion in the navy but he was anxious to get home to start work with his father, helping him in his herbarium, writing his accounts of the work he had done and preparing a paper, worked up from Darwin's collection, on the plants from the Galapagos Islands.

Although this work kept him busy on his return, he was determined to extend his botanical acquaintance and experience and planned a great European tour. Time and money restricted his travels but he went to Paris, Berlin and several cities in the Netherlands, visiting botanical gardens and making new friends. He arrived at Le Havre and left by diligence for Rouen, where the railway to Paris had been built. The train took him there "100 miles for 16 francs, 14 stoppages, 4 hours in passage, 3 tunnels, one 3 miles long". Here he was excited to meet the great naturalist and traveller Baron Friedrich Alexander von Humboldt (1769-1859). He wrote that he had found:

> A paunchy little German instead of a Humboldt... I expected to
> see a fine fellow 6 feet without his boots, who would make as
> few steps to get up Chimborazo as thoughts to solve a problem.

However, they got on well, for Humboldt was most interested in Ross's expedition and kept asking questions about the voyage and filling in each account he received with detail, derived from his marvellous memory, of his own expeditions. Travel in Europe at that time was slow, difficult and hedged around by regulations. Hooker's passport had to be signed by the British Ambassador in the country he was leaving and also by the Ambassador from the country of his destination before he could start, and then his passport must be signed by the Prefect of Police. Thus numerous delays for officialdom were added to those due to the atrocious condition of the roads in winter and the frozen rivers. Hooker used his hard-won opportunities not only to further his botanical education but to visit art galleries. He planned one visit to Haarlem so that he might hear the organ there. He was widening his experience of art as well as science.

Back at Kew he set to work again on his *Flora Antarctica*. He was persuaded to give a course of lectures in Edinburgh but, unlike his father, he found this a difficult and uncongenial task, though he improved as he went along. Professor Graham, whose botany course he had undertaken because of his illness, died, and Hooker was proposed as his successor. Local interests and politics combined to obstruct the appointment and Hooker returned to Kew. A post was found for him to work on British flora, extant and fossil, and their connection with geological formations, allowing him time to continue with his reports on his Antarctic findings. The geological work introduced him to a new group of scientists which included Sir Richard Owen (1804-1892), doctor-anatomist, the man who coined the name Dinosaur and was a pre-Darwinian advocate of branching animal development but based on a unified, underlying plan of creation. Owen was unable to accept the idea of natural selection and wrote a bitterly critical review of Darwin's *Origin of Species* (1859). He developed a persistent antipathy to the Hookers, chiefly because they represented Kew which Owen had failed to have placed under the administration of the British Museum.

1847 was a busy year: Hooker became engaged to Frances Henslow, a friend of his sister Elizabeth and the daughter of the Cambridge Professor of Botany, who had been instrumental in persuading Darwin into a scientific career, he was elected a Fellow the Royal Society with the largest number of votes recorded in his day, in October he was invited to stay at Down House, Darwin's Kentish home, where they formed the close friendship which lasted for the remaining thirty-five years of Darwin's life, and lastly, in November he sailed for India on his second great botanical expedition.

This trip started with a piece of luck. Lord Dalhousie was about to take up his appointment as Governor-General of India and agreed to let Hooker sail with him in the *Sidon*. Hooker wrote that Lord Dalhousie had "a lamentably low opinion" of natural history and was "a perfect specimen of the miserable system of education pursued at Oxford". However, despite their divergent training and conflict of interests, they enjoyed each other's company and formed a mutual regard, indeed Dalhousie became an unstinted supporter of Hooker, took him into his suite and later was to prove a staunch friend when he was in trouble in India. The *Sidon* called at Lisbon, Gilbraltar, Malta and Alexandria, Hooker plant collecting on the way, except in Cairo which he found interesting for everything except botany. His letters now included those to

Frances Henslow, so they gave a lighter account of his travels than before; for example, he told Frances how in Malta he had been offered some fossil shark's teeth as authentic relics of St Paul. He visited Mahomet Ali in the train of Lord and Lady Dalhousie, and his description of the cortège and their reception might well have come out of the *Arabian Nights*.

> We were rather late, and arrived just after the Governor, as the guns were pealing forth a Royal Salute. Passing under the gates, through a most splendid new and half finished alabaster Mosque, we arrived at the Quadrangle, where the Governor was getting out of a splendid six-horse coach, like the Lord Mayor's with Egyptian Lancers as outriders: the band played a sort of "God save the Queen" to him, and I know not what to the second carriage, with Fane* and Courtenay*; but I got the Bohemian Polka for my share of reception outside... In a few minutes each, Lady Dalhousie included, was furnished with a pipe 6 feet long, having amber mouthpieces full of brilliants, the mouthpieces as thick as my arm almost, and 8 inches long. The bowl was placed in a silver dish on the ground; and we all whiffed away. The servants then brought coffee in little egg cups, set in gold filagree holders blazing with diamonds... We all retired much pleased with all we saw.

They travelled overland to the Red Sea, as this was thirteen years before the Suez Canal was started, and had a rough journey with terrible jolting, for although the Arab tribes removed the larger boulders from the track, when they were not paid they put them back again. At Suez they embarked in the *Moozuffer* for a dull journey over the Indian Ocean and round to Madras, where they were greeted with a fine military display, and then on to Calcutta. Hooker was learning Hindustani and tried out his new attainment by engaging servants for his journey. In Calcutta the Dalhousies insisted that he stay at Government House an honour and a kindness but, unfortunately, this was five miles from the Botanic Gardens; his father's old friend Sir Lawrence Peel's house, "the Chatsworth of India", with wonderful gardens of its own, was only just across the river.

---

* Francis Fane, A.D.C. later Earl of Westmorland and F.F. Courtenay private secretary.

Hooker's first botanical excursion was in south-west Bengal to the Kymore hills and then north to Mirzapur above Benares on the Ganges. He then travelled slowly down the river for three weeks, writing his notes and letters home, leaving the Ganges to travel north to Darjeeling. His letters were full of excitement: his ascent of the sacred mountain of the Jains, his passage through the jungle with two elephants, so useful in obtaining otherwise inaccessible specimens for him, and his view of a wonderful display of the Aurora. The sight of the Aurora was rare so near the tropics, and his account was received with some disbelief at home as an example of "travellers' tales". He wrote to his father, obviously piqued by this doubt of his veracity, and, with the eager hard-working scientist's haughty attitude to his compatriots, said that seeing the Aurora had not seemed so extraordinary to him as to cause surprise much less argument, adding "in such a country as India, where every Englishman eats a heavy dinner at 8 and goes to bed at 10, it is not astonishing that these spectacles have been hitherto unobserved". He wrote to Darwin answering many of his questions about such things as the habits of the Cheetah and the extension of different species, confessing himself bewildered by the facts hourly thrown before him.

In Darjeeling at the foot of the Himalayas his work in India really began. He was fortunate to meet there Brian Hodgson, who had been dismissed from his post as Resident at the court of Nepal, against the wishes of the Nepalese, by the previous Governor-General of India in one of his petulant fits of determination to undo everything done by his predecessor. Hodgson was a notable scholar, a student of Oriental lore, a linguist, ethnologist and geographer, the donor of the Hodgson natural history collection to the British Museum and a mine of information on all things Indian. Hooker became his student, confidant and medical adviser, and made his house his home. He named after him one of the first new rhododendrons discovered in Sikkim, *R. hodgsonii*, with a dark magenta-purple flower. Another valuable friend with a delightful family was the Political Agent in Sikkim, Archibald Campbell, whose wife also had a rhododendron named for her. The Campbell children called him "Hooker doctor" and were much impressed by his ability to ride "the naughty pony".

From Darjeeling Hooker planned to reach the Himalayan snows between which and the humid valleys of lower Sikkim "lay a whole botanical world, with a range equal to that from the tropics to the pole". The Sikkim Rajah proved an obstacle, for he barred travellers from his country under the influence of China, fear weighing effectively against distrust despite the fact that he derived most of his income from the British. When the Governor of Bengal doubled the Rajah's revenue to ease matters, his natural suspicion saw this move as an example of foolish British duplicity embodying a deep plan to take over his country. Hooker appealed to Lord Dalhousie for help and at last under this pressure the Rajah felt obliged to give his reluctant assent for the trip. The Nepalese, disgusted by the Sikkim Rajah's pettiness, sent a Ghurka escort to see Hooker and the Campbells through their territory to the Tibetan Passes by routes never before traversed by a European. Hooker wrote a glorious description of the Sikkim delegation which was sent to the border in a last attempt to obstruct his entry with instructions that, if forced to give in, they should do so with as bad a grace as possible. The insight, vivid description and imperial assumptions, revealed in his account of this Himalayan encounter one hundred and forty years ago paint the scene with its pictorial appeal and artful guile.

First there was the Rajah's Vakeel, a portly, tall and muscular Thibetan, clothed in a long red robe like a Cardinal's, looped across the middle, and round his neck and down his shoulders hung a rosary. His face was not strongly Chinese at all, stern, grave and solid, thoroughly obstinate and impracticable... A stiff black, small cap, with high brim standing up all round, rather set off the repelling look he maintained. Taken to pieces he might be described as a funny mixture of the old woman, from his beardless face, the Lama priest, from his dress and rosary, and a burly, well-to-do Landamman, departed from some Swiss Canton to resist to the uttermost the demands of a dangerous neighbour power... These qualities, together with an unblushing effrontery and consummate skill in fabrication and a large interest in the monopoly of Sikkim trade, rendered him a fit tool for the Rajah... A real character stands at his elbow, a little old withered Thibetan, leaning on his long bamboo bow, simply clothed in a woollen robe, his grey hair floating in the wind, bowed with age, of mild expression and stone blind. He is a Seneschal to the party, devoted to his country, and the Companion of the Rajah's deputations to the Political Agent of the powerful Government whose advances his master rejects. When he speaks, and this is very seldom (and it is always in his own half Chinese tongue no Englishman can interpret it) the burden of his story passes from tongue to tongue; he is evidently the oracle of the party; his placid looks and grey hair would lead me to confide in him and address him as Father, but I have a grim suspicion that his views narrow as his years go on, that he was bereaved of his best and brightest sense before our power showed itself in these hills, and that his crafty companions have taken advantage of this and done more than leave him in the dark as to our real power to punish, but wish to reward and encourage... The attendants upon these... were short, stout, thick-set Bhoteas, clad in purple worsted dressing gowns, fastened round the middle by a belt, bare headed and footed, very dirty and ill-favoured withal.

This extraordinary gathering was regarded by the beautiful Campbell children with only mild interest verging on indifference.

Entry of the expedition to the country was just the beginning of their difficulties. Hooker found at first that he had no chance of pulling a plant "without disturbing the *Gods*, in other words exciting suspicion". However, his natural frankness, assumption of superiority and open expression of a flattering opinion of the people, backed by the prestige won through his useful doctoring, left an impression of his wisdom and kindly strength. He soon became so well regarded that his visit was affectionately recalled to travellers and botanists who followed him fifty years later. The officials, on the other hand, took Hooker for a brother spy and continued their attempts to obstruct him in every way possible. The botany went well; loads of plants were dispatched to Calcutta for shipment to Kew, the supply was inexhaustible, but many dried out and died on the journey.

Campbell had been instructed to secure a meeting with the Rajah himself for diplomatic negotiations. Too prevent anyone entering the capital of Sikkim the Rajah was compelled to take his court and go forward to the river and meet Campbell. There, on the banks of the Teesta, in a makeshift hut sitting on a shaky raised platform, they found the Rajah, a little man "swathed in yellow silk with a pink broad-brimmed and low-crowned hat on".

Hooker's first exciting Himalayan journey, despite the harassment, was a great botanical success. So many new plants were found and distributional evidence collected that a second, longer journey to the mountains was planned. He set out again in May 1849 for a three-month trip but, did not manage to get back to Darjeeling until Christmas Day. For the first part he was without Campbell, received a welcome and much help from the mountain people, and suffered no more than some official passive resistance, though he had at one time to withstand intimidation by twenty uncouth barbarians who imposed every kind of delay and interference with the receipt of his supplies. He dealt with them with firmness and courage and was able to cross into Tibet, climb to 19,000 feet and discovered many new plants. He came down to Choontam, where Campbell joined him for what was to be the last part of his expedition. Things changed with the arrival of the official Political Agent, and they were both seized and held hostage for nearly two months while attempts were made to extort better terms for the Sikkim-India treaty. The prize was irresistible to the crafty henchmen of the Rajah. Hooker and Campbell were confined in a miserable hovel under wretched conditions. Hooker was able to continue writing his notes and sorting his plants, but it was the middle of November before he was allowed to send out a letter. His appeal to Lord Dalhousie produced an instant response. Troops were sent to Darjeeling and an ultimatum, backed by military force, went to the Rajah which was something he understood. In December he sent the prisoners back with an escort, the leader being told to travel "as slowly as he could contrive to crawl". They found at Darjeeling that 14,000 Sepoys and European troops with guns under a whole staff of officers had arrived to put a stop to such nonsense as arresting two Britons, an official and a friend of the Governor General. Lands given to the Rajah were taken back, his pension withdrawn and Southern Sikkim annexed. Such was the penalty for flouting the authority of the British Raj.

Hooker embarked on one more expedition in 1850 with his

167

friend Thomas Thompson (1817-1878), the Superintendent of the Calcutta Botanic Garden, a grand affair taking them to the Khasia Mountains and lasting nine months, with elephants and one hundred and ten coolies. They collected 2,500 plants and 300 kinds of wood. They got to Chittagong but were prevented by head hunters from reaching the higher hills.

Hooker got back to England in March 1851 after an absence of three and a half years and was married that August to his patient Frances. His great work in India had assured his scientific position but no suitable post was immediately available. On half-pay as a Naval Surgeon while busy arranging his collection and writing his report, times were hard. However, to his surprise, the Admiralty made him a most welcome grant of £500 in recognition of his "zeal, perseverance and scientific ability in his botanical services". In 1854 Hooker produced his *Himalayan Journals*, nine hundred pages of adventure, scientific notes, descriptions of bizzare people and secluded places, dedicated to Charles Darwin and with a new influence on his style provided by his wife. It was a great success, was reissued the next year and again in 1891 and 1905. Well over two hundred of his scientific works, ranging from multi-volume books to short papers, contributed greatly to the outstanding position he attained in the history of botany, but his *Himalayan Journals; or Notes of a Naturalist in Bengal, the Sikkim and Nepal Himalayas the Khasia Mountains Etc.* assured him a lasting place in English literature.

Hooker was maintaining that species were variable before Darwin had declared his theory of evolution by natural selection. He had reached this conclusion independently through his own observations at a time when there was a newly developing view of the origins of man, but when the Bible story of the direct creation of all God's creatures was still the accepted dogma. Darwin had written to him in January 1844:

> At last gleams of light have come, and I am almost convinced (quite contrary to the opinion I started with) that species are not (it is like confessing to murder) immutable.

Hooker, the professional botanist with an interest in the geographical distribution of plants was invaluable to Darwin the philosophical naturalist, because he supplied both supporting, botanical evidence for his research and expert discussion of his theories, while pointing out difficulties in the way of his hypotheses and suggesting solutions. Darwin wrote to Hooker (October 19th 1856) that "fighting a battle with you clears my mind wonderfully", and there were battles, because, although Hooker came to accept Darwin's main contention with enthusiasm, he maintained a cautious, critical attitude towards the mechanisms proposed.

Hooker's introduction to his *Flora of Tasmania* (1859), the completion of the account of the research he had done on Ross's expedition, was one of the first works to offer open support for Darwin and a landmark in its own right. In this he wrote: "Geographical Distribution will be the key which will unlock the mystery of the species". There had been another doctor who was among the first to put forward the concept of the descent of man: Edward Tyson (1650-1708), anatomy reader at Surgeon's Hall, suggested a place for the orang-outang in a line of descent to man in a monograph published in 1699, *Orang-Outang sive homo sylvestris; or the Anatomy of a Pygmie Compared with that of a Monkey, An Ape and a Man.* Hooker's friendship and correspondence with Darwin made him an important influence on the new revolution in ideas which was to dethrone man from the pinnacle of direct creation, as the physician Nicholas Copernicus (1473-1543) had deprived the Earth of its place at the centre of the Universe.

Hooker was caught up in the great events which followed when the news of evolution broke as Charles Darwin and Alfred Wallace (1822-1913) made their joint communication on natural selection to the Linnean Society in July 1858, and Darwin published *The Origin of Species* in November 1859. Huxley reviewed the book in *The Times* on Boxing Day 1859, and few book reviews can ever have had a greater effect. A faint ripple of interest turned into a flood of speculation which was given its impetus by the great confrontation which took place at the meeting of the British Association for the Advancement of Science in Oxford in 1860. The famous clash between Bishop Samuel Wilberforce and Thomas Huxley was not a simple matter. Wilberforce, primed by Richard Owen (the one with the old grudge against the Hookers), ridiculed Darwin's theories and was foolish enough to ask Huxley to explain on which side of his family he was descended from an ape. Huxley's reply has been variously reported, shortened and improved into what James Agate used to call "the higher truth", it declared that he would rather be descended from an ape than from a man in high position who misused his talents to attack a theory he did not understand. There was an uproar, ladies fainted and Robert Fitzroy, Darwin's old Captain on the *Beagle*, stalked up and down the room waving a Bible above his head and shouting "The Book, the Book". There were many scientists, however, who did not believe that accepting the undoubted fact of evolution entailed adopting a purely materialistic view of life, believing that man's development occurred solely by chance, or having a completely new ethical basis imposed on the conduct of man. Disraeli's counter found many a sympathetic response when he said that given the choice of treating man as an ape or an angel, he was "on the side of the angels". Nevertheless, the way we see ourselves had been forever changed.

Hooker wrote to Darwin on the 2nd of July 1860 giving his account of the extraordinary meeting and of his own part in it:

Well, Sam Oxon got up and spouted for half an hour with inimitable spirit, ugliness and emptiness and unfairness. I saw he was coached up by Owen and knew nothing, and he said not a syllable but what was in the Reviews; he ridiculed you badly and Huxley savagely. Huxley answered admirably and turned the tables... Lady Brewster fainted, the excitement increased as others spoke; my blood boiled, I felt myself a dastard; now I saw my advantage; I swore to myself that I would smite that Amalekite, Sam, hip and thigh if my heart jumped out of my mouth, and I handed my name up to the President (Henslow) as ready to throw down the gauntlet... It became necessary for each speaker to mount the platform, and there and then I smashed him amid rounds of applause. I hit him in the wind at the first shot in ten words taken from his own ugly mouth; and then proceeded to demonstrate in as few more: (1) that he could never have read your book, and (2) that he was absolutely ignorant of the rudiments of Bot. Science. I said a few more on the subject of my own experience and conversion, and wound up with a very few observations on the relative positions of the old and new hypotheses, and with some words of caution to the audience.

It was not exactly the model for an objective, truth-seeking scientific discussion but it certainly made history. It set the scene for a long-continued, fiercely maintained, Darwinian defence against all comers, a defence not only of evolutionary views against the creationists, but of the whole canon of gradual, inevitable, biological advance through the natural selection of small variations in individuals as a slow, regular and continuous process.

Today when there has been a decent interval for reassessment and the science of genetics has added its telling contribution, there have been renewed anti-Darwinian movements, scientific as well as theological. These have been many and various, such as the assertion that the theory of evolution is impossible to confirm or to falsify and so is basically unscientific despite the fact that the modern dating of fossils shows such records following evolution in an ordered sequence. The validity of Darwin's concentration on the individual organism as the unit of selection has been questioned. "Altruistic" traits, such as warnings given by danger signals, should reduce the sentinel's chance of survival even though assisting the group; natural selection would be expected to eliminate the look-outs, unless it was able to act in some way on the group. The forces driving evolution may be many and various, including mutation, environment, competition and a form of natural selection based on population genetics. Just as there is a general pattern of control over the growth and development of the whole individual, so there must surely be some controlling influence over the general characteristics of the group. Doubt has also been cast on inevitability and gradualism in evolution; the long-time fixity of some species, the elimination of others, gaps in the geological record, doubts about the adequacy of the time available for small variations alone to have worked the miracle, and revolutions in social change have all encouraged ideas of far greater forward bounds in evolution than were allowed for in Darwinian theory. On the fringe-theological side, Creationists who hold to the strict belief taken from the book of *Genesis* that all species were once miraculously and rapidly created, have recently gone so far as to attempt to ban the teaching of "the atheistic philosophy of evolution" in schools in some parts of America, or, alternatively, to make the artful suggestion that it would be only fair to give equal teaching time to a strict Bible interpretation of the origin of man. The struggle for existence, and the grand endeavour to understand the workings of nature, seem dull and uninspired to some people when compared with their hope for the revelation of a divinely programmed march towards perfection. The freedom to proceed without inevitability into the unexpected should surely be one of the highest aspirations of man.

There has been a tendency to underestimate directional influences which act on chance, for chance only provides random variables for selection by an advancing trend. Random variations are made use of to promote a non-random sequence, being selected in a stochastic process where mutations supply the new, and influences such as the environment and competition determine the outcome. Pasteur said "All great discoveries are the result of chance but chance favours the prepared mind"; chance also favours a prepared organisation. Organisms develop through the uses made of increased potential. Richard Dawkins in *The Blind Watchmaker* (1986) wrote:

> I want to persuade the reader, not just that the Darwinian world-view *happens* to be true, but that it is the only known theory that *could* in principle, solve the mystery of our existence.

Will and habit improve individual men, they do not change the inheritance of mankind. Intention is a force for change in society not in genetics. A random element inherent in the ascent of man can do nothing to diminish personal achievement. Men not only pass on their genes to their descendants but add the priceless gift of the store of knowledge and of art they have accumulated over the centuries.

The theory of evolution set up a revolution in thought about man's place in the world. Variety, fertility, transformation and extinction appeared as necessary components of development. There was a reason for death and for the elimination of millions of species never to be seen again, of which some of the largest such as mammoths, giant sloths and sabre-toothed tigers were only the more obvious. Such ideas moved into the realm of natural, explained reality. The appearance of new species took on an air of inevitability. The need either for a directing authority outside nature, or for an inherent preplanned purposefulness in the natural order itself, were not disproved, but they had been questioned. The point of divergence lay in the fact that to theologians truth is revealed, while to scientists it is doubt and uncertainty which make progress in understanding possible. Even Samuel Johnson defined evolution as "To unfold: to disentangle".

Small genetic changes occurring by chance, building up over vast periods of time, may under favourable circumstances, allow almost anything to happen. Some of the results will provide survival advantage thus influencing the selection of the individuals who are to furnish the next generation, however, the question debated is whether such a process alone could possibly account for the whole story of the rise of sentient man from the primordial slime. Certainly people have detected puzzles, such as how the complex arrangements of the eye or the brain – what Darwin called "the organs of extreme perfection" – could possibly have evolved through multiple, small, random changes unless they were acting in harmony. Such highly organised structures they believe must be planned and coordinated both structurally and functionally. As John Dryden (1631-1700) in his poem *A Song for St Cecilia's Day* (1687), a favourite of Goldsmith's, put it,

> From harmony, from heavenly harmony,
> This universal frame began:
> From harmony to harmony
> Through all the compass of the notes it ran,
> The diapason closing full in man.

There are features in certain organisms which developed before there was any obvious demand for them; trends in development have continued in one main direction for long periods of time; transmitted changes in behaviour which secure survival may occur in advance of any observed structural alteration and many other observations suggest that there must surely be some programme at work. Flexibility, new potential derived from increasing complexity, a built-in ability for self-assembly, and the overall miracle of organisation all come into the story. That evolution occurs gradually in a step-by-step manner where each change is a chance improvement relative to the past is not really in doubt, but the sequence of accumulating change is certainly not random, it is directed by survival with improvements chosen by

173

selection. Evolution occurs – it is not to be expected that it may be simply explained. *How the Camel Got his Hump* and *How the Leopard Got his Spots* are more than *Just so Stories for Little Children*. The Countess in Christopher Fry's *The Dark is Light Enough* (1954) said, always with the voice of Edith Evans,

> The arithmetic
> Of cause and effect I've never understood
> How many beans make five is an immense
> Question, depending on how many
> Preliminary beans preceeded them.

We start our lives with inherited organising and selecting abilities and we learn by referring experience to these ancestral dispositions (Chapter 2); the rise of man must also involve some element of such a group dispositional system. The growing potential for advanced performance must be accompanied by the organisation of increasingly elaborate relationships for its fulfilment. Loren Eiseley in *The Immense Journey* (1946) wrote:

> Men talk much of matter and energy, of the struggle for existence that molds the shape of life. These things exist, it is true; but more delicate, elusive, quicker than the fins in water, is that mysterious principle known as "organisation", which leaves all other mysteries concerned with life stale and insignificant by comparison. For that without organisation life does not persist is obvious. Yet this organisation itself is not strictly the product of life, nor of selection. Like some dark and passing shadow within matter, it cups out the eye's small windows or spaces the notes of a meadow lark's song in the interior of a mottled egg. That principle – I am beginning to suspect – was there before the living in the deeps of water.

Perhaps the most abiding qualities of life may after all be ethereal. There is an exciting day just around the corner for biology.

Hooker's travels took him to Palestine and Syria in 1860, where he saw the Cedars of Lebanon in the Kadisha Valley at 6000 feet. There were four hundred or so in one group, four hundred yards in diameter, forming a black spot in a landscape where no other trees or shrubs were to be seen. Some of the cedars might, he thought, be 2,500 years old. His notes and measurements of this group were published in May 1884. Three-quarters of this famous Kadisha grove was destroyed in the 1914-18 war, the timber being used by the Turks for fuel on the Palestine railway. The first Lebanon cedars were planted in Britain towards the end of the seventeenth century, the other great cedars came here much later, the blue Atlantic cedar not until 1845. The cedar avenue at Kew was planted in 1871 at the same time as the Pinetum.

In 1869 Hooker was off to Russia with his wife on a six-week private visit. On the train journey from Berlin to Moscow he met General Todleben, the defender of Sebastopol:

> A grand old fellow, full of wounds and honours – lame of both legs – an English bullet in *one*, and a French in the other, which shattered the bones; he has a huge hole in the neck, caused by a bayonet thrust, and a wound *through* the bridge of the nose, from a Turkish poniard.

In 1871 Hooker went to Morocco where he had difficulty in explaining his intention to study the flowers and vegetation in the mountains – anything so simple and truthful was bound to conceal a sinister purpose. However, coming from the Royal Botanic Gardens, he was thought to be collecting herbs to cure disease which made his activities more believable; but this idea was soon changed into the belief that he was on a mission sent by the Sultana of England to find a plant for her which would make her live for ever. When their botanical endeavours in the Great Atlas Mountains were seen to involve a lot of climbing and hard work it was said that "The Sultana of England is a severe woman, and she has threatened to give them stick (the bastinado) if they do not find the herb she wants!"

In 1877 Hooker went to the United States. It was his last important botanical expedition. He reached 14,500 feet in the Rockies, ascended the Sierra Blanca, and travelled beyond Colorado Springs to Pike's Peak. He went on to Denver leaving for Georgetown and Gray's Peak and then to Salt Lake City for a botanical excursion into the Wahsatah Mountains. They took the train to Reno and Carson City and went by wagon across the Sierra Nevada to San Francisco. His non-botanical comments on American life were typically forthright, prejudiced and mixed.

> Today we called on Brigham Young and had a chat with him. He is about 70, stout, well dressed, and with a rather refined

countenance. He reminded me more of a stout, elderly and *thoroughly respectable* butler, than anything else. In person and conversation he is less of a Yankee than 9/10 of the gentleman I have been introduced to. Of course he is an arrant impostor, but nothing in speech, look or manner differs from those of a quiet well-bred English gentleman...

Hooker called Georgetown "the extreme finger-end of civilisation" and wrote that although the streets were better watered than at Kew, people slept with no locks on their doors, the fire-engines were well-manned and in capital order, and there was no end of food.

The New Englanders are most like us in language, speech and habits... Their high sharp voices, and of the women especially, is the most grating feature of their life to us. In other respects they are superior to us, as in education, civility, great desire to oblige and take trouble for you, – decent cleanly manners, clean shirts and a far superior condition and manner of the official and subofficial classes attached to public conveyances and to Hotels, etc. These people are most universally well conducted, civil and obliging to all, far more so than with us.

Things have changed a bit, there and here, since 1877, but this was high praise from a condescending, travelling, Victorian Englishman of the period looking at those whom he regarded as having been "Colonials" less than 100 years before. Dickens in 1842 and Trollope in 1868 experienced the understandable sensitivity of Americans to condescending English criticism, and both failed, in the climate of that time, to have a gross injustice to British authors removed by an international copyright agreement between America and Great Britain, not achieved until 1891.

On his father's death in 1865, Joseph Hooker was appointed his successor as Director of Kew Gardens. Sir William Hooker had found Kew in poor condition with no herbarium, museum or library. He brought his own collections from Glasgow and in 1853 the herbarium and library of Dr W.A. Bromfield were added, with George Bentham's (1800-1884) collections coming the next year. Bentham, with wealth, time and enthusiasm and no official post, worked with Joseph Hooker to produce *The Handbook of British Flora* (1887). At Kew Hooker took over a going concern which he had already helped to develop and applied immense enthusiasm and hard work to its improvement. He built a new range of greenhouses, changed the water supply and installed a new heating system. He fought a battle for two years with Acton Smee Ayrton, Gladstone's First Commissioner of Works, an affair known at Kew as "The Ayrton Episode", when Hooker tried to prevent him from turning Kew into no more than a public park and recreation ground and so forcing him to resign. Ayrton engaged Sir Richard Owen, long committed to attacks on the Hookers, to produce an official, damaging report on Kew, which he published without first showing it to the Director. This action brought many to Hooker's defence, and a report on the history of Kew and its debt to the Hookers was signed by many leading scientists, including Bentham, Darwin, Huxley, Lyell and Tyndall, and presented to Parliament by Sir John Lubbock. Ayrton was transferred to another post and in 1874 failed to be re-elected to Parliament. Hooker continued his work at Kew: a laboratory was built in 1876, a wing to the herbarium in 1877 and a new extension was added to the museum in 1881. He involved himself in every detail of building and organisation whilst engaged in his own botanical work and preparing his many publications.

In 1874 Hooker's wife Frances died, leaving him with six children. Theirs had been a most happy marriage and she had been a constant support and helper in his work. In 1876 he married again. His second wife was Hyacinth, the widow of Sir William Jardine. They had a son in 1877 who became a soldier and served in the Boer War and in India. He preserved his father's instructive and affectionate letters from his schooldays onwards, eventually published as *The Lion Letters*. Hooker's daughter Harriet married the Assistant Director of Kew, W.T. Thiselton Dyer (1843-1928) in 1877, and, as he followed her father as Director, this maintained the Hooker/Kew connection.

When Hooker retired from Kew he bought a plot of land near Sunningdale where he built a comfortable house called "The Camp". Troops had camped there after the battle of Culloden so as to keep them a little way out of the town. The soldiers had been kept employed by making the lake at Virginia Water. Hooker planted trees around his house and made a garden full of rhododendrons. There he continued to work for the rest of his life. He had described three new species of mosses in 1837. In the last year of his life he was still establishing new species at the age of ninety-four. At eighty-two he made a speech at the unveiling of Darwin's statue in Oxford. In 1901, as the only surviving officer of Ross's expedition, he was consulted about Scott's new Antarctic expedition and paid a farewell visit to the *Discovery* the day before she sailed. He was there to welcome Scott on his return three years later and able to see the photographs they had taken, a method of recording which had not been available to him.

In August 1902 he attended the coronation of Edward VII and wrote in his usual style,

> The Archbishop and Dean were both evidently very frail, the latter literally tottering along, and the D. of Cambridge was rather dragged than walking. The King and Queen bore themselves with quiet dignity... The solemnity of the whole ceremony was most impressive, and I am glad I went, though I was bothered by my gorgeous, voluminous sky-blue satin mantle for C.G.S.I. with a gold star on it as bit as a soup plate, and a heavy gold collar on my shoulders.

In 1907 Hooker was awarded the Order of Merit, which had been established in 1902. His ninetieth birthday produced addresses sent to him from seven foreign countries, he wrote that "the cumbrous address I have received in Latin and German are terrors to translate and stupefaction to answer". At the 1908 Jubilee celebrations of the presentation of the Darwin/Wallace address to the Linnean Society, Hooker, the sole survivor of those most closely concerned, and the last of the three great scientists, Lyell, Huxley and himself, who had been Darwin's chief support, delivered the address. He was ninety-one. The next year he attended in Cambridge the three-day celebration of the centenary of Darwin's birth. He did feel unable to travel to see Scott off on his last expedition in 1911. He died that December, peacefully in his sleep, somewhat enfeebled in body but lively in mind until the end.

Bateson, Gregory *Mind and Nature* Wildewood House, London, 1979.

Beer, Gillian *Darwin's Plots* Routledge & Kegan Paul, London, 1983.

Bowler, Peter J. *Evolution. The History of an Idea* University of California Press, Berkeley, 1984.

Dawkins, Richard *The Blind Watchmaker* Longmans, London, 1986.

de Beer, Sir Gavin *Charles Darwin. Evolution by Natural Selection* Thomas Nelson & Son, London, 1963.

Hooker, Joseph *Himalayan Journals.* 1854.

Huxley, Leonard *Life and Letters of Sir Joseph Dalton Hooker O.M., C.G.S.I.* John Murray, London 1918.

Smith, John Mayard (Ed) *Evolution Now* Nature and Macmillan, London, 1982.

Taylor, Gordon Rattray *The Great Evolution Mystery* Secker & Warburg, London, 1983.

Turrill, W.B. *Joseph Dalton Hooker* Thomas Nelson, London, 1963.

CHARLES LEVER

CHAPTER NINE

Two Irishmen and Another

THERE MUST, one would suppose, be limits to credulity. Surely most novelists would think seriously before writing a story containing the extraordinary events in the lives of these three Irishmen. One, a tall, handsome, athletic man became a Red Indian, and abandoned a lucrative medical practice to become a best-selling but often impecunious novelist; another, a small, dynamic and internationally famous surgeon, with a tragic prodigy for a son, made a name for himself as a writer and had his career wrecked by a woman; the third made a dramatic escape when he was taken away to be shot, became a senator and acquired a wide-spread reputation both as a surgeon and a poet.

Charles Lever (1806-1872) wrote more than 30 novels in 35 years, from *The Confessions of Harry Lorrequer* (1837) to *Lord Kilgobbin* (1872), practised medicine in Ireland through a cholera epidemic and in Belgium where he attended aristocrats and diplomats of the British colony in Brussels, was acquainted with King Leopold, and charged fees five times those of the local practitioners. As a student in Germany he was an attendant at a duel and in Canada he escaped death from a Red Indian tribe. He was a graceful dancer, a proficient fencer, a lover of horses, perpetrator of elaborate hoaxes and a notable wit and raconteur. He married his schoolgirl sweetheart and lived happily with her and their children for the rest of her life. He tried to explain Ireland to Garibaldi. He was appointed Vice-Consult in Spezia and became Consul in Trieste, where he died.

William Wilde (1815-1876) founded the Dublin eye hospital, wrote a standard work on aural surgery and books on travel, exploration, archaeology, the beauties of his country and a well researched account of Dean Swift's last illness. He had three illegitimate children. The two girls, at 21 and 23, were tragically burned to death at a ball, the crinoline of one caught the fire as she danced by and the other was enveloped in flames when she tried to save her. There were many such accidents at the time

181

when a ball-dress might be seven feet across and composed of four skirts containing five-eighths of a mile of combustible tulle. The boy followed his father as surgeon to the eye hospital. Wilde had two legitimate sons, one a charming failure and one a tragic genius. He showed the battlefield of the Boyne to Macaulay. His wife, a large woman of striking appearance, wrote poetry under the name of Speranza and, at one time, fiercely nationalistic articles for *The Nation* under the name of John Fenshaw Ellis. As she grew older she became a strange figure holding a *salon* "enthroned behind a tea-table looking like a sort of female Buddha", according to Frank Harris. On his deathbed, Sir William was visited each day by a mysterious woman, dressed in black and closely veiled, who mounted to his room, unhindered by his wife, to sit by the end of his bed without speaking or raising her veil.

Oliver St John Gogarty (1878-1957), whose father, grandfather and great-grandfather had been doctors, was surgeon, author, aviator, master of repartee and friend of Arthur Griffith (1872-1922), the founder of Sinn Fein, and of Michael Collins (1890-1922), one of its most famous leaders. His portrait was painted by Augustus John, Sir William Orpen and Gerald Brockhurst. He owned a Mercedes-Benz and a yellow Rolls Royce – the Mercedes was described by Horace Reynolds as "All yellow hood and mahogany trimmings, shiningly sinister". As a wild young man he shared a brief period of dissipation with James Joyce before becoming a well known surgeon, an Irish senator and a fine poet.

Despite the fact that Charles Lever's father was an Englishman, himself was as Irish as they come. His father, an architect and builder, had arrived in Ireland in 1787 aged 27 and lived and prospered in Dublin where he married an Irish Protestant of English descent, Julia Candler. He was employed on some Government contracts, including those for the Customs-house and General Post Office. He acquired a great reputation as a story teller.

There were two sons ten years apart: John, who became a parson, and Charles.

Charles's first school in Dublin was kept by Mr Ford, a man who regularly flogged his pupils until the day when an enraged father turned on him, as Nicholas Nickleby was to turn on

Wackford Squeers a few years later, and beat him with such violence that he fled yelling into the street. Charles next went to Mr McCarthy, an accomplished man with eighty pupils. There he met John Ottiwell, who became his boyhood hero and inspiration: an ill-looking customer, full of wit and resource, who rode, swam, sang, jumped and composed verse better than anyone else. Ottiwell was called to the bar but died early on, a disappointed man. Next Charles went to the Rev George Newenham Wright, another who had a great influence on his early life for, though a stern disciplinarian, he found Charles's flow of talk as engaging as did the pupils who were kept amused by his stories and practical jokes. Wright taught him much, including dancing and fencing, at which Lever became adept and was said to be all grace and agility. In later life Charles Lever told a revealing story about himself at that time. He used to follow a poorly-dressed old man he had seen wandering from bookstall to bookstall stopping to read at each. Charles would take up the book the old man had just put down to see what he had been reading and to wonder how he had come by his pursuit of learning and why it was such an obvious source of happiness to him. Another incident in his school days was to influence his whole life. He was attracted to a pretty girl at the Hibernian Marine School and persuaded his companions to distract the janitor's attention while he gave her flowers. She was Katharine Baker who was to become his wife.

At 16 Charles decided against the career of architect proposed for him by his parents and chose to study medicine. His childhood had been more fortunate than that of his friend and contemporary Charles Dickens, who was working in a paste-blacking factory when he was 12, for Lever had a pliant father, a devoted mother, and a pony to ride, was tall, athletic and full of fun, but, like Dickens, he was a great reader. In October 1822 Lever entered Trinity College, leaving without distinction, if more creditably than Oliver Goldsmith had done some 70 years before. He did not get his B.A. until the Autumn of 1827, in fact his elaborate pranks nearly cost him his matriculation. Here he developed his love of Dublin ballads and indulged in the craft of street ballad singing, once returning to college with thirty shillings in half-pence for his efforts. He composed some ballads of his own to sing such as:

Och, Dublin city, there is no doubtin',
Bates every city upon the say;
'Tis there you'd hear O'Connell spoutin',
An' Lady Morgan makin' tay.
For 'tis the capital o' the finest nation,
Wid charmin' pisintry upon a fruitful sod,
Fightin' like divils for conciliation,
An' hatin' each other for the love of God.

After college Lever took several trips abroad, the most important being to Germany to complete his medical education. One, however, was to Canada where, with his love of horses, he became enthralled by the wild open life of the prairies and was admitted to the fellowship of a Red Indian tribe. When he tired of this experience and wanted to return to his own people he learned that one of his "tribal privileges" for desertion would be death by tomahawk. However, he escaped, helped by a squaw and an Indian traveller named Tahata who brought supplies, being smuggled back to Quebec in moccasins and head-feathers. After a short visit to America he returned home bringing with him a Canadian canoe to try on the Grand Canal near Dublin.

In Germany he walked the hospitals and was a student in Göttingen. Writing was now becoming part of his life and his impressions of Europe were submitted to *The Dublin Literary Gazette* and published as *The Log-Book of a Rambler* (1830). This is an entertaining, light-hearted account of his travels, with side-lights on German University life. There are a number of good stories and a dramatic account of a duel, fought because one participant had refused to pledge the other in beer when he was drinking coffee, in which the poor coffee-drinker was so severely wounded that he had to leave the University. There is an account of a student rebellion in Heidelburg held in protest against an "act of oppression on the part of the professors" when the students of Göttingen, in sympathy, invited those of Heidelburg to visit them. Student unrest and student violence are nothing new, even if individual armed combat has given way to more organised confrontations, in which, as Swift said, "a crowd is a mob even if it is composed of bishops". Lever's account of his travels is much enlivened by descriptions of people he met such as mine host of the Boar's Head in Rotterdam, the most famous gastronome in the Low Countries, whose eye "alternately opening and closing seemed as it were to relieve guard upon the drowsiness of his features"; and a tall, gaunt Prussian "who was vainly endeavouring to mould his cast-iron features into an expression of softness to salute some fair acquaintance".

Back in Ireland finding life dull Lever started a club on German student lines for good talk and witty fooling, the members wearing scarlet vests and skull-caps with tassels. Naturally Lever was President and Grand Lama. The members were required to abjure the use of white hats, to abstain from oaths, to contribute to the amusement and good-fellowship of the club without exceeding in liquor, and to address all office-bearers by their proper titles. One, for example, Samuel Lover (1797-1868), painter, poet, musician, novelist and dramatist, was known as "Minstrel". The eccentric resident surgeon at Dr Steevens's Hospital where he trained, James William Cusack, was in the habit of lecturing his class at home from his bed. One day Charles Lever arrived early to find that Cusack had gone out and left a note saying that the lecture had been cancelled. He took down the notice, jumped into bed, put on Cusack's red silk night cap and when the eight other sleepy students arrived began conducting the class by first calling the roll and finding Lever absent.

Lever became a Bachelor of Medicine in 1831. He worked through a cholera epidemic with wonderful cheerfulness. In 1832 he married Kate Baker. Lever then went to Derry and practised at Portstewart near the Giant's Causeway, a summer watering place amidst glorious scenery which in winter turned into a dismal village of poor fishermen. Here he met William Hamilton Maxwell, Rector of Balla in Mayo, a successful novelist who greatly influenced his writing. When tired and jaded by work he returned to his old student relaxation of elaborate practical jokes and noisy enjoyment for which, as an established community doctor, he was much criticised. He once took a party to a fancy-dress ball in a furniture van and a hearse. Returning in the early hours they broke down and tried to obtain shelter at Castle Coe but were taken for travelling showmen and forced to spend the night in the van. Next morning with fresh horses they made a triumphal entry into Coleraine all in their fancy dress. In 1839 he wrote in *The Dublin University Magazine*:

Nothing is too severe: nothing too illiberal to be said if the doctor, when the hours of a painful and laborious day passed, should he either unbend in the lighter amusements of the world, or avail himself of the recreations which to over-worked minds are almost a necessity of existence. No, no – we never can forgive the man who has listened to our narrative of gouty suffering or dyspeptic ill-temper, if he be seen the same evening enjoying himself at the opera, or the next morning breathing the free air of the hunting field.

An accumulation of frustrations and discontents which he called "the fidgets" assailed him; he decided to resign his post in Portstewart though he scarcely knew why. The Surgeon General, Sir Philip Crampton, who boasted that he could swim across Lough Bray, ride into town, and amputate a limb before breakfast, had suggested to Lever that he might do well in Brussels where Crampton's son was then secretary to the British Legation; so Lever set off armed with a letter of introduction. He soon established a good practice supported by the British aristocratic and diplomatic communities. More of his time was now spent in writing, and when his friend Dr William Wilde came to visit him he gave him a manuscript for his opinion. Wilde took it to read in bed and reported that the old four-poster had shaken with his laughter. Together they visited the field of Waterloo, featured in Lever's novel *Charles O'Malley* (1840) which ended with the battle and the Duchess of Richmond's Ball, (Byron's "There was a sound of revelry by night"), an effect which Thackeray liked so well that he adopted it for *Vanity Fair* (1847).

By 1840 Lever was talking of throwing physic to the dogs, and in January 1842 finally gave up prosperous medicine for uncertain literature and returned to Ireland to edit the *Dublin University Magazine* and write *Tom Burke of Ours* (1844). While still affluent he took Templeogue House, which had once belonged to the Knights Templar, and there entertained men from many walks of life renowned for their brilliant conversation. William Wilde was often of the company, and Thackeray said that he "had met no such collective agreeability anywhere". Lever kept a dozen horses, as well as ponies for his children, who rode out with him over the Wicklow Hills. He sustained a vicious attack from S.C. Hall for an article in *The Dublin University Magazine* for which, though he had not written it, he was held responsible as editor. The article was entitled *"Modern Conciliation: Mr Hall's Letter to the Temperence Societies"*. Hall attacked Lever in print accusing him of slandering his native country and its people. Lever was so incensed by this savage attack that he travelled to London to call out Mr Hall for a duel to be fought at Chalk Farm. When Lord Ranelagh, acting as mediator, succeeded in calling off the affair he said "I suppose this is the first time four Irishmen met to shoot an Englishman and didn't do it".

As his income and the quality of his guests' conversation declined, Lever, who needed someone to match his brilliance to bring out the best in him, began to live more quietly and to write more consistently. Though much of the editorial work was now being done by others, the magazine had become a burden benefiting him "neither in fame nor pocket" and Lever was often heard declaring that he would tear up his roots, leave Ireland and live more cheaply abroad. In May 1845 he finally decided to go and was off on his travels, first back to Brussels and then to Bonn, Carlsruhe and Baden-Baden. He rented an ancient castle, Rieder Schloss, on Lake Constance, where he finished *The Knight of Gwynne* (1847), and then went on to Mantua, Verona, Rome and Venice. By 1847 he had settled in Florence which was to be his home for more than 20 years. Here, in Italy, he wrote book after book with scenes laid in Ireland, grew fat, and was a familiar figure driving his fine horses with his family through the town. He paid a number of visits back to Ireland where he was entertained by Sir William Wilde amongst others and where, always at his best with an appreciative audience, he enjoyed a feast of good talk.

Lever, Trollope, Dickens and George Eliot, with Thackeray some way behind in sales, were the most popular novelists of their time. Dickens was six years younger than Lever but died three years before him. Their books appeared at the same time published in eagerly awaited parts, both had some of their work illustrated by Hablôt Browne ("Phiz"). Dickens invited Lever to write for his publication *All the Year Round*; but *The Day's Ride*, which he supplied, and which included the adventures of Algernon Sydney Potts an apothecary, was not a success. Nevertheless they became good friends, despite some early rivalry and Lever dedicated *The Barringtons* (1862) to Dickens with warm appreciation.

There are many exciting incidents in Lever's books, interesting historical scenes and a great deal of grand Irish humour. Tom Burke is a naive romantic, always ready to respond to an insult by striking the speaker in the face with his glove, though he only fights one duel. Bret Harte does better in *Terence Deuville* (1869), his parody of Lever, for Terence kills five men in duel but spares Lord Henry Somerset, for the sake of the Hon. Blanche Fitzroy Sackville, when they exchange nineteen shots and at each fire Terence shoots away a button from Lord Henry's uniform. Tom Burke is there through the Napoleonic wars always devoted to, but steadily disillusioned with, the Emperor, for whom he frequently risks his life.

Though Lever had neither the quality and lasting appeal of Dickens's humorous humanity nor his variety of characterisation, he tells a fine story, and it is easy to understand his popularity and interesting to speculate on his influence on Dickens. Captain Bubbleton, with his fantasies and expectations that something would turn up, preceded Micawber but is not his match. The flogging of the headmaster at Lever's school by an enraged parent may have inspired Dickens's account of the thrashing of Wackford Squeers. The court scene in *Tom Burke* in which the cunning old Darby M'Keown in the witness chair turns the whole court in Tom's favour as he is examined by the prosecuting counsel is a fine example of Lever's skill. This episode is comparable to that memorable scene in *Pickwick Papers*, at the law suit brought by Mrs Bardell for breach of promise, with Sam Weller's telling replies and calm refusal to be bothered by Sergeant Buzfuz. The "Phiz" drawings of these two court scenes make a remarkable pair. When Hablôt Browne died in 1882 *Punch's* tribute said:

> The lamp is out that lighted up the text
> Of Dickens, Lever – heroes of the pen.
> *Pickwick* and *Lorrequer* we love, but next
> We place the man who made us see such men.
> What should we know of *Martin Chuzzlewit*,
> Stern *Mr Dombey*, or Uriah Heep –
> *Tom Burke of Ours?* – Around our hearts they sit,
> Outliving their creators – all asleep!

No sweeter gift e'er fell to man than his
Who gave us troops of friends – delightful "PHIZ".

One of Lever's frequent visitors in Italy was Thackeray, who dedicated his *Irish Sketch Book* (1843) to him. Lever was introduced to the Brownings in 1849 but though Robert then called on him he failed to return the visit, and Elizabeth wrote to Miss Mitford telling her how much she had enjoyed meeting Lever, though she did not much care for his books, and how disappointed they were by his neglect. Mary Russell Mitford (1787-1855), the daughter of a spend-thrift physician and a staunch Lever supporter, told Elizabeth Browning that she thought him one of the best living writers of fiction. Anthony Trollope was an intimate friend, but Lever in Florence had frequently to manoeuvre to avoid Trollope's formidable mother. Maria Edgeworth, nearly 40 years his senior, was enchanted by Lever's books and read them aloud to her nephews and nieces. She wrote charming and helpful letters to him; he visited her at Edgeworthstown, where Sir Walter Scott had been to call on her in 1825. *Tom Burke* is dedicated to her.

To help his uncertain finances the post of Vice-consul in Spezia was found for him and later Lever was made Consul at Trieste. When appointing him Lord Derby said "Here is £600 a year for doing nothing; and you, Lever, are the very man to do it".

A change came over Lever's style of writing, more gravity and dignity replacing much of the old rollicking fun. A number of factors contributed to this fairly radical change as seen in *The Fortunes of Glencore* (1857). Thackeray had made a good natured, amusing and telling parody of Lever's style which, though he took it with good grace, made him think, for he was a man who depended much on praise and encouragement; then William Hamilton Maxwell, who had inspired his racy Irish humour, died in 1850; and then again he was older and more settled. First Lever talked of giving up writing, but it was in his blood, his daily occupation; so the new style was adopted retaining the fine gift of dialogue and this carried him forward to a new audience even though the change was regretted by some of his old admirers.

Thus he continued to the end. When Kate became ill, Lever nursed her with devotion; she had been the centre of his life, the person to whom he referred all his work. When she died in 1871

WILLIAM WILDE

he was devastated by his loss; theirs had been a married life of pure felicity. He finished the novel he was working on, *Lord Kilgobbin* (1872), but never wrote again. He died the next year; they are both buried at Trieste. *The Times* said that thousands of readers of all ages deplored his loss as a personal misfortune.

William Wilde's family, unlike that of Charles Lever, had been long in Ireland. Ralph Wilde came from Durham to Connaught and married Margaret O'Flyn of an ancient Irish family. One of their sons, Thomas Wilde became a doctor in Roscommon, doing his rounds on horseback. He married Emily Fynne of an important if notoriously unstable family, and the youngest of their sons was William born in 1815 at Kilkeevin near Castlerea. He was a small, bright boy who went to school in Elphin when he wasn't off poaching or fishing with his friend Paddy Walsh. Paddy taught him much that he couldn't learn at school, for Paddy, with one leg shorter than the other, was a fiddler, singer, fisherman, and expert shot who "understud distillin".

William decided to follow his father into medicine and in 1832 set out for Dublin to attend the Park Street School of Medicine and to be apprenticed to Abraham Colles. Colles (of Colles's fracture) became professor of anatomy, physiology and surgery and twice president of the Royal College of Surgeons in Ireland; he was a celebrated surgeon at Dr Steevens's Hospital, where Swift had been a trustee and later a governor. Change was in the air and Wilde was fortunate to work under some of the pioneers of modern medicine in Ireland. He assisted Colles with his research on bone growth and the healing of fractures and he was taught by Robert Graves ("he fed fevers") and William Stokes (of Cheyne-Stokes phenomenon the rhythmical waxing and waning of respiration, and Stokes-Adams's syndrome of extremely slowing of the heart sometimes with loss of consciousness) at a time when, with Dominic Corrigan, these men were adding a wealth of clinical description to medicine and establishing a school of bedside teaching. The cholera epidemic arrived when Wilde was 17 and he was sent home to Connaught while Charles Lever, nine years older was in the thick of it. However, Wilde made quite a name for himself while staying with the Fynnes. He was sent for to Kilmain where a man was dying from cholera. He could not save the man and could only get one person to help him, but together they dug a grave, buried a rough coffin in quicklime and set fire to the house and contents. No further cases occurred in the village; so Wilde got the credit. The reputation of this 17 year old medical student increased further when one Sunday on the way to church at Ballymagibbon a small boy was seen turning blue with a piece of potato stuck in his windpipe and Wilde did a tracheotomy on the spot with a pair of scissors under the eye of the congregation.

Lever and Wilde came back to Dublin, but Lever was soon off to practice in the North and Wilde remained as resident at Dr Steevens's for four years with a spell at the Rotunda Hospital where he won the annual prize for midwifery. In 1837 he obtained his licentiate of the Royal College of Surgeons but soon afterwards developed a severe fever, possibly typhus, which, combined with his asthma, lowered his health. He became clinical clerk and museum curator at Dr Steevens's. His superiors, having a good opinion of his abilities and seeing how slow was the recovery from his fever, recommended him to the wealthy Mr Robert Meiklam as medical attendant on a voyage Meiklam was to take for his own health to the Holy Land. This voyage of the *Crusader*, a fine topsail schooner, gave Wilde a view of the world and started him on two of the great interests of his life. He saw a great deal of eye disease, particularly trachoma, and studied at the hospital in Egypt where Antoine Clot ("Clot Bey") and Franz Pruner ("Pruner Bey") were in charge of ophthalmology. He was also able to explore the tombs and pyramids of Sakaru and Dashur, which aroused his life-long interest in archaeology. They went to Rhodes, Telmussus, Tyre, Jaffa, Jerusalem and visited Greece before turning for home.

Arriving back at Kingstown, they took the train to Dublin on one of the first railways of the world, designed by Ferdinand de Lesseps as a young man. Wilde showed Dublin's fair Georgian city to the Meiklams where Charles Lever's father, who had arrived just before the French Revolution, had taken a hand in some of its finest buildings. Here, at that time, could be seen the stark contrast which existed between the gentry in their grand colourful clothes driving fine horses in a variety of elegant carriages and the poor ragged beggars. In this city William Wilde set up his medical practice at the age of twenty-three and began to acquire a reputation through his lectures to learned societies, especially the Royal Irish Academy, on the experience gained on his travels. This brought him into contact with important people such as George Petrie (1789-1866), the archaeologist, musician and painter in watercolours, best known for his proof that the Irish round towers were Christian ecclesiastical buildings. Petrie asked Wilde to help him in an investigation of a bone heap at Langore in Meath which was to provide evidence of the first lake-dwelling, or Crannog, found in Ireland. This started Wilde on a long-term excavation of ancient sites all over Ireland. He also met that most remarkable man William Rowan Hamilton (1805-1865) mathematician and poet who, like Dr Thomas Young before him, knew thirteen languages by the age of 15. A third doctor with a phenomenal gift for languages was a contemporary of Thomas Young, John Leyden (1775-1811), who learned Arabic, French, German, Icelandic, Italian, Hebrew, Persian and Spanish and then became a doctor in order to have the opportunity to travel and to learn the languages of the East. Hamilton, while still an undergraduate, was appointed Professor of Astronomy in Dublin in 1827 and later made Astronomer Royal.

In 1839 Wilde was elected to the Royal Irish Academy at the early age of twenty-four. On the voyage of the *Crusader* he had dissected porpoises and studied the problem of breast feeding in aquatic mammals which need to keep surfacing for air. He described the compressor muscle, which reduces suckling time by enabling the mother to inject milk rapidly into her young. Like Lever, now in Brussels, he wrote a long series of articles on diverse subjects for publication in the *Dublin University Magazine*. He was also writing his first book to have a great success, being an account of his travels on the *Crusader*, known, for obvious reasons, as *Wilde's Madeira*, for its full title had fifty-one words, if we include an "etc.". Published in 1839, the first edition of 1250 copies was soon sold out.

Wilde was becoming quite a figure in Dublin society. Though a small, pale and not very handsome young man, he was much admired by women, whom he seems to have courted whenever opportunity offered. His first illegitimate child was born in 1838, the mother unknown, and given the name of Wilson for Wilde's son. His reputation began to spread beyond Ireland; Maria Edgeworth, by then a famous old lady, became a kind of patron, and when he attended the meeting of the British Association in Birmingham in 1839, he had a great success and met many more influential people.

Now he was enlarging his experience – first by working at The Royal London Ophthalmic Hospital, founded in 1805 and known the world over as Moorfields. He was there for many months studying ophthalmology, and also worked at the Hunterian Museum of the Royal College of Surgeons. At the same time he was pouring out biographies and articles of such varied kinds as on the Irish elk, an influenza epidemic and the structure of the Giant's Causeway. He never neglected society to which he was introduced by Sir James Clark, physician to the Queen, remembered for his attendance on the dying Keats and for his blunders in diagnosing pregnancy in the Lady Flora Hastings affair when she was suffering from a malignant abdominal tumour, and in failing to diagnose typhoid in Prince Albert. This was unfortunate, for he was a kind, considerate physician who achieved something, especially in organisation, helping to found London University and improve the medical curriculum at Oxford and Cambridge.

Wilde moved on to Vienna to work at the *Allgemeine Krankenhaus* with over 2000 beds where the excellent teaching was carried out in Latin backed by six monthly public examinations for the students.

Again he was able to meet the great men of medicine – for example Karl Rokitansky, the first of the outstanding full-time hospital pathologists, who with Skoda and Semmelweiss were making the Vienna medical school famous. Wilde attended the department of ophthalmology under Professor von Rosas, and the army opthalmic clinic under Christopher Jaeger and his son. He was shocked by the inhumane treatment of patients with mental disease, which lagged far behind the methods already developing elsewhere. Midwifery had unusual aspects in that private rooms for those who could pay, and free wards for the poor, existed where the strictest secrecy was observed. Ladies could be admitted veiled, masked or disguised, no questions of identity were raised, and no visitors, whether friends or relatives, were admitted without the patients' permission. After delivery, the baby could be taken home by the mother or be admitted to the foundling hospital. The free-ward patients were required to nurse their own, and one other child, for two months. The ratio of illegitimate to legitimate births in Vienna at that time was 1 to 2.24. There was a terrible loss of life from puerperal fever, and Wilde wrote scathing remarks about the treatment. He became a friend of Ignaz Semmelweiss, and they corresponded for many years, but Semmelwiss's great discovery of the transmission of infection in hospital leading to the prevention of puerperal fever, for which he had to suffer ridicule and abuse, was not made until seven years after Wilde had left. Once more Wilde threw himself into social life, that of Vienna, with its balls, carnivals, and those famous restaurants frequented by so many ladies, was much to his taste. He called at Munich, Prague, Dresden, Heidelberg and Berlin, where introductions from Maria Edgeworth opened many doors for him. On his way home he went to stay with Lever in Brussels.

Back in Dublin with a wide and varied experience he started to practise as an eye and ear surgeon. Special hospital facilities for the poor, always one of his main considerations, were totally inadequate and he set out to create a Moorfields in Dublin. He started in a stable which he fitted up and soon had a flourishing practice. He was appointed lecturer in diseases of the eye and ear at his old Park Street school where some of his previous teachers were still on the staff. He started a new hospital on a subscription basis taking over the old hospital of St Nicholas which in 1844 became St Marks Ophthalmic Hospital and Dispensary for Diseases of the Eye and Ear. Robert Graves became his consultant physician and Sir Philip Crampton his consulting surgeon, but Wilde did the work as the only regular attending surgeon. The hospital was soon attracting students from all over the world.

Wilde's next book was about the literary life and the scientific and medical institutes of Austria and was packed with well tabulated information. As a result he was asked to take the post of Medical Census Commissioner which he held for the rest of his life. He threw his extraordinary energy into the task of establishing a registry of births, deaths and marriages and reporting on disease incidence, especially of the infectious fevers, and on the effects of vaccination. Then he was off on archaeological expeditions whenever he could get away, always, despite mistakes, contributing something of value. With Lever

195

back in Dublin there were people to meet and great talk at his parties and as usual women to pursue. One of his failures was the lovely actress Helen Faucit, quite the rage in Dublin, who married Sir Theodore Martin biographer of the Prince Consort. Always writing, he produced in 1849 his best loved book, *The Beauties of the Boyne and Blackwater*, as well as volumes on history, archaeology and fishing. Twenty years later he was to write another well loved handbook *Lough Corrib and Lough Mask* (1867). During the terrible Irish famine Wilde produced long detailed reports on its medical aspects, one of which was about the outbreak of trachoma which he had studied in Egypt.

In 1842, three young men, Duffy, Davis and Dillon, founded a newspaper dedicated to Irish national independence. Thomas Davis, a Protestant, was the first editor of *The Nation*, followed by John Michel. The journal was dedicated to breathing life into the national movement. One of the contributors to the paper was John Fenshaw Ellis. Duffy paid a visit to this new force in Irish politics only to discovery that "he" was a very tall twenty-year old girl, Miss Jane Francesca Elgee, who wrote poetry under the name of Speranza. When Duffy was prosecuted for high treason on account of two articles inciting to rebellion ("Now is the moment to strike; and by striking save, and the day after the victory it will be time enough to count your dead") there rose high from the body of the court the surprising figure of Speranza whose voice rang out "I am the culprit, I wrote the offending articles". This was the woman William Wilde was to marry in 1851. Wilde at thirty-six, was small, wore a black beard, without moustache, had sharp eyes, a long nose and a large mouth. Speranza 10 years younger with black hair, was tall, stately and handsome. They entered into the social life of Dublin, Speranza even agreeing to be received at the Castle. Their sons William Charles Kingsbury Wills Wilde and Oscar Fingall O'Flahertie Wills Wilde were born in 1852 and 1854. In 1850 Wilde moved St Marks Hospital to better quarters in Park Street which he bought, remodelled and then gave free of rent to his committee. It was a great success, patients coming from all over Ireland, and the fees paid by students, especially from England and America, adding to the income. Wilde remained the only regular surgeon to the hospital. His book, *Aural Surgery*, was published in 1853. He had become one of the leading members of the medical profession in Europe before he was forty years of age.

The Wildes moved to a fine house in Merrion Square, the Harley Street of Dublin which the wags called "The Valley of the Shadow of Death". Besides doctors, lawyers and a few peers lived there and judges and members of parliament were soon to come. There was now a daughter, Isola Francesa, and Speranza was entertaining many people, including Rowan Hamilton and the poet Aubrey de Vere. The Medico-Philosophical Society, a hundred years old, was revived, and dinners were held at the members' houses, including Wilde's where the talk was not at all confined to medico- philosophical subjects. Wilde was conducting a busy practice, doing archaeological research, producing statistical reports for the census, making a catalogue of the antiquities in the museum of the Royal Irish Academy in time for the Dublin meeting of the British Association and organising an excursion for seventy members to the Aran Islands where he and Petrie were to hold forth to them on the antiquities. Wilde toured museums in Berlin, Copenhagen, Lund, Stockholm and Christiania. His Dublin museum was becoming famous; he took the Prince of Wales round it when he visited the city. Charles XV of Sweden gave him the order of the Polar Star after Wilde had operated on the King for cataract. He bought a piece of land on the shores of Corrib and built himself a small house, Moytura, for holidays. Strangers, preferably of some intellectual or artistic distinction, were frequently asked to assemblies in Merrion Square where Speranza, in flowing robes adorned with ornaments modelled on those of ancient Irish Queens, held court, growing more and more eccentric. Honours poured onto Wilde from European Universities; and in 1864 he was knighted at the Castle by Lord Carlisle the Lord Lieutenant.

He was at the height of his fame when things began to go wrong. Mary Travers, the neurotic daughter of Dr Robert Travers, Professor of Medical Jurisprudent at Trinity College, had been sent to Wilde as a patient by Dr Stokes when nineteen years of age. She became his mistress and they consorted for some years. Speranza got to know of this liaison and tackled Miss Travers on the subject. Wilde grew tired of the troublesome Mary Travers who had been getting money out of him and tried to bring the affair to an end while avoiding a scandal, but Mary wanted revenge. When he refused her demands she chose her moment, when he was to give a public lecture on *Ireland: Past and Present: The Land and the People*. It was a great occasion attended by a throng of Dublin society; she engaged boys to distribute outside the hall a highly damaging and wildly embroidered account of their relationship in which the parties were referred to as Dr Quilp and Florence Price. The principal was clearly recognisable as Wilde who, as Dr Quilp, was accused of attempting to seduce Florence with the help of chloroform. She then wrote to the press, anonymously, enquiring why, if the story wasn't about Wilde or wasn't true, he didn't sue the author. When this failed to provoke him she published some of his letters setting off the gossips all over Dublin. Mary Travers pursued her plan of forcing Wilde to take action against her without result, but eventually succeeded in her aim of public scandal by invading his house, confronting Speranza and the children, upsetting Isola, who couldn't understand what was going on, and provoking Speranza into the mistake of writing a furious, accusing letter to her father, Dr Robert Travers. He threw it aside, but it was discovered a week or two later by Mary, who used it to serve Speranza with a writ for libel. The trial was a great affair; Mary now claimed that Wilde had seduced her using force and nearly choking her in his study while his wife and family were away. Her story grew more dramatic and more improbable as the trial proceeded, including a statement that she had borne him a child. The defending counsel succeeded in showing her to be unreliable and vindictive and Speranza, when called, kept up a loyal defence throughout a grilling by Mr Butt acting for Mary Travers. Mr Butt, all righteous indignation, made a fiery speech, the judge summed up showing a good deal of disbelief in Miss Travers' testimony, but the jury still found for the plaintiff though they only awarded her one farthing damages.

The damage to Wilde, however, was terrible, it did him much harm with his colleagues that he had not himself gone into the witness box. He never recovered. He became untidy, even dirty at times, lost his old flair, though he continued writing, and took refuge in his house, Moytura, in Connemara, where he became pre-occupied with the distant past. His illegitimate son, Henry Wilson, who had been well trained and had become his assistant, took over at St Marks Hospital. His other two boys were doing well at school and spent their holidays at Moytura. Wilde did return to his practice in Dublin for a while but he had lost much of his interest in medicine and his health had deteriorated. He attended dinners and Speranza continued here celebrated *salons*. He published one of his most popular works, *Lough Corrib*, with illustrations by his son Willie Wilde. His much loved daughter Isola died in 1867 and the tragic death of his two illegitimate daughters, brought up by his brother the Rev Ralph Wilde, was another terrible blow. His deterioration proceeded, his hair grew long, he took on a dejected air and died in 1876. Despite his sad last years he was well remembered; at his funeral a great concourse followed the cortége, including the President and Council of the Royal Irish Academy.

The estate, seriously diminished in Wilde's last years, left Speranza far from well off. She finished the *Memoir of Gabriel Beranger* which her husband had been publishing in parts in the *Journal of the Royal Archaeological Association of Ireland* and saw it through to book form in 1880. Henry Wilson died of pneumonia in 1877. Willie was an unsuccessful barrister but Oscar, an outstanding figure at Oxford, went on an expedition to Greece and returned to obtain a first in "Greats" and to win the Newdigate Prize for poetry.

When Willie Wilde deserted the Irish Bar for the life of a journalist, Speranza went with him to London. There were still some glorious days to enjoy. Willie and Oscar were often there to support their mother's increasingly eccentric *salon* where she held court on Saturdays "from five to seven" wearing outlandish make-up and exotic clothes, with curtains drawn and soft pink lights. W.B. Yeats visited her but the crowd that attended were mostly on the fringe of the literary and artistic world. Speranza in her fading glory still understood the art of entertaining, introducing everyone with aspirations as having just written a delightful poem or being the new novelist every-one is talking about. Dr Macdonald Critchley (1969) included Speranza in his list of sufferers from what he called "The Miss Havisham Syndrome" when catastrophic disappointment, bereavement or rejection, usually in domineering, intelligent, aristocratic beauties, may cause them to hold back time, exclude

OLIVER GOGARTY

the day, seclude themselves and dress in the costume and jewels of their prime.

Oscar married in 1884 the lovely and devoted Constance. "The House Beautiful", the aesthetic movement, and their sensational public appearances together coincided with his extraordinary creative period of 1888 to 1895. The terrible tragedy which followed derived from Oscar's homosexuality and the English law, but it was the hatred between the real villains, Lord Alfred Douglas and his father the Marquis of Queensbury, combined with Oscar's own arrogance, which brought him to gaol and his lonely death in Paris. The spiteful speculations contained in some of his biographies ill accord with the compassionate, generous and kindly man who emerges from his letters. One of the saddest scenes of this tragic story is that of Oscar and Constance's two sons at school hiding under an assumed name, bullied and afraid, finding to their horror that they might be betrayed by the old nametapes still sewn on to their white flannels. What would Sir William have thought had he known that one day his grandsons would be found in uncomprehending shame, frantically hacking away with a penknife to remove the illustrious name of Wilde from their clothing?

A few years after the death of these two Irishmen another doctor-writer, Oliver Gogarty, appeared in Dublin as if to remind the world that the mould had not been broken. Gogarty and James Joyce took a Martello tower in 1904 overlooking Dublin Bay. When a British warship, anchored offshore, interfered with their view from the tower, Gogarty and Joyce wrote to the Admiralty and had it moved. Staying with them there one night was their friend Samuel Chenevic Trench (the unlikeable Englishman, Haines, in *Ulysses*). Gogarty described the incident that occurred in his book *It Isn't This Time of Year at All* (1954).

> One night about one-thirty Trench awoke from a nightmare screaming: "Ah, the black panther!" As he yelled, he drew a revolver from under his pillow and fired two shots at the hallucination before falling back exhausted. Quietly, I took the revolver away. Again he woke screaming: "Leave the menagerie to me" I said; and fired the remaining shots into the cans over Joyce's head. One by one they fell into his bed. He scrambled out, dressed, took his ash plant, and left the Tower never to return.

Joyce nearly got into this book in his own right for he went to Paris intending to become a medical student with a letter of introduction to Alexander Rivière (1859-1946) a specialist in physical medicine and a pioneer in the treatment of cancer by x-rays and radium. Joyce, however, preferred lectures on literature and philosophy to those on medicine. The early part of Gogarty's life came back to embarrass him when he had become an eminent surgeon and a respectable Irish senator, for Joyce used him as a model for Buck Mulligan in *Ulysses* (1922), where the book starts in their Martello tower.

There are many stories about Gogarty. He saved Michael Collins' life (for a while at least) when the I.R.A. came to his house looking for him by covering him with a sheet and half opening the door to curse the intruders for disturbing a surgeon at work on an operation. In January 1923 Gogarty was kidnapped by armed men but escaped by asking them to hold his overcoat and then running twenty yards to dive into the freezing Liffey and swim for his life under a hail of bullets. He was no stranger to plunging into the river fully clothed for he had once received a medal for saving the life of a man who was drowning. He later liberated a pair of swans onto the river in a ceremony of thanks for saving his life, which was attended by Yeats, and called a collection of his poems published in 1923 *An Offering of Swans*. When Yeats went to Spain, Gogarty wrote to a Spanish doctor to look after him and received a letter back referring to Yeats as "an antique cardio-sclerotic". Yeats, to Gogarty's distress insisted on reading the letter but seemed only concerned with the fine sounding words saying, "I would rather be called cardio-sclerotic than 'Lord of Lower Egypt'".

Gogarty practised for a while in London. "Here", he wrote, "the doctors are so kind and professional, conduct is so nice that they never contradict each other. To maintain this harmony it is taboo to make a diagnosis." Eventually he settled in New York. Through it all he was writing novels, fanciful reminiscences *As I was Going Down Sackville Street* (1937), and the more auto-biographical *It Isn't This Time of Year at All* (1954) dedicated "To myself for a lifelong attachment", articles and much good poetry. He was noted for his facility with parody and for his bawdy limericks. Many of his sayings are delightfully quotable. For example, "There is nothing more sinister than the humility of the mean". Of the man given a gold medal in error by the Pope on being told that it was a mistake, "Have you lost your faith in Infallibility?" Of Browning's obscurities, "When I read his translation of Aeschylus, I find it very useful to have the Greek beside me so that I may find out what the English means". Of poor Father McQuisten overcome by the sight of ladies' underwear dancing in the breeze on the line over the garden hedge, "He was as much the victim of propinquity as of delinquency". Of a man coming out of a pub and consulting a compass (where else but in Dublin?), "He goes home by compass! He cannot trust the ebbing town". He said, "Reason was given us for a safe-conduct through our daily life; but magic deals with eternal values." He also wrote

> To be as magical as Life itself, and as irresponsible; to be
> irrational enough to temper Justice with Mercy, and to be able
> to adjust oneself to the changes in intensity which the waxings
> and wanings of Reality assume in the shimmerings of its cloud –
> this would be an ideal adjustment and a poetic opposition to
> outrageous Fortune.

Gogarty's real claim to literary fame lies in his *Collected Poems* (1951). His friend Yeats wrote in the introduction to *The Oxford Book of Modern Verses* (1936) "I gave him considerable space, and think him one of the great lyric poets of our age". Yeats has been accused of over-valuing Gogarty's work by including seventeen of his poems in this collections, but one should be chary of dismissing Yeats's judgment on poetry, even on that of a friend.

Gogarty never quite achieved the heights of his profession or the full recognition of his literary worth; people famous for their wit have difficulty in acquiring the highest level of regard from their contemporaries whether in art, administration or scholarship. Sidney Smith said that he had been sunk by his own levity while his theologian brother had risen by his gravity. James Stephens told Gogarty that it was unlikely that he would be praised as a poet as he should be until fifty years after he was dead; there are still some eighteen years to go. Gogarty certainly had a wonderfully light touch, whether serious or gay.

> Was there ever beauty yet
>   Time forgot to counteract?
> If by Sorrow unbeset,

Did her city go unsacked;
Nor some accident disguise
The Immortals' jealousies?

Beauty never comes on earth
  But an equal Grief is born;
Hidden, maybe, in the dearth
  Of the hours ere the Morn;
Or that in her core are strife,
Gain of Love and loss of life.

There is nothing new at all;
  We have heard it all before;
Beauty one side of the Wall,
  On the other side, the War.
Love and Death; and no denying
These things do not end by dying.

Joseph Campbell, in a preface to *The Collected Poems* said of Gogarty,

> He does not belong to our spindling, self-nauseated age, he is a Buck of the robust, devil-may-care 18th century, born out of time to our delight.

George William Russell, Æ (1867-1935) the Irish poet, in his preface to the poems, called Gogarty "the wildest wit in Ireland" but also wrote of him:

> The ideal of Oliver's genie was beauty and mystery achieved by precision... He has never made a business of beauty: and, because he is disinterested in his dealings with it, the Muse has gone with him on his walks and revealed to him some airs and graces she kept secret from other lovers who were too shy or too awed by her to laugh and be natural in her presence.

One of Gogarty's delightful poems, called *The Plum Tree by the House* contains:

There must be things which never shall
Be matched or made symmetrical
On Earth or in the Air;
Branches that Chinese draughtsmen drew,
Which none may find an equal to,
Unless he enter there
Where none may live – and more's the pity! –

204

The Perfect, The Forbidden City,
That's built – Ah God knows where!

Sir William Watson (1858-1935) the English poet wrote of Gogarty, who lived for three years in Stephen's Green near the Shelbourne Hotel, in *Retrogressions*,

> Three Olivers before your time
> Were not unknown in prose and rhyme;
> One was the paladin or pal
> Of him who faught at Roncesvalles;
> One gave Drogheda to pillage;
> And one wrote "The Deserted Village";
> But sorra an Oliver ever was seen
> Compares with him of Stephen's Green.

Amor, Anne Clark *Mrs Oscar Wilde. A Woman of Some Importance* Sidgwick & Jackson, London, 1983.

Critchley, Macdonald *The Miss Havisham Syndrome* Hist. Med. 1969, 1, 2.

Downey, Edmund *Charles Lever. His Life and Letters* William Blackwood & Sons, London, 1906.

Fitzpatrick, W.J. *The Life of Charles Lever* Chapman & Hall, London 1879.

Lyons, J.B. *James Joyce and Medicine* The Dolman Press, Dublin, 1973.

Lyons, J.B. *Oliver St John Gogarty. A Man of Many Talents* Blackwater, Dublin, 1980.

Ober, William B. *Oliver St John Gogarty, M.D.* N.Y. St. J. Med.

O'Connor, Ulick *Oliver St John Gogarty. A Poet and His Times* Jonathan Cape, London, 1964.

White, T. de Vere *The Parents of Oscar Wilde* Hodder & Stoughton, London, 1967.

Wilde, W.R. *The Closing Years of Dean Swift's Life* Hodges & Smith, Dublin, 1849.

Wilson, T.G. *Victorian Doctor. Being the Life of Sir William Wilde* Methuen & Co., London, 1942.

Wyndham, Horace *Speranza. A Biography of Lady Wilde* Boardman & Co., London, 1951

RICHARD AUSTIN FREEMAN

CHAPTER TEN

Detectives and Doctors

A SURPRISING aspect of the medico-literary scene is that so few of the doctors who took to writing fiction adopted medical jurisprudent as their theme, one to which their training would seem to have fitted them so well, and one which the non-medical detective-fiction writers have so often adopted. Perhaps doctors who write fiction mostly do so to escape from their daily concerns. Dr Robert Eustace Barton was consulted on the matter and appeared as "Eustace R." co-author with Mrs L.T. Mead of *The Sorceress of the Strand (Madame Sara)* (1902) and as "Robert Eustace" with Dorothy Sayers in *The Documents in the Case* (1930). Two doctors who wrote detective fiction, however, performed to such effect that they acquired great international reputations and faithful followings which continue enthusiastically to this day. They are Sir Arthur Conan Doyle (1859-1930) and Dr Richard Austin Freeman (1862-1943).

Austin Freeman wrote more than 30 novels and, like Conan Doyle, made one of his chief characters a doctor. His Dr John Evelyn Thorndyke of No. 5A King's Bench Walk was, unlike Conan Doyle's Dr Watson, the great man himself – tall, imposing, dignified, handsome and impressive, characterised by H.M. Brock's portrait in Pearson's Magazine of 1908. He was both doctor, barrister and criminologist, with a fine logical way with him in court, and a lecturer in medical jurisprudence. His solutions were achieved with skill even if once, in *For the Defence Dr Thorndyke* (1934), he was allowed the easy task of saving a client from being convicted of his own murder.

Dr John Thorndyke was based on Professor Alfred Swaine Taylor (1806-1880), Professor of Medical Jurisprudent at Guy's Hospital from 1831 to 1877, who delivered the first course of lectures on the subject to be given in England. Taylor was born at Northfleet in Kent and apprenticed in medicine to Dr McRue in the lovely small town of Lenham between Maidstone and Charing. He set off on a medical pilgrimage to Europe, walking 2,700 miles to visit medical schools in Italy, Switzerland and Germany. When he returned he worked his way up in specialist medicine to become the leading medical jurist of his day and to be consulted in many of the main criminal investigations, one of which was the affair of Dr William Palmer, the Rugely poisoner of 1856, whose trial was the first in which life insurance was shown to be the incentive for a murder. Taylor wrote books on medical jurisprudence and on poisons. He lived at 15 St James Terrace, Regents Park and, among his other accomplishments, helped William Henry Fox Talbot (1800-1877) to develop hyposulphate of lime as a fixative in photography. He was to Austin Freeman what Joseph Bell was to Conan Doyle. Dr Christopher Jervis who assisted Thorndyke and played the Watson role in the stories, was neither so obtuse nor so endearing as Holme's questioning companion; Nathaniel Polton, Thorndyke's laboratory assistant, photographer and general aid, was the more interesting character.

There is no English biography of Austin Freeman but there are two from abroad: *In Search of Dr Thorndyke* (1971) by Dr Norman Donaldson from America and *R. Austin Freeman. The Anthropologist at Large* (1980) by Dr Oliver Mayo from Australia. Freeman's early life is rather mysterious, partly because he disliked publicity and partly because he deliberately concealed much of his history from his family. We know he was the youngest of five children born in North London where the boys used to swim in Kenwood Lake. His grandfather was an innkeeper and his father became a tailor in Soho, rose to be manager of the business and to inherit it when the proprietor died. Freeman's father seems to have been a talented man, possibly an alcoholic, with his own unusual but, as it proved, quite successful ideas on education for his children. Dr Mayo suggests that the portrait of the narrator's father, in *Pontifex, Son and Thorndyke* (1931), is based on Freeman's own father:

> He could construe the most difficult passages from the ancient authors and work out intricate problems in spherical trigonometry, when, from causes which I need not dwell upon, the functions of his legs were in temporary abeyance; on which occasion he would sit on the floor, for the excellent reason – as he lucidly explained – that the direction of the forces of gravity being geocentric, it was impossible for him to fall off... A man must be accounted more than ordinarily gifted in whom, once

more to adopt his admirable phraseology, "the effect of alcoholic stimulation is merely to induce motor inco-ordination unaccompanied by phychical confusion".

Freeman was apprenticed to an apothecary and, in *Mr Polton Explains* (1940), based on this work, he gave an account of the job of an apprentice delivering medicines for Dr Pope – as Bob Sawyer's boy Tom did in Bristol in his own peculiar way, modified to promote the interest of "Sawyer's, late Nockemorf's Physicians". Freeman's experience delivering medicines may well have been the foundation for the extensive knowledge of the by-ways of London he later displayed in his books. He became a medical student at the Middlesex Hospital in 1880 at the age of eighteen, qualified L.S.A. in 1886 and then M.R.C.S., L.R.C.P. after a year as a house-surgeon.

In 1887 Freeman applied for the job of Assistant Colonial Surgeon on the Gold Coast in West Africa, and was duly appointed, but had to leave his bride in Mitcham to take up his post almost immediately after his marriage, returning home for two months leave in 1888. Freeman, always interested in sociology and eugenics, strongly disapproved of the Colonial Administration's method of dealing with the Africans. In his book *Travels and Life in Ashanti and Jaman* (1898) he wrote:

> With the unerring instinct of a professedly philanthropic nation, they have selected the sturdiest, most enterprising and most courageous tribe as the special object of hostility, and have consistently endeavoured, after the fashion too common among philanthropists, to secure in the most perfect manner the survival of the unfittest.

Freeman, aged twenty-seven, was on the Ashanti expedition of 1889, "trudging through the dismal wilderness of Adansi" suffering many hardships, concerned for the health and welfare of the force of one hundred men he served under the supervision of Dr McCarthy the Chief Medical Officer. They arrived in the Kingdom of Bekwé where Freeman described their welcome by the court with a perceptive, sympathetic amusement, embellishing his detailed observation in a manner which was later to contribute to his success as an author.

> I do not know why it is so, but evidently to the African mind an

umbrella is a special symbol of magnificence and dignity. Not only in these interior countries where the umbrellas are of local manufacture and of really gorgeous appearance, being covered with velvet of various and brilliant colours, hung with gold fringe and studded with gold ornaments, but on the coast and even in so comparatively civilised a place as Sierra Leone, the umbrella is the outward and visible sign of the dignity and importance of its possessor.

They pressed on to Kumasi to be received by the Asantehene, the king of Ashanti, the band playing "Bonnie Dundee" and "Just Before the Battle Mother" while the Ashanti fired off small arms in all directions "somewhat after the fashion of a travelling circus". The effect of this reception on Freeman was marred by the onset of malaria which forced him to lie watching lizards and rats while large doses of quinine took their effect. Kumasi, he noted, had never recovered from the destruction wrought by the British force under Sir Garnet Wolseley in 1874. Freeman found

> hints of departed prosperity and evidences of a culture far superior to anything seen in the littoral regions; and as I looked round on the blighted city with its demolished buildings and its demoralised citizens, I could not help reflecting on the strange and regrettable fact that its ruin had been accomplished by a nation that yearly spends millions on the conversion of the heathen and the diffusion of civilisation.

It is difficult for us to see ourselves in the position, and to understand the upbringing, of those who exercised colonial power at that time, assured of the benefits of their mission not only to themselves but to the natives, but it is relieving to find that there were some people on the spot who could reflect on the effects of arrogant, good intentions and think that they might be "strange and regrettable".

The expedition continued and Freeman recorded many of their encounters and the interest they aroused. He was seeing to the sick, arranging for litters to carry them, making maps and studying wild life. They found that the French had been there before them, and that King Ajiman had already signed a treaty with them, but he quickly handed over the treaty and the French flags and, gaining in experience, agreed to sign a new one with the British so long as they promised to leave at once.

210

The expedition eventually returned to Accra in April, when they were granted a spell of leave at home.

Freeman's attacks of malaria recurred, and the severe form of blackwater fever which then developed had such an effect that he was invalided out of the service without a pension in 1891. One result of his African experience was his first novel, *The Golden Pool* (1905), in which the hero, unlike the author, returned to England a rich man with wonderful prospects. Back home Freeman attempted medical practice but his health was poor; he was kept busy writing his *Travels and Life in Ashanti and Jaman* (1898) and making reports to the Royal Geographical Society. His writing career was being slowly established. His first short stories had appeared in the *Cassell's Magazine* of 1898 and brought him a little much needed money. His two sons were born in 1893 and 1897. At a bad time he was fortunate to meet Dr James Pitcairn, the medical officer to Holloway Prison, who took the family to live with him and gave Freeman a job in the Prison. This was a turning point in his fortunes for together they produced two series of stories in 1902 and 1903, *The Adventures of Romney Pringle* by "Clifford Ashdown", a pseudonym composed of one of Freeman's sons' names and Pitcairn's mother's maiden name. Dr Mayo described their character, Romney Pringle, as "a robber of thieves, a taker-down of con-men, a defrauder of frauds". The association also produced *From a Surgeon's Diary* in 1904 but they could find no publisher for their last work and this brought their collaboration to an end.

Freeman found a house in Gravesend which he occupied in return for educating the owner's four children along with his own two sons. The education supplied was unusual, including such topics as ancient Egyptian history and the evolution of the steam engine. The children had difficulty in getting into University with no mathematics, nevertheless the two boys of his landlord became a research chemist and an accountant and Freeman's eldest son matriculated at his first attempt though neither of his two boys had much success in life, both, in their different ways, being war casualties, one eventually committed suicide. Freeman, before his time, taught his pupils about sex, fully and frankly. In *Pontifex, Son and Thorndyke* Freeman's narrator announces what was probably his own opinion,

> I enjoyed the supreme advantage of having escaped education
> – or rather, I should say, the particular brand that is supplied
> by the State. Other boys of like indigence were handed off to
> Board Schools, where they contracted measles, chicken-pox,
> ignorance and a most hideous accent.

Freeman's brother Henry took the tailoring business to Maddox Street and the rest of his family were all said to be creatively inclined.

Freeman's first lone effort at detective fiction, *The Red Thumb Mark* was published in 1907. Sir Francis Galton (1822- 1911), Charles Darwin's cousin, the famous geneticist who founded the study of eugenics, had written his important book *Finger Prints* in 1892. In this novel Thorndyke, speaking of Galton's statement that a finger print affords evidence requiring no corroboration, called it, with admirable foresight,

> a most dangerous and misleading statement which has been
> fastened upon eagerly by the police, who have naturally been
> delighted at obtaining a sort of magic touchstone by which they
> are saved the labour of investigation. But there is no such thing
> as a single factor that "affords evidence requiring no
> corroboration". As well might one expect to make a syllogism
> with a single premise.

As usual Freeman had done the test and was "able to produce quite good prints" of his own finger prints, demonstrating that, however difficult, counterfeit prints were at least a possibility. He established that they can be forged though most experts would recognise such a forgery. Freeman gave up medicine and was writing at Gravesend until he died aged 81, with an interval during the 1914-18 war when he joined the R.A.M.C. and was appointed O.C. of Field Ambulances in the Home Counties. It was not until thirty-six years after his death that a ceremony, with the Mayor of Gravesend present, was held to place a proper memorial stone above his neglected grave.

Austin Freeman was an expert bookbinder, a good amateur painter and kept a laboratory where he performed every experiment which he described in his fiction. He said of his work that:

> In each book, a particular problem in medical jurisprudence is
> worked out, and although the cases are fictitious, the facts are

real facts and in many cases contribute new matter to science.

Some of the actual laboratory tests used in his stories are said to have been adopted by the police, though much more has been written about the influence of Conan Doyle's less precise but more imaginative methods on scientific crime detection (*The Debt of the Police to Detective Fiction* (1932) and *Sherlock Holmes. Father of Scientific Crime Detection* (1970) for example).

Freeman had a great love for the works of Dickens and is one of the many who have offered solutions to *The Mystery of Edwin Drood*. Dorothy Sayers writing in the *Dickensian* in 1930 discussed Freeman's *The Mystery of Angelina Frood* (1924) with its theory of a woman disguised as a man and his comment that burial in quicklime preserved rather than destroyed a body. Freeman also commented on Arthur Morrison's book *The Chronicles of Martin Hewitt Investigator* (1895), suggesting a way in which the ship's crew could have stolen the gold bullion using the high density of gold in place of Morrison's implausibility. Freeman's medical training, prison service, craftsmanship and even his painting (*The Jacob Street Mystery* 1942), were all put to good use in his work. He introduced new developments in pathology and medical research and used knowledge from many branches of medicine to make his Dr Thorndyke the most scientific of all the fictional criminologists. He used radiology in 1911 to show that a mummy case in the British Museum really contained the skeleton of a vanished Egyptologist, recognised because it could be seen on the x-ray that he had had his fractured patella wired. Thorndyke's blood examinations, detailed autopsies and clear professional reports as he solved the problems and presented the solution to everyone's satisfaction are models of their kind. Thorndyke carried a "little green case", which, like the "Bertillon Box", named after the famous French criminologist, contained all the instruments necessary for rapid investigation. Freeman's characters are drawn with literary skill and some are particularly memorable. Many of the plots are original, cleverly constructed if rather complicated and bizarre at times, and the ingenious way they are unravelled and presented in court is admirable.

Freeman has been much appreciated in America where a twice yearly journal, *The Thorndyke File*, was started in Maryland in 1976.

His work had many similarities and some rivalry with that of Conan Doyle. Neither of them introduced much love interest, though an occasional marriage occurred: John Osmond did get his enterprising Elizabeth Burleigh in *A Certain Dr Thorndyke* (1927), where Larkson died from blackwater fever with hepatic complications, but generally they both stuck to the business in hand. Dr Thorndyke introduced scientific methods unknown to Sherlock Holmes and the technical side of the detective work is better done by Freeman than by Doyle. Freeman's main characters, however, Dr Thorndyke himself, the romantic associate Dr Jervis and the laboratory assistant Nathaniel Polton, are just a bit too ordinary in themselves so that they fail to catch the imagination and become famous in the way that Holmes and Watson, with their likeable eccentricities and peculiar characters, have done. Perhaps the occasional late entry of Thorndyke into the mystery may have lessened his personal if not his professional appeal. Then the early account of the crime and identification of the criminal before the work of detection began in some of his stories, though admired for their skill, removed the suspense. Most important of all, is the fact that the reader while unable to compete in the interesting and complex laboratory work of Dr Thorndyke, always feels that he might manage Sherlock Holme's deductions if only he was clever enough. With Doyle there is the excitement of taking part, '"Come, Watson, come!' he cried. 'The game is afoot.'" Conan Doyle and Austin Freeman were masters of their chosen art and complementary rather than in competition for the highest awards in fictional criminology.

Freeman wrote one historical novel, *The Unwilling Adventurer* (1913) set at the end of the eighteenth century and dealing with adventure, sailing ships, a pirate captain who prospers and retires, and a slave-trading, christianity preaching, captain who comes to a sticky end. He also wrote a book on sociology, *Social Decay and Regeneration* (1921), a curious, illogical attempt to stem the decline of Western civilisation which he thought was due to dilution of the superior beings which had resulted from evolution by a too rapid increase in population – man's alteration of the ways of nature, securing the survival of the unfit and outbreeding of the better by the inferior. Some of his sociological ideas, and many of his value judgements, were nonsensical, even if he did discuss a

214

few of the important issues at a time when the application of genetics to social thought was new and even more confused than it is today. He would have done better to have stuck to his detective fiction. He is to be remembered for his offering of detective stories which provide good problems with intellectual satisfaction and with admirable scientific backing for fair and feasible solutions. These were his regular source of income, and his puzzles have given much pleasure over many years. They achieved their purpose which was to interest and entertain, and that is something which a number of more ambitious authors have been less successful in securing.

Conan Doyle was born in Edinburgh, had a hard schooling there with severe corporal punishment, a year at school in Germany and a return to the University of Edinburgh to qualify in medicine. His restless spirit was always causing him to seek adventure: he went whaling in the Arctic as ship's surgeon while still a third year medical student and, when qualified, on a voyage to West Africa. He went into practice for a brief period in Plymouth with his university friend Dr George Turnarene Budd. The relationship between the two has been well described by Hesketh Pearson (1943). Budd, erratic, friendly and murderous by turns, always about to make millions with his latest inventions, nevertheless, had an undoubted influence on Doyle as a doctor, but was indirectly instrumental in helping to turn him into an author. Doyle soon left the stormy Budd practice and, after a visit to Tavistock, settled into another medical practice in Southsea where he took to more serious writing to supplement his income. He had written a number of stories, sold for a few pounds each, when the idea of Sherlock Holmes came to him and *A Study in Scarlet* (1887) was produced for which he received £25. His next book was an historical novel *Micah Clarke* (1889), a fine adventure story built around the Monmouth rebellion ending with a stirring account of the battle of Sedgemoor and a fine sketch of the terrible Judge Jeffreys. It contains a grand character, Decimus Saxton, who buys Micah off the prison ship bound for slavery in Barbados with a degree of good luck which did not come the way of Dr Peter Blood, the real life hero of Rafael Sabatini's book *Captain Blood: His Odyssey* which gave Errol Flynn one of his most dashing parts in the Warner Brothers film of 1935 (Smithers 1986). *Micah Clarke*

ARTHUR CONAN DOYLE

came back from several publishers, with the usual polite, depressing rejection slips, until Andrew Lang read it for Longmans and recommended it for publication. By then, however, Sherlock Holmes had begun to make his impact and when Oscar Wilde read *Micah Clarke* and praised it and other literary figures added their support, Conan Doyle was launched as an author. Doyle's interest in psychic studies started before he left Southsea and lasted the rest of his life, becoming his major preoccupation as he grew older, especially after the loss of his son who died in the influenza epidemic of 1918 after being seriously wounded during the battle of the Somme. Doyle then began to accept pleasing explanations too easily and his wishful thinking allowed him to be hoaxed, particularly over the case of The Cottingley Fairies.

Doyle got married while in Southsea and moved to South Norwood where he decided to concentrate on making writing his main source of income. His wife developed tuberculosis, which led them to Switzerland and Egypt for her health. In Egypt he served as a war correspondent for a while in 1896. They returned to live in Hindhead until he was off again, this time to the Boer War. He twice stood for parliament but "the electors returned him to the bosom of his family". They finally moved to Crowborough and he threw himself into sport and travel until 1914 when, first as a private in a Volunteer Regiment, and then commissioned to write articles for the government which appeared in the "Daily Chronicle", he managed, with his usual determination to be in the thick of things. He got to the British, Italian and French fronts, writing all the time wherever his travels took him. He was a remarkable mixture of bluff adventurer and thoughtful mystic, a conjunction which gave his work much of its appeal.

There is quite a body of writing about detective fiction: its history, its authors, its rules, and the fine distinction between crime or mystery stories and police novels. They are social documents in their way, being products of a specific time and place. Ronald Knox laid down "Ten Commandments of Detection" and others, Austin Freeman and Dorothy Sayers for example, have had their say over the basic formula and about not allowing the heros too much nonsense on the side when they should be concentrating on the job of detection. Of the books written on the subject of writing detective novels one of the best is Howard Haycraft's *Murder for Pleasure* (1942) but Julian Symons's *Bloody Murder* (1972) is the more thorough. The latest and perhaps the best is *Murder Will Out*, T.J. Binyon (1989).

Fascination with detective stories has many aspects: light, concise, easy reading, with interesting characters, preferably familiar ones, a good plot, not too elaborate, and a feeling of participation in the enquiry, all contribute to the enjoyment. Accidents must not be allowed to help the detective; coincidence must be avoided and intuition suppressed. The clues must give the reader a fair chance but the end should still surprise him without cheating or disappointment through wild improbability. The methods of detection must be cunning and interesting in themselves, special knowledge and acute observation on the part of the detective who outdoes his rivals, usually the police as well as the reader, are expected. The crime is incidental, a necessary preliminary to the business in hand which is detection. There should be character, suspense and intelligent detective work allowing enough anxiety to build up while awaiting the release brought about by the final solution so that it becomes difficult to put the book down. The next step must always be eagerly anticipated. If the main characters can acquire a special appeal, capture the imagination and become the very embodiment of detection so much the better. Justice must be seen to be done. Hazlitt wrote in 1828:

> Fiction, unlike history, has the softenings of fancy and sentiment; and we read on in the hope of something like poetical justice to be done at last, which is more than we can reckon upon in reality.

Detective stories are a form of relaxation indulged in by those who read little else to those engaged in the most important and demanding work. An extraordinary mystique has grown up around Sherlock Holmes and Dr Watson which almost meets the dictionary definition of a cult as: "a group having an exclusive ideology and ritual practices centred on sacred symbols, esp. one characterised by lack of organisational structure". Holmes and Watson have been provided with a fame and an existence all their own, to some they have even seemed more real than their creator who was once described as "Dr Watson's literary agent".

The apparent neglect of the author, which in reality is a special kind of acclaim, an affectionate intellectual banter which has a fine effect as sales promotion, is one which most writers would gratefully accept. Nevertheless it has led to a defence reaction. Dr Alvin Rodin of Dayton, Ohio and Jack Key, the Mayo Foundation librarian, (1982) have supported Conan Doyle's medical reputation and attempted to reinstate him in the public mind as a doctor by giving an account of his medical publications, as, for example, his work on gout and his early incrimination of syphilis as having a role in the causation of tabes dorsalis, and other such aspects of his medical career as might emphasise his medical abilities. Conan Doyle was indeed quite well known as a doctor. He was knighted in 1902 for his Boer War service with the Langman Hospital through a typhoid epidemic in Bloemfontein and for his writing on the history and conduct of the war. He only becomes lost to view behind two characters of his own making a quirk of public choice which was selected one facet of his work from an output of over 80 books for their special enjoyment. Drs Rodin and Key in their *Medical Casebook of Doctor Arthur Conan Doyle* (1984) have however done much more, for their research and admirably annotated reporting gives the most complete account not only of Conan Doyle's medical writings but of all the many doctors appearing in his fiction. Conan Doyle included over one hundred doctors in his non-Sherlock Holmes stories, the best known probably being Professor Challenger in *The Lost World* (1912). However, had it not been for Holmes and Watson they would not have spent so much time adding to our enjoyment through that part of their research which deals with Doyle's interesting if modest medical achievements. Who is to say that the public is not right in its choice of what to remember about an author, it is for them that his books are written. If there has really been any lack of regard for Conan Doyle's literary achievements it has been in undervaluing those of his works which have nothing to do with Holmes and Watson, for example such excellent tales as *Micah Clarke*, *The White Company* (1891) and *Rodney Stone* (1896).

Dr John Watson was created to speak for Sherlock Holmes, to be mystified and to ask for those explanations which we, the readers, are so anxiously awaiting. Watson, like some of Dickens's characters and for the same reason, grew in stature with time, his role changing in emphasis as the stories progressed. Serial presentation permits readers to exert an influence on the development of characters, for they may observe things about them sometimes even before the author has appreciated their hidden possibilities and certainly before he has understood some aspects of their public appeal. Holmes once said to Watson "Your mental processes may be slow but they are never obscure", and in the same brief self-parody *The Field Bazaar* (1981) written for the Edinburgh University *Student*:

> You will not, I am sure, be offended if I say that any reputation for sharpness which I may possess has been entirely gained by the admirable foil which you have made for me. Have I not heard of debutantes who have insisted upon plainness in their chaperones? There is a certain analogy.

We may be thankful for the doctor's leisurely mind, humanity, good feeling and outstanding literary ability. But the solid, brave Dr Watson when claiming "an experience of women which extends over many nations and three separate continents" was surely rather overdoing it, was he really married two or three times? He did, however, display some sensitivity and even, on occasion, delivered a dry pleasantry, though Conan Doyle himself said that he "never shows one gleam of humour or makes one single joke".

Watson was not very often called on to use his medical skill in assisting Holmes, though he once resuscitated a criminal who had tried to hang himself. Thirty-four (or is it thirty-seven) other doctors appear in the Holmes stories from Stamford in *A Study in Scarlet* (1887) to Ray Ernest in *The Retired Colourman* (1927), or alphabetically from Moore Agar in *The Devil's Foot* (1910) to Wood in *The Valley of Fear* (1915). Most notable of these doctors is the horrible Grimesby Roylott in *The Speckled Band* (1892), of whom Holmes said:

> When a doctor does go wrong he is the first of criminals. He has nerve and he has knowledge. Palmer and Pritchard were among the heads of their profession.

Only two doctors consult Holmes as clients, one is Percy Trevelyan in *The Resident Patient* (1893) who is fooled by a simulated attack of catalepsy even though it is his own speciality, the other James Mortimer in *The Hound of the Baskervilles* (1902). Dr Barnicot comes in because he is an enthusiastic admirer of Napoloeon, and his plaster cast of the Emperor is smashed to see if it contains the most famous pearl in the world. Holmes and Watson meet the grim, ascetic, formidable Dr Leslie Armstrong in Cambridge only to find in the end that they are on the same side. A number of diseases are introduced into the stories, for example John Turner "With his deeplined craggy features and his enormous limbs" in *The Boscombe Valley Mystery* is dying of diabetes, Godfrey Emsworth in *The Adventures of the Blanched Soldier* has ichthyosis and Lord Mount James in *The Adventures of the Missing Three-Quarters* is nearly eighty, and so cram full of gout that they said he could chalk his billiard cue with his knuckles.

The character, appearance and talents of Sherlock Holmes were based on an amalgam of many people. The chief of these was a real doctor, Joseph Bell, a surgeon in Edinburgh who lectured at the Infirmary and who engaged Arthur Conan Doyle as his out-patient clerk. Dr Doris Ball who wrote *Crime in Our Time* (1962) and many thrillers adopted the pseudonym of "Josephine Bell". Other Holmesian ingredients came from fiction: Edgar Allan Poe's Dupin, and Emile Gaboriau's Lecoq, although such suggestions caused Holmes to "sniff sardonically", and in real life from Henry Irving as Hamlet, seen from the gallery for six pence night after night, and Douglas Maclagan, Professor of Medical Jurisprudence in Edinburgh. There was also his uncle, Richard Doyle, who played the violin and, like his father John Doyle, a well known caricaturist, did drawings for *Punch*, including the famous, long-running cover design, and later became an illustrator for Dickens and Thackeray. Arthur stayed with his uncle Richard on his first visit to London when aged 15. Then there is obviously something of Conan Doyle himself in both Holmes and Watson who combine his scientific, observational, dreamy love of the occult side, with his earthy, adventurous disposition which led him to have "a life of variety and romance" described in his *Memories and Adventures* (1924).

Joseph Bell the chief model for Sherlock Holmes was "thin, wiry, dark, with a high-nosed acute face, penetrating grey eyes, angular shoulders, and a jerky way of walking". It was from him that Conan Doyle derived Holmes's "methods". He recorded an introduction to Bell's clinic of a civilian patient when the enquiry proceeded as follows:

"Well, my man, you've served in the army."
"Aye, sir."
"Not long discharged?"
"No, sir."
"A Highland regiment?"
"Aye, sir."
"A non-com. officer?"
"Aye, sir."
"Stationed at Barbados?"
"Aye, sir."

Thorndyke speaks for Freeman, who, with some professional jealousy, was critical of Holmes's "methods", when he made the point,

A guess is a particular and definite conclusion deduced from facts which properly yield only a general and indefinite one. Let us take an instance, he continued. Looking out of the window, I see a man walking round Paper Buildings. Now suppose I say, after the fashion of the inspired detective of the romances, "That man is a station-master or inspector," that would be a guess. The observed facts do not yield the conclusion, though they do warrant a conclusion less definite and more general.

"You'd have been right though sir!" explained Polton, who had stepped forward with me to examine the unconscious subject of the demonstration. "That gent used to be the station-master at Camberwell. I remember him well." The little man was evidently greatly impressed.

I happen to be right you see, said Thorndyke; but I might as easily have been wrong.

"You weren't though, sir," said Polton. "You spotted him at a glance." In his admiration of the result he cared not a fig for the correctness of the means by which it had been attained.

Now why do I suggest that he is a station-master? pursued Thorndyke, disregarding his assistant's comment.

"I suppose you were looking at his feet," I seem to have noticed that peculiar, splay-footed gait in station-masters, now you mention it."

Quite so. The arch of the foot has given way; the plantar

ligaments have become stretched and the deep calf muscles weakened. Then, since bending of the weakened arch causes discomfort, the feet have become turned outwards, by which the bending of the foot is reduced to a minimum; and as the left foot if more flattened, so it is turned out more than the right. Then the turning of the toes causes the legs to splay outward from the knees downwards – a very conspicuous condition in a tall man like this one – and you notice that the left leg splays out more than the other.

But we know that depression of the arch of the foot is brought about by standing for long periods. Continuous pressure on a living structure weakens it, while intermittent pressure strengthens it; so the man who stands on his feet continuously develops a flat instep and a weak calf, while the professional dancer or runner acquires a high instep and a strong calf.

Thorndyke then listed other occupations involving prolonged standing, eliminating each one because of a characteristic gait, coming down on the probability of the observed subject being a station-master. But he emphasised that, though the observed facts justified the inference that the man's mode of life necessitated a good deal of standing, the rest was guess work.

"It's wonderful," said Polton, gazing at the now distant figure; "perfectly wonderful. I should never have known he was a station-master."

You will observe, said Thorndyke, with a smile, that a fortunate guess often brings more credit than a piece of sound reasoning with a less striking result.

Holmes was, of course, an author is his own right. His work *Upon the Distinction Between the Ashes of the Various Tobaccos* listed 140 forms of cigar, cigarette and pipe tobacco. He also wrote on other aspects of his art such as tracing footsteps, the influence of a trade on the form of the hand and a monograph analysing 160 separate ciphers. He was a better chemist than a biologist. He was, however, a limited man in other respects. He had never heard of Thomas Carlyle, was quite ignorant of cosmology, and entertained the false notion that you can over-stock the mind until a point is reached when every addition of knowledge involves forgetting something known before. In the first case in which Dr John H.

Watson was involved, Holmes looked out of the window and seeing a messenger advancing with a letter for him told Watson, correctly of course, that the man who was coming was a retired sergeant of marines.

Crime writers have had an undoubted effect on scientific crime detection. Sherlock Holmes has naturally received most attention both because of his fame and for the imaginative attention to detail which Conan Doyle supplied. Sherlock Holmes's study of tobacco ashes was quite a new idea the importance of which was soon realised. Mud, dust, stains, foot-prints were all given new significance through the stories. Alphonse Bertillon (1883-1914) the French criminologist, who has been called the creator of forensic science and started the routine front-and-profile, mugg, photographic, criminal record, admitted his debt to Sherlock Holmes and recommended the adoption of his method of reasoning by all professional police.

The very first encounter between Holmes and Watson takes place in the chemical laboratory at St Bartholomew's Hospital, *A Study in Scarlet* (1887), when Holmes shouted "I've found it!" as he demonstrated his infallible test for blood stains. The spectroscopic identification of haemoglobin was indeed achieved but a few years later but blood grouping, discovered in the early 1900's, did not have its potential in crime detection exploited for some time, the first grouping was tested in Italy in 1916. The fact remains that despite this early discovery Sherlock Holmes never made use of his infallible test for blood stains in any of his reported cases. His observation and his reasoning are superb but his laboratory work is suspect. In this department at least, Thorndyke has the edge. When Watson discovers Holmes at the beginning of *The Naval Treaty* (1893) doing a chemical experiment Holmes says "If the paper remains red, all is well. If it turns blue, it means a man's life", but they quickly pass on to other things in case someone might ask what possible alkaline fluid detection could ever provide the crucial evidence on which a man's life might depend. The first report of the identification of typewriting is due to Conan Doyle and appeared in *A Case of Identity* (1891) according to David Crown writing in *The Journal of Criminal Law, Criminology and Police Science* (March 1967). The technical literature on powder marks defining the distance at which a gun was discharged followed a few

224

years behind comments on the subject made in *The Adventure of the Dancing Men* (1903). There are many other instances of the remarkable influence which Conan Doyle's imagination had on forensic science.

The Holmes-Watson cult has led some, whom Bernard Darwin called "alarmingly intelligent persons", to "devote treasures of careful scholarship" to aspects of the stories which the author had either not considered or of which he was quite unaware. The fun has been to discover and become involved in obscurities, inconsistencies and hidden evidence. The game is dear to the hearts of the initiates and has added to the general enjoyment of these stories while remaining an interesting phenomenon in itself: something more than a game though less than a serious literary investigation. There was, for example, a heated dispute about which University Holmes attended, the honours going to Cambridge with Fenners having something to do with it, though we know, of course, that Watson went to Edinburgh University. There is the little mystery of why Mary Watson in *The Man with the Twisted Lip* (1891), talking to her friend Kate Whitney, referred to her husband as James, which may be attributed to a not uncommon ailment amongst authors of unreliability in proof reading, the more easily missed because Dr James Watson was a friend of Conan Doyle's in Southsea. Then there was an investigation about train journeys taken by Holmes and Watson: a train from Paddington to Exeter was caught an hour or two after they had had breakfast at 221B Baker St. and travelled so that it was evening before they arrived at Tavistock, on that occasion they came back on a night train. Much searching of old railway timetables was involved in this side issue but it was a memorable journey for better reasons. This was the occasion of one of Holmes' rare, admitted blunders. Silver Blaze, the favourite for the Wessex Cup had disappeared, and Holmes had failed to hurry down because he could not believe it possible that the most remarkable horse in England could long remain concealed. As a result of this experience he would no doubt have set off for Ireland immediately on hearing that Shergar had been abducted. This story is famous for its animals: lame sheep, the curious incident of "the dog in the night-time", and a murder, albeit in self defence, committed by a horse. All was well in the end, for Silver

Blaze was recovered despite the work of the old horse-faker Silas Brown who did not leave a white hair on its body, and, still disguised, won the Cup. Conan Doyle knew nothing of racing and made so many errors in this story that he told how a sporting paper had explained "the exact penalties which would have come upon everyone concerned if they had acted as I described. Half would have been in jail and the other half warned off the turf for ever". The train journey had led others to some mathematical calculations trying to judge the speed of trains by Holmes's method, whereby he estimated that the express was travelling at 53½ m.p.h. determined by the rate of passing of telegraph poles 60 yards apart.

To be fully-developed the Holmes-Watson devotee requires an early start in life, it is then that a life-long affection for absurdities can be acquired and a fascination with Holmes's methods may most easily take hold. With the passing of time the endings tend to seem less satisfactory than they did; resort to bigoted, vindictive Mormons and a diminutive aboriginal from the Andaman Islands of terrifying aspect spitting poisoned darts from a blow pipe are sadly less appealing to a second than to a first childhood. Fortunately Holmes, Watson and "my methods" retain their interest and charm. These stories end with the thanks of the Prime Minister for saving the nation from war and Holmes declining to tell him how it was done: "'We also have our diplimatic secrets' said he, and picking up his hat he turned to the door."

After they had collaborated in a theatrical production that proved to be a failure, Sir James Barrie wrote to Sir Arthur an amusing parody of Holmes. Watson was writing *The Adventure of the Man without a Cork Leg* which had so puzzled the Royal Society and Holmes was amusing himself with a little revolver practice when the clients arrived – Doyle and Barrie. Through the window Holmes could see that they were obviously two collaborators in comic opera, and that their play had not been a triumph. They were flinging little pieces of blue paper angrily from them which were clearly press notices held in such quantity as only criminals, dramatists and actors receive and, as no actor would come in a carriage, they were clearly authors, one from South Norwood and one from Scotland. Holmes shrank away to nothing before the harsh commands of his master, the larger man, who demanded that he cut out the first four pages and get on with it; Holmes's last words were:

Fool, fool! I have kept you in luxury for years. By my help you have ridden extensively in cabs, where no author was ever seen before. Henceforth you will ride in buses!

The brute from Norwood sank aghast into a chair. The other author did not turn a hair.

Ashton-Wolfe, H. *The Debt of the Police to Detective Fiction* Illustrated London News, 1932, 180, 320 and 328.

Berg, Stanton *Sherlock Holmes: Father of Scientific Crime Detection* J. Crim. Law, Criminology and Police Science 1970, 61, 446-452.

Binyon, J.J. *Murder Will Out* Oxford University Press, 1989

Böttinger, L.E. *The Murderer's Vade Mecum* Brit. Med. J. 1982, 285, 1819-1821.

Darwin, Bernard *Pack Clouds Away. Old Friends and Old Books* Collins, London, 1941.

Donaldson, Norman *In Search of Dr Thorndyke* Bowling Green Univ. Popular Press, Ohio, 1971.

Doyle, Sir Arthur Conan *Memories and Adventures* Hodder & Stoughton, London, 1924.

Haycraft, Howard *Murder for Pleasure* Peter Davies, London, 1942.

Higham, Charles *The Adventures of Conan Doyle* Hamish Hamilton, London, 1976

Mayo, Oliver *R. Austen Freeman. The Anthropologist at Large* Investigator Press, Hawthorndene, S. Australia, 1980

Pearson, Hesketh *Conan Doyle* Methuen Co, London, 1943

Rodin, Alvin *Journal of a Quest for the Elusive Doctor Arthur Conan Doyle* Davies Printing Rochester, Minnesota, 1982

Rodin, Alvin and Key, Jack *Medical Casebook of Doctor Arthur Conan Doyle* Robet Krieger, Malabar, Florida, 1984

Smithers, D. W. *Medicine, Adventure, Pirates and Castaways* N.Y. ST. J. Med, 1986, 184

Symons, Julian *Bloody Murder* Faber & Faber, London, 1972

WILLIAM SOMERSET MAUGHAM

CHAPTER ELEVEN

Tales of Human Behaviour

THIS LAST chapter is about a man who wrote from experience with a fine understanding of the vagaries of human behaviour under the stresses and temptations of life but was determined to conceal his own nature, failings and misfortunes. He attempted to mislead posterity about his doings by suppressing evidence, and accepting inaccuracies and distortions. A great storyteller, with a gift for presenting the problems, frailties and misbehaviours of his fellows, he feared to allow his own fallibilities to be revealed.

Frederic Raphael, in a perceptive review in the *Times Literary Supplement* of Robert Calder's *Willie: The Life of W. Somerset Maugham* (1989), wrote:

> He was never entirely at home anywhere; his conformity was the measure of his alienation. Observing the very rules he was amused to bend, he had the temperament and the nerve of the classy spy. His cover-story was like Willie Ashenden's, consistent with the truth but not with the whole truth. He was a man who put his cards on the table the better to conceal the ace he kept up his sleeve.

William Somerset Maugham (1874-1965) gave instructions to his literary agent that he was not to authorise any biography nor was he to assist anyone who attempted such a publication. He begged his friends to destroy all letters they had received from him. Specific instructions to this effect were incorporated in his will. He got his secretary, Alan Searle, to help him destroy piles of letters he had himself received from many people. This effort to conceal his private affairs naturally added to speculation about them and aroused increasing public interest in his life-style, peccadilloes, indiscretions and misdemeanours. Biographies began to appear during his life and a flood of material about him was released by his death. Collections of his letters, gleaned from auctions and from dealers, accumulated in the libraries of American Universities. There was a rush to cash in on the Maugham saga, with revelations, exposures and tittilations about private matters, led by his own nephew Robin Maugham.

Had Somerset Maugham been less worried by the fate of Oscar Wilde, and known that intelligent public opinion would develop a kinder, more understanding phase in its view of homosexuality he might have been less concerned and not quite so anxious to cover his tracks. This not uncommon aspect of the nature of men and women is less often regarded as opprobrious or dishonourable today even if regrettable, though the spread of Aids has done something to impede the changing attitude. It is a matter of degree, but homosexuals are what they are, that is the way it is. In Somerset Maugham's day homosexuality involved a risk of prosecution, social exile, disgrace and calumny which could only be partly overcome by fame. It was also a difficult problem for Maugham to reconcile within his own person as his numerous affairs with women, his genuine love of Ethelwyn "Sue" Jones, the original of Rosie in *Cakes and Ale* (1930), and his disastrous marriage reveal. A matter of more general interest is whether some forms of perceptive, artistic achievement may have an unusually high incidence amongst homosexuals or whether we are just more likely to hear that someone is a homosexual if he has been successful in the arts.

Knowledge of the life of artists and the times in which they live can increase understanding of their work but gossip about their sexual behaviour fails as a rule to tell us much about their creative ability. Their works may not be entirely self-sufficient but they are what matter. Though we cannot divorce Somerset Maugham's nature from his work, it is regrettable that a disproportionate interest in his private life, stimulated by his own efforts at concealment, has too often deflected attention from the proper assessment of his place in literature, whatever that may be. Some have placed him in the top class of novelists considering the cogency of fiction to be fully expressed in providing entertainment and relaxation. Dr Saunders, a character of Maugham's in *The Narrow Corner* (1932), was one of those:

> who liked books that displayed the oddities of human nature...
> He read neither for information nor to improve his mind, but
> sought in books occasion for reverie.

On the other hand those who believe that the really great novels should have more substance, display a finer imagination and portray a greater variety and depth of human awareness, only place Maugham in the realm of the successful second class. He described himself as just a storyteller but he aspired to greater recognition and deeply resented exclusion from lists of the most outstanding novelists. His favourite themes kept recurring: infidelities were seldom omitted, the petty prejudices of provincial and colonial societies were regularly censured, marital clashes due to differences of class, education and taste and the potential of morality to act as a destructive influence were frequently paraded. His style was simple, his sentences usually short, his meaning clear, his stories riveting, his determination, work-rate and tenacity undoubted. His vast public loved him.

With so much written about him, anyone now attempting a discussion of his life would be faced with a formidable research task. Fortunately my interest is centred on his writing and particularly on the influence which his medical experiences and training had on his work, a matter which, amidst all the hullabaloo and literary criticism, has received comparatively little attention. He made his own assessment of this aspect of his art in *The Summing Up* (1938), when referring to his training as a medical student at St Thomas's Hospital where he started in 1892.

> For here I was in contact with what I most wanted, life in the raw. In those three years I must have witnessed pretty well every emotion of which man is capable. It appealed to my dramatic instinct. It excited the novelist in me. Even now that forty years have passed I can remember certain people so exactly that I could draw a picture of them. Phrases that I heard then still linger on my ears. I saw how men died. I saw how they bore pain. I saw what hope looked like, fear and relief; I saw the dark lines that despair drew on a face; I saw courage and steadfastness. I saw faith shine in the eyes of those who trusted in what I could only think was an illusion, and I saw the gallantry that made a man greet the prognosis of death with an ironic joke because he was too proud to let those about him see the terror of his soul... All this was a valuable experience to me. I do not know a better training for a writer than to spend some years in the medical profession.

In a long experience of dealing with serious disease amongst people of all classes and many nationalities, I found no group better able to face personal disaster with pride and an "ironic joke" than the cockneys; they were lovely patients to deal with. I came to regard an ability to confront the physical deterioration and personal disaster of serious disease with cheerful courage and consideration for the family as the highest manifestation of the human spirit; George Crosses have been awarded for less. Ted Morgan, (*Somerset Maugham* 1980), quotes another comment on the value of medical experience to a writer taken from a letter Maugham wrote to a Mr Wilenski in 1938 now in the Yale library:

> The life of a writer is extremely specialized and by following some other avocation it is likely that he will gain experience which will be a great value to him afterwards. So far as I am concerned I can only wish that I had remained a doctor for three or four years instead of writing books which have long been dead as mutton.

Frederic Raphael, discussing writers who had an influence on his adolescence, referred to a doctor and two sons of doctors: Somerset Maugham, Sinclair Lewis and John O'Hara. He wrote:

> All three had the habit of iconoclasm. They were free, or seemed to be free of literary affectation. Their mode was literal rather than metaphorical. They were impatient with the metaphysical and of humbug. They were unshockable and so they could afford to be accurate.

A first hand account of life as a medical student at St Thomas's Hospital in the early nineteenth century is given in a unique series of letters preserved by the Weekes family. They are mostly written by Hamilton Weekes from St Thomas's to his father Richard who practiced in Hurstpierpoint, but some of his replies are included. The collection was edited by John Ford and published in 1987 by the Wellcome Institute. Richard Weekes charged fifteen shillings for the delivery of a parish patient and attended between two and three thousand births in 28 years, (Letter 111).

Thirty-seven years behind, I followed Somerset Maugham to St Thomas's Hospital and, like him, found the experience of district, delivering babies in Lambeth, one of the most memorable. *Liza of Lambeth* (1897), the first work to bring Maugham recognition, is located in a part of Lambeth I once knew well. It is told with acute observation and insight and written under the influence of Guy de Maupassant if without his polish. Vere Street is so like the Tyre Street of my day and the people so true to life that *Liza* makes memories flood back to me. We would got to the street number we had been given for "Mrs Somebody, three rings" which meant that she had a room on the third floor. We would turn children out into the passage or into the room of the people opposite and usually be left with the patient, her mother and the trainee midwife. We drank terrible black tea with condensed milk in it to be friendly and helped another infant into the world, just as Somerset Maugham had done. We heard a lot of intriguing talk without taking notes or thinking of the experience as literature as Maugham was doing but we absorbed an understanding of how the Lambeth poor then lived, of their vitality and their exhaustion, of their reaction to wanted and unwanted babies, and of their rough and ready goodness to each other, lessons which coloured our lives no less than they did Maugham's. Maugham wrote a summary of this his first book when submitting it for publication:

> This is the story of a nine-day wonder in a Lambeth slum. It shows that those queer folk the poor live and love and die in very much the same way as their neighbours in Brixton and Belgravia, and that hatred, malice, and all uncharitableness are not the peculiar attributes of the glorious British Middle Class, and finally it shows that in this world nothing much matters, and that in Vere Street, Lambeth, nothing matters at all.

He might have added that as Liza dies of puerperal fever following the miscarriage of her illegitimate child, she has become a social outcast in her slum no less certainly than, under the same circumstances, a middle class girl of her day might have been. *Liza* contains more violence and horrors than we saw in Lambeth but it is written with a restraint which emphasises the hopeless inevitability of the effects of a slum environment. It is a fine performance for a first novel based on observation and understanding for Maugham was writing about what he knew. He describes the conditions of his day, the terrible lack of privacy in Vere Street, the prodigious number of babies, the absence of any castigation of society or of government, in fact the lack of protest or real complaint against slum conditions, a lot of fun, and how Liza's lazy, drunken mother is respectable because she has her marriage lines to prove it.

Far greater changes have taken place in Lambeth since my time there than occurred between Maugham's and mine. Bombs did much to clear the area but the vastly improved living conditions and social security of to-day are associated with the highest incidence of mugging in London in those very streets where we were able to leave our bicycles day or night and later the old yellow, open, unlockable, two-seater Morris, shared by my partner Robert Yeo and me, without fear of theft or vandalism.

I saw Somerset Maugham just once as an old man, most appropriately in the Hong Kong Yacht Club, when invited to lunch there, we found ourselves at the next table to his party. I have dipped into many books about him and have a special preference for Robert Lorin Calder's *W. Somerset Maugham and the Quest for Freedom* (1972), though he has since written a full biography, *Willie: The Life of W. Somerset Maugham* (1989). I have taken most information from Ted Morgan's biography *Somerset Maugham* (1980), but my prime concern has been with the novels and the plays, related with a skill born of intense concentration on the technique of his art, abounding with astute observation and sharp insight but varying greatly in quality, especially when he departed from his own experience. Elizabeth Bowen in *The Heritage of British Literature* (1983) wrote "Somerset Maugham in *Our Betters* wrote perhaps the best social comedy of the century, and in *The Sacred Flame* he certainly wrote one of the worst dramas". His characters are too often dislikable or worthless and their behaviour distasteful to do full justice to his expert professional ability. His greatest success seems naturally to have been obtained in the theatre and the cinema where a good story and sharp dialogue come into their own. His incessant repetition of variations on the theme of brief affairs and infidelities based on immediate sexual attraction, seems to underline his difficulty in comprehending and his failure to portray, sustained love. There is a dearth of quotable observation of wider issues, not of human relationships but of motive, understanding, intellectual depth and that imaginative perception which illuminates greater novels. William Ober (*A Few Kind Words About W. Somerset Maugham*, 1969)

234

wrote "Larry Darrell's wisdom gained from years of study of Hindu mysticism in *The Razor's Edge* would not enlighten a sophomore". The failure, Cronshaw, in *Of Human Bondage* (1915) who knew Pater, Oscar Wilde and Mallarmé, and the average of every first-class cricketer for the last twenty years, talks with a certain vigour but talks nonsense. Clutton does a little better on the subject of why artists paint and can become self absorbed to the point of abandoning comfort, home, money, love, honour and duty for the sake of getting on to canvas the emotion the world has given them. What carries you on with Maugham is not the glorious, re-readable asides which form such a memorable feature in many of the works of the greatest writers but the flow of his story – you turn the page because you have become engrossed in the progress of the narrative. One should not underestimate the achievement of an outstandingly successful storyteller.

Somerset Maugham's restricted upbringing after his parents died led him to a quest for freedom and a hunt for a wider experience. He was born in France in the British Embassy in Paris, to avoid the law that children born on French soil acquired French citizenship and so were liable for conscription. He lived well for the first ten years of his life in the English society of Paris but his later, less happy, orphaned childhood, brought up by his elderly uncle and aunt in their Vicarage at Whitstable, coloured his life. Speaking French as easily as English and deprived at eight years of age of his mother's demonstrative love, the change to the care of an old, childless couple in a parsonage in a Kentish seaside town was sudden and dramatic. He developed a passion for freedom, the will to do as he pleased, to escape from the narrow restrictions of his new life and the persistent sense of loss of the mother he had known so little but remembered so well. This desire to escape was part of his love of travel with its new experiences and lowered responsibilities. He developed a special partiality for the East where change and variety provided new ideas and backgrounds for his stories.

During his long life he wrote some twenty novels and some thirty plays, one at times being transformed into the other, also short stories and much non-fiction in a productive period lasting from 1897 to 1962. After *Liza of Lambeth* he wrote a number of fairly undistinguished novels and a volume of short stories as he tried to earn money, using subjects he hoped would have popular appeal such as imperialism, the Boer War and the occult. The first of these *The Making of a Saint* (1898), departed from his own experience as he attempted an historical adventure tale related by a fifteenth century Italian soldier of fortune which included assassination, stabbing, hanging, dismemberment and betrayal. *The Hero* (1901) is about James Parsons, returning from the Boer War with a Victoria Cross, who finds himself unable to bear the petty prejudice of provincial society, a common theme of Maugham's, or to abide his energetic, charitable, self-assertive fiancé who will rearrange a sick man's pillows to her satisfaction and his discomfort. He shoots himself. *Mrs Craddock* (1902 revised 1928) shows some improvement though Maugham described it later as written by "a foolish young man; he was supercilious, cock-sure and often wrong-headed". In another of his favourite themes of marriage based on physical attraction but wrecked by differences in education, artistic appreciation and intellectual ability, Bertha Craddock, intelligent and well educated, marries a handsome, strong, large-framed, Kentish farmer for whom she has a fiery passion. She soon finds him ignorant, complacent and lacking in any appreciation of the things she loves. After a long and painful labour, during which her guardian Dr Ramsey has to call in Dr Spencer for help, her child is stillborn. Disillusioned she falls in love, passionately once more, with a scamp of nineteen but, trapped by marriage, she contemplates suicide. Unlike James Parsons, however, she is granted an escape when her unwanted husband is killed falling from his horse.

Mrs Craddock is saved by Bertha's aunt, Mary Ley, a character based surprisingly, according to Maugham, on the portrait-statue of Agrippina the Younger in the museum at Naples.

> She had the same lined face, with its look of rather scornful indifference for mundane affairs, and that well-bred distinction of manner which the Empress had acquired through the command of multitudes but Miss Ley, more finely, through the command of herself.

He refers to Agrippina again in Ashenden (1928) when he goes to Naples with The Hairless Mexican who kills the wrong man, and sees her statue which "he had particular reasons for remembering

236

with affection". Miss Ley is plain-spoken, has a keen wit and an independent spirit with a gift for ridicule. She holds a delightfully crisp dialogue with Dr Ramsey and Miss Glover, the sister of the Vicar of Leanham, when she shocks them with the news of Bertha's engagement to Edward Craddock. Miss Ley rested easily in a condition of satisfied doubt, her attitude towards life indicated by a slight shrug of the shoulders.

We are happy to meet Mary Ley again in *The Merry-Go-Round* (1904), which contains a number of Maugham's comments on medicine. This consists of three stories running loosely together, and linked by Miss Ley and Dr Frank Hurrell who is based on Maugham's idea of himself as a successful consultant in Harley Street and physician on the staff of his old hospital. One part is taken from his play *A Man of Honour* (1903), about another doomed marriage, this one between Basil Kent a law student, and Jenny a beautiful barmaid. He marries her, as a man of honour, when she becomes pregnant, bringing out a favourite theme of Maugham's, the destructive potential of morality. Jenny's family are intolerable and after the baby is stillborn he and Jenny have little in common beyond their sexual attraction. Jenny drowns herself. Another part is the story of a Dean's daughter in her forties and a young poet dying of tuberculosis whom she loves and marries to care for him. The poet goes to see Frank Hurrell, the consultation being set out in some detail. Hurrell makes the diagnosis from the patient's white skin, emaciated body, clubbed fingers, recent night sweats, family history and crepitations at the apex of the right lung, and confirms it by finding tubercle bacilli in the sputum. The third story is of yet another woman who has an affair with an attractive, young wastrel on the way to returning to her husband a better wife. Frank Hurrell, like Maugham, wants to give up medicine and travel because he tires of a life in which he sees only sickness. He lets off steam to Miss Ley about the pervading idea that pain ennobles a man, "it doesn't refine, it brutalises" and refers to "the frightful egoism of physical suffering". *The Merry-Go-Round* didn't sell very well despite some good reviews so Maugham changed his literary agent when he really needed to change his plots.

Maugham's references to medical matters become less frequent with time as memories of hospital life receded. Some of them might have been written by any author of fiction, like Dr Brandon the murderer in *The Happy Couple* from *Creatures of Circumstance* (1947), Dr Harvester who connived in a murder in *The Sacred Flame*. Dr Charles Bishop in *Virtue* from *First Person Singular* (1931) who committed suicide, or his accounts of several characters who developed malaria. However, a number faithfully reflect his medical experience. The blind Prior in *Faith* from *Orientations* (1899) dies of advanced, untreated buccal cancer with lymph node involvement, where the signs and symptoms are presented in a way which clearly reflects personal observation. Despite severe pain and slow starvation the Prior still believes in the merciful goodness of God. Then the death of Elliott Templeton from renal failure in *The Razor's Edge*, published in 1944, though one of his last novels, is still described with the clarity of a well remembered experience of uraemia. In *A Bad Example*, from the collection of stories, James Clinton is certified insane by two doctors, just in time to save his wife from penury, because he quotes the Bible and does what it tells him to do: love his neighbour as himself, clothe the naked, feed the hungry and sell all that he has and give it to the poor. This theme was expanded in the play *Sheppey*. Mrs Grange in *Flotsam and Jetsam*, from *Creatures of Circumstance* has a tic "that made her jerk her head as though she were beckoning you to an inner room" and a left hand which at regular intervals went into a state of almost constant movement. Yaws, elephantiasis and measles all appear in *Rain* from *The Trembling of a Leaf* (1921).

Maugham turned to the theatre in 1903 with a stream of plays. *A Man of Honour* was produced for two performances by the Stage Society. *Lady Frederick* (1907), his first success, was turned down by seventeen managements but was eventually produced as a six-week stop-gap at The Royal Court Theatre. The news caught Maugham penniless in Sicily and he had to bluff and gamble his way through to get home for the opening. With its crackle of smart, amusing dialogue and glossy setting it played for 422 performances in the West End. It portrayed the author's life-long preoccupation with money and ways to escape from penury, on this occasion by an older woman who, to discourage a young suitor, makes up on stage before him changing from a dishevelled, haggard frump in a kimono into her attractive, society self. The managers had thought that no actress would accept such a part, but Ethel Irving made a great success of it and so did Ethel Barrymore when she played Lady Frederick in New York.

As success arrived Maugham began to dig out his rejected plays: Charles Hawtry appeared in *Jack Straw*, Marie Tempest in *Mrs Dot* and Lewis Waller in *The Explorer* all in 1908. By then he had four plays running in the West End at the same time, he was famous, money was rolling in and continued to do so for the rest of his life. He was said to be mean, he certainly remained careful with his money and stowed bits away in different places for safety, but he had known poverty, liked to live well, both for pleasure and for show, and could be most generous at times. In 1909 Marie Tempest was in *Penelope* (1909), Marie Lohr in *Smith* (1909), and *The Explorer* had been revived. He wrote one play in two weeks and said he wrote others in three or four. He had become a celebrity and was meeting the star personalities of the day. He was eventually to have twenty-nine plays produced.

By 1913 Maugham had written eleven of his plays and decided to devote his talents to the theatre which had by then been the source of his success. However, he couldn't resist a return to the novel for he had a draft, made fifteen years before, called "The Artistic Temperament of Stephen Carey", an immature attempt at autobiography. He set out to turn this into an autobiographical novel, the story of his youth with fact as its background though reality was not strictly adhered to. This novel *Of Human Bondage* (1915) marked a welcome change in his literary output, he was back to the days of *Eliza* writing about his own experiences, a move he seldom abandoned again. Occupation and characters were changed, Stephen became Philip Carey, his own personification, with a club foot to cause him rejection and embarrassment instead of his own stutter, written with a newly acquired experience of his art. Philip Carey, sensitive, perceptive, gifted, has a desperate struggle with poverty and his own nature particularly over the wretched, vulgar, slut Mildred, whom he loves and despises at the same time, and who so nearly wrecks his life. He seems to be compelled to submit to bondage to his upbringing, to his physical defect and especially to the woman he hates himself for loving. Maugham's friend, Harry Philips, with whom he seems to have had a love affair, told Joseph Dobrinsky, a French expert on

Somerset Maugham, "Mildred was a composite figure and certain episodes connected with incidents in his life. The real Mildred was a youth".

The book was roughly handled by many of the critics as being morbid, distasteful, depressing and thoroughly unwholesome. Theodore Dreiser, however, saw the book as a work of genius to be loved if not completely understood and felt compelled to designate it as a work of art. It had some success which grew with time and has persisted with growing critical acclaim; people related to the misery of Philip's life and to his weakness of character, many responded to his unhappy childhood. The terrible Mildred, and Philip's obsession with her, occupies almost a third of the novel pushing aside interesting characters like Thorpe Athelny and his family and the artists, Lawrence, based on Sir Gerald Kelly, and Clutton who disappears too soon. There is no Mary Ley to enliven this rather depressing chronicle. It is, nevertheless, one of Maugham's greater achievements, an affecting, emotional study though lacking sufficient amiable or convivial appeal for the full appreciation of many people.

Medicine carries a thread through the novel; not only does the story contain an absorbing account of midwifery on district in the slums but also a vivid description of the conduct of hospital out-patients practice at the turn of the century. The large dark waiting room with the characteristic dull two colours dividing the walls, with long benches packed with waiting patients suggesting "the grim drawings of Daumier". The old patients dealt with after the 1.30pm bell before Dr Tyrell arrives at 2pm to see the new patients, all gathered at once without appointments to await a turn with the great man.

> Sometimes they put on shabby clothes in order to pretend they were poor; but he had a keen eye to prevent what he regarded as fraud and sometimes refused to see people who, he thought could well pay for medical attendances.

Anyone who doubts the wonders of our National Health Service, established by the most imaginative piece of legislation passed in my life time at a moment of post-war financial stringency, should read Chapter 81. Nevertheless, most of the hospital out-patients of that time:

where under the impression that the hospital was an institution of the state, for which they paid out of the rates, and took the attendance they received as a right they could claim. They imagined the physician who gave his time was heavily paid.

Now that it is, and the doctors are, the inevitable defects and financial difficulties of an expanding, comprehensive health service paid for out of taxation is subject to public outcry for its short-comings and far too little is to be heard of its magnificent achievements.

Philip is taken ill in his lodgings as a medical student and Dr Deacon from the hospital comes to see him. In the book he has a severe bout of influenza whereas, in life, Somerset Maugham contracted a potentially more dangerous illness, a septic infection from doing a post-mortem examination, which he probably thought unsuitable for repetition in the novel as he had already used it in *The Merry-Go-Round*. Others doctors appear in *Of Human Bondage*: Dr Chandler, the senior obstetric clerk, is called in by Philip on district when a sixteen year old is dying in childbirth. Dr Wigram attends his uncle in Blackstable; and the lonely old Dr South with whom he goes into practice at Farnley in Droset when he marries Sally Athelnys.

The war brought about a great change in Maugham's life. He joined a Red Cross Ambulance Unit in 1914 and went with the British Expeditionary Force to France. He was an ambulance driver during the battle of Ypres, shared a billet with Desmond MacCarthy, managed to correct the proofs of *Of Human Bondage*, dressed wounds in a Field Hospital and met Gerald Haxton, the love of his life. After the actress, Sue Jones, had turned down his offer of marriage he had an affair with Syrie Wellcome, the daughter of Dr Barnardo and the wife of Henry Wellcome, (the founder of the great pharmaceutical firm), whose lovers included Gordon Selfridge the owner of the famous store. Syrie persuaded Maugham that they should have a child and their daughter, Liza, was born in Rome in September 1915. Henry Wellcome had hired detectives to provide evidence of Syrie's infidelities and chose Maugham as co-respondent in his divorce because he was single and solvent. When the divorce became absolute, Maugham, in his role of Man of Honour, felt bound to marry her. She introduced

THE JESTER

him to Sir John Wallinger who recruited him to intelligence work because of his fluency in languages and, as having a reasonable excuse for going to Lucerne as a writer to find peace for his work. He travelled regularly to France to report and to receive new instructions. While there he wrote a play *The Unattainable* later called *Caroline* (1916), with a bearing on Syrie and himself, about an eminent lawyer who loves a married but, when her husband dies and she is no longer unattainable, loses interest. Dr Cornish understands it all. There is a typical piece of Maugham dialogue in which the doctor explains middle age to Caroline but when she tries to persuade him to marry her so that, unattainable once more, she will regain the lawyer's love, he resurrects her husband and packs him off to Texas to conceal his deception which is designed both the restore the status quo for her and to save himself.

At this time, Maugham's lover, the American Gerald Haxton, whom he had met in the all male environment of the Ambulance Unit in France, got into trouble in London accused of committing a homosexual act but after an expensive trial, was acquitted. However, he was later deported as an undesirable alien, on what was thought to be security grounds, but, oddly enough, his papers were closed to inspection by the Home Office for a hundred years. Maugham got home for the opening of *Caroline* but was soon back in Switzerland where he met Compton Mackenzie and Edward Knoblock doing the same sort of work and providing him with extra material for his *Ashenden* (1928) stories.

In August 1916 Maugham sailed for America followed by Syrie and Liza. With her divorce not yet absolute he took the opportunity to set off that November with Gerald for the South Seas to gather material for a novel about Gauguin. Gerald was a problem, drinking, gambling and running into debt whenever opportunity offered but was an invaluable asset on their travels collecting information for Maugham's work. Maugham was reserved and found communication with strangers difficult. Gerald was amiable and gregarious, making friends easily. He brought interesting characters with tales to tell to talk to Maugham, expanding his sources so that most of his best work was done while he and Gerald were together.

Clutton in *Of Human Bondage*, an artist Philip met in Paris, had talked of a man he met in Brittany who had forsaken a good job, wife and family to become a painter, gone to Tahiti, nearly starved to death and become a great artist. This formed the basis for his trip to Tahiti and a novel, *The Moon and Sixpence* (1919), about Gauguin who died in 1903. He and Gerald stopped in Hawaii on the way and met two people who in very different ways were to become important to Maugham: Bertram Alanson who was to invest his money for him and make him a great fortune and, on the boat leaving for Samoa, Miss Thompson with her "gentlemen callers" who was to be the model for Sadie Thompson in one of his best known stories *Rain* in *The Trembling of a Leaf* (1921). In February 1919 they were in Tahiti researching for the novel, they met a number of people who had known Gauguin and found a door, in a shabby house where he stayed when ill, containing glass panels painted by him which Maugham bought for $200 and sold in 1962 for $37,400.

Back in America, Maugham married Syrie in May 1917 in Jersey City to avoid the New York press. Maugham then embarked on an extraordinary double life, leaving his wife for half the year when he was off with Gerald collecting material for his work. It was hardly an ideal arrangement for a successful marriage. Syrie opened a shop and became well known and most successful as an interior decorator and seller of antiques. She was well liked for her enthusiasm, good taste and warm personality. Her marriage to Maugham lasted ten exasperating years. One result of their unusual association was an amazing great grandson. In July 1989, just ten years old, born weighing on 1½ lb., blind from birth, he has become a remarkable pianist making his debut with the Philharmonic Pop Orchestra at the Barbican.

In June 1917, newly married and just back from the South Seas, Maugham was asked to go to Russia to help keep that country in the war. He was fortunate to meet an old friend, Sasha Kropotkin, who acted as his interpreter and introduced him to Kerensky. He gathered useful information and finally returned to England to deliver by hand a message from Kerensky to Lloyd George, but it was too late for action the Bolsheviks were turning Kerensky out and making peace with Germany by the time he arrived home.

While in the South Seas Maugham's play *Our Betters* (1917) had caused a furore in New York being a satire on wealthy Americans selling themselves in marriage to find their way into London Society. The language and the behaviour of the characters were described by the critics as sordid and offensive thus ensuring its success on Broadway. Maugham who had developed pulmonary tuberculosis, made worse by his Russian trip, had to spend some time in a Scottish sanatorium. In Scotland he was writing plays again, *Love in a Cottage* (1918) and *Home and Beauty* (1919), and, as ever, using a new environment to produce a story. *Sanatorium* from *Creatures of Circumstances* (1947) accurately depicts the curious, restricted life led by many tuberculosis patients in the days before streptomycin, confined within a small community where they were preoccupied with their own symptoms and chance of recovery, where love affairs did a little to relieve the boredom and friendships, antagonisms, gossip and bridge formed a major part of life, while degrees of courage or self-pity disclosed their personalities. In the film made of this story, Ashenden's chest x-ray was shown for a moment in the doctor's consulting room revealing the right apical lesion from which Maugham himself had suffered.

Early in 1918 he was well enough to return home to work on *The Moon and Sixpence* (1919) and another play *Caesar's Wife* (1919). Gerald had been in a prisoner-of-war camp in Germany, had then gone to Denmark but his attempt to join Maugham in England was foiled as he was deported, still an undesirable alien, as soon as he arrived. Maugham and Gerald were off together again in China at the end of 1919 which produced *On a Chinese Screen* (1922), *East of Suez* (1922) and *The Painted Veil* (1925). This last contains another of Maugham's assaults on middle class values with a silly young woman, Kitty Fane, dominated by her socially ambitious mother who plans to see her married to wealth. She fails to find the husband her mothers thinks suitable in three seasons and in panic, marries Dr Walter Fane a stuffy bacteriologist she doesn't love. She has an affair in Hong Kong with the good looking, exciting and popular Charles Townsend. Her furious husband in revenge takes her off with him to work in a remote cholera-ridden region where her survival is improbable. There is nothing about cholera in this story except odd references to death. Here French nuns run an orphanage and Waddington, the understanding deputy commissioner, runs the district and lives with a Manchu lady of a great family. Kitty discovers suffering, sacrifice, death, faith and the tender care of children, one with hydrocephalus, who have been rejected by the Chinese. She works with the nuns developing her character and acquiring concern for others. Walter is unchanged, still obsessed with her infidelity. "But soon a wonder came to light" as one of the greatest doctor-writers said, and as he is dying of cholera Walter quotes "The dog it was that dy'd". Kitty returns to Hong Kong and, in the original ending, falls for the worthless Charles Townsend yet again, her passionate nature temporarily overcoming her spiritual regeneration. Another of Maugham's characters, Ginger Ted, finds redemption in a cholera epidemic, helped by Miss Jones and treacle pudding, in *The Vessel of Wrath*, from *Ah King* (1933).

Maugham's next trip with Gerald was to the Malay States in 1920 producing *The Casuarina Tree* (1926) and another of Maugham's best known short stories *The Letter*, turned into a play with Gladys Cooper (1927), and a film with Bette Davis. One of his own favourite plays *The Circle* (1921) also came out of this trip. John Gielgud played in the 1944 revival. In September 1922 the pair took their most adventurous trip to Ceylon, Burma, Siam and Indochina. They travelled for twenty-six days through jungle by mule to reach Kengtung, a peaceful Burmese village near the Tibetan border which a man had told them was the place where he would rather live than anywhere else in the world. While on this difficult and uncomfortable journey Maugham's highly successful play, a dramatised version of his story *Rain*, opened in New York. Many actresses wanted a chance to play the prostitute, Sadie Thompson, and three film versions were made: with Gloria Swanson and Lional Barrymore in 1928, Joan Crawford and Walter Huston in 1932 and Rita Hayworth and José Ferrer in 1953. Dr Macphail tries to hold the situation on some level of good sense while the medical missionary Davidson struggles with himself and God to convert Sadie only to succumb to temptation himself and then to cut his throat.

They were off once more to New York, Mexico, Havana, Jamaica and Guatermala but stories did not offer themselves as freely as before, there was no settled British colony in Mexico to be chastened. In 1925 they went to Singapore but a desire for a home of his own was growing, for though Maugham and Syrie at this time were on fairly good terms they led quite separate lives. Maugham fancied the South of France for its climate and because Gerald was banned from England. He began long negotiations to buy, alter and decorate a house at Cap Ferrat, between Nice and Monte Carlo, in eight acres of land looking over the bay of Villefranche, which he called Villa Mauresque. While this was going on he went back to New York for the opening of *The Constant Wife* (1926) once again about an affair, one which Constance's husband the surgeon in Harley Street, Sir John Middleton FRCS, has with her best friend and, as she takes her revenge by preparing to go off to Italy for six weeks with an old admirer because she wants to be loved, she is begged by her husband to stay. The audience is left expecting her to return as she says "I may be unfaithful, but I am constant. I always think that's my most endearing quality".

Maugham moved into his lovely house in June 1927 and started a new phase of his life. Syrie divorced him in May 1929 and received their home in London, a Rolls Royce and £2,400 a year for herself and £600 a year for Liza. Maugham was upset at losing the respectable cover which marriage provided for his life with Gerald and never forgave Syrie for spreading the story that their marriage breakdown was due to his homosexuality. In his lovely Riviera Villa with thirteen servants, filled with the beautiful things he had acquired, including his Gauguin glass painting, he ran everything to a routine designed to suit his regular morning work and his entertaining. Many people came to stay mostly the famous, the wealthy, and attractive young men. Half the year he travelled to England, where he kept a London flat, and to America for the opening of his plays or the launch of other works. He went to Switzerland to a clinic for "the cure" and to Spain. *Ashenden*, held back for security clearance, was not published until 1928 the first in line of the contemporary trend in spy stories, a forerunner to the great improvements of John Le Carré, where the agent is not heroic and does unromantic work which is often dull or morally indefensible.

Maugham's relations with women were thoroughly unsatisfactory, although he loved the actress Sue Jones, had numerous affairs and a wife, he didn't appear to like them much.

He was often hard and insensitive with actresses who aspired to parts in his plays. However, he did have one female friend for more than thirty years with whom he was not emotionally involved, Barbara Back, the elegant, blond and beautiful wife of the well known surgeon to St George's Hospital, Ivor Back. She acted for Maugham as hostess from time to time on opening nights, was often a guest at Mauresque, partnered him at golf and bridge and for many years kept up a lively correspondence with him retelling all the Mayfair gossip. Beverley Nichols said it was probably the happiest friendship with a woman that Maugham ever enjoyed.

In 1930 *Cakes and Ale* was published. This was for Maugham an especially happy book, he found it amusing to write and liked it the best of his novels. Its refreshing gaiety made it an instant success. He had long wanted to base a fictional character on the actress Sue Jones so he presented Rosie as a warm hearted, delightful character, the common, amusing, unfaithful wife of an aging novelist, Edward Duffield. This character was partly based on Thomas Hardy, whose longevity rather than his talent was presented as the reason for his elevation to the status of Grand Old Man of English Literature. The portrait was resented by many of Hardy's admirers who said Maugham had trampled on his grave but their reactions were mild compared with those of Hugh Walpole and his friends to the character of Alroy Kear, a self-promoting, favour-currying, talent-lacking writer all too obviously representing Hugh Walpole. The malice in this portrait shocked Walpole who had thought of Maugham as his friend. The literary storm which resulted with its accusations, denials and general indignation promoted the sales just as scandal, banning and notoriety do to-day, it also obscured for some time, the excellence of what is generally regarded as Maugham's best work.

The Breadwinner opened in London in September 1930 with Ronald Squire, Marie Lohr and their stage children, Patrick aged 18 and Judy aged 16, played by two young people on their way to fame, Jack Hawkins and Peggy Ashcroft. It is about a stockbroker who allows himself to be hammered when he could have prevented it and walks out on his family because he is bored with them and wants to start a new life on his own. It was light hearted with a series of amusing conversations between father, mother,

248

children and solicitor but had the disadvantage of being put on at the same time as Noel Coward's *Private Lives*. *The Painted Veil* was adapted for the stage and for Gladys Cooper. Another collection of short stories *First Person Singular* was published in 1931.

In 1932 *The Narrow Corner*, resurrected an old character, Captain Nichols, from *The Moon and Sixpence*. It was written in the mould of *The Ebb Tide*, with a schooner, islands, villainy and even vitriol, but the villain isn't a patch on Robert Louis Stevenson's Huish. Captain Nichols hides a young man on his schooner who is running away from a charge of murder and Dr Saunders travels with them. The young man wins money from the Captain at cards and after some adventure goes overboard to the sharks one night in a calm sea off the coast of Java as the Captain plans to repossess his losses while retaining his thousand pounds paid for secreting the young man. Dr Saunders watches philosophically over the adventure. He has been struck off the medical register in England, settled in the Dutch East Indies and is a good doctor with a special bent for ophthalmology – "He knew exactly what to say to alleviate the terror or pain of the moment and he left no one but fortified consoled and encouraged". He performs a cataract operation on the wealthy Kim Ching, notes Nichols's blotchy skin, high colour and purple flush over the cheek bones as signs of long-standing heart disease and refers to a man as aimlessly snuffed out by Flexner's dysentery bacillus.

Maugham took Gerald off on another of their trips in 1935 to French Guiana collecting material for *Christmas Holiday* (1939). They visited the penal colony where they saw a guillotine kept for use in a small room and learned that the motive for murder was almost invariably money.

Liza was married in 1936 to Vincent Paravicini, the son of the Swiss Minister to England and Maugham went to the wedding where he met Syrie again but hardly spoke to her and refused to have themselves photographed together.

By 1937, Gerald at forty-five was bored with life, fifteen years of luxury living, with little to do but attend to Maugham's needs and a diminishing opportunity for adventurous travel, had begun to pall. His gambling became wilder, his drinking heavier and his behaviour in front of guests worse. He then became so ill that he thought he was going to die and so frightened that he gave up drink being threatened with dismissal if he ever started again. In 1933 Maugham had taken him on a grand tour of India where, predictably, he found the narrow provincialism of the British yet another example of the self-satisfied insularity he had railed against for so long. The Viceroy, Lord Linlithgow, invited Maugham to lunch but he refused because they would not receive Gerald.

Back at Mauresque, entertainment of guests was renewed with the addition of the Duke and Duchess of Windsor creating problems over titles and precedence. It was probably through the Duke of Windsor that Maugham heard of Dr Paul Niehans. Niehans had a clinic near Vevey where he treated the famous and the wealthy for certain diseases and for rejuvenation with injection of cells taken from unborn lambs. He claimed that he rejected nine out of ten of the people who applied to him, certainly he was careful in his selection of those to receive his cellular therapy by their ailments, if any, and their bank balances. Maugham had used his medical training as a chance to observe people freed from reticence and anxious to talk about themselves, rather than for any serious scientific training. He showed how little depth there was to his medical understanding and how great was his personal vanity by submitting himself to a rejuvenation clinic purveying a brand of classical, medical confidence-trickery compounded of diagnosis by a urine enzyme reaction and treatment by dramatic injections of a "Miracle serum". The methods used in such concerns are invariably made precise enough to provide an air of certainty and not easily to be duplicated by rivals or evaluated by testing sceptics. Dr Niehans had his own slaughter house were he kept pregnant ewes so that cells obtained from a foetus could be injected within the hour. Niehans had all the trimmings: tall, distinguished looking, reassuring, complimentary and confident, given additional prestige by a mother said to be the illegitimate daughter of Frederick III, King of Prussia who married Victoria, Princess Royal of England in 1858. Niehans congratulated Maugham on his youthful body, healthy skin and the excellent condition of his sexual organs. Vanity, wishful thinking, and uncritical acceptance of the practiced aplomb of the presenter is a well known combination for relieving the wealthy of their money.

With the war came the collapse of France; Maugham escaped on a coal barge from Cannes taking twenty days of great discomfort to reach England. Gerald was left behind to close Mauresque and sell the yacht. Maugham went to America and made speeches for the British war effort until America came into the war. Gerald joined him there having left the cook, the maid and a French boyfriend of his to look after Mauresque. Maugham was writing *The Razor's Edge* (1944), Liza was having a daughter and Gerald was drinking in secret. Aldous Huxley, Christopher Isherwood and Gerald Heard, literary friends of Maugham's spent the war in America and were studying a Hindu system called Vendanta, they provided Maugham with material for *The Razor's Edge* where a young American, Larry Darrell, seeks a meaning to life through Hindu philosophy.

Maugham's publisher built a house for him in South Carolina where he could work in peace and he lived there on and off for four years. While there he had a recurrence of malaria and went to New York to see Dr Max Wolf, a follower of Dr Niehans, who made a serum called Bogomolets from goats. He diagnosed a large, benign tumour of the stomach, kept Maugham in hospital for three weeks and treated him with enzymes and a huge injection of quinine after which both the tumour and the malaria miraculously disappeared. Maugham was loud in praise of the wonderful Dr Wolf. Gerald didn't like South Carolina and was eager to lead his own life for a change. Alan Searle was taking his place. Gerald found a clerical job in Washinton with the O.S.S. telling his friends that he was doing top-secret intelligence work. Maugham finished *The Razor's Edge* in August 1942. This story of an American drop-out who abandons what he sees as materialism and seeks a new faith, anticipated a widespread movement by the young in the 1960's which caused quite a stir in America. The book had a first edition of 375,000 copies; Maugham always commanded high sales in America. Just when things were going well, Gerald developed pleurisy and was found to have tuberculosis. Maugham visited him every day in Doctors Hospital, New York, and was shocked at his wasted condition. All his past misbehaviour was forgotten, he took him to the Adirondacks to a place full of nursing homes and hospitals where he improved for while and then, still seeking help, to Boston and back to hospital in New York where Gerald raved, denouced Maugham and screamed obscenities at him. An operation revealed a stomach

251

ulcer, he was not well enough for a thoracoplasty to be performed and he died on November 7th, 1944. Maugham had stayed by him for months remembering old times and forgiving so much. Maugham found Gerald's death a grievous blow; he had gone his own way, had been drunken, dishonest, promiscuous and self-indulgent, he had caused him distress and embarrassment in front of his guests but he had loved him and for so long he had been his light-hearted and most rewarding companion.

Mauresque had been occupied by the Italians and then the Germans, the British had shelled it from the sea and the Americans had captured it and turned it into an officer's rest home. Maugham and Alan Searle set about the task of repair while living in a nearby hotel. The Germans had drunk all the wine, the cars had been stolen but some of the servants remained to help. Maugham had been in Hollywood working on the screen version of *The Razor's Edge* for which his fee was a Pissarro of the harbour at Roen to add to his growing collection of Impressionist paintings. No word of his adaptation was ever used. Tyrone Power got his first film role as Larry Darrell.

Alan Searle who had taken Gerald's place as secretary and companion spent the last twenty years of Maugham's life with him in anxious devotion, dull compared with Gerald but with no sarcasm and no scenes. Liza had been married again, this time to Lord John Hope MP, the son of Lord Linlithgow who as Viceroy of India had refused to receive Gerald. At the wedding reception at Claridges Maugham met Syrie again but they sat at opposite ends of the room. Maugham's collection of paintings were mostly bought in Liza's name and had become one of great importance, it included a Bonnard, Matisse, Picasso, Pissarro, Sisley, and a Toulouse-Lautrec to go with his Gaugin.

Maugham continued to travel and to write but was becoming increasingly discontented and querulous as he became more famous. Honours were heaped on him. He had written *Then and Now* (1946), a novel about Renaissance Italy with an initial printing of 825,000 copies and his last novel *Catalian* (1948) was set in seventeenth century Spain. Four million copies of his books had been sold world wide. *The Razor's Edge* alone sold 1,367,283 copies. He had made four million dollars from his writing, he was the most popular novelist alive, constantly followed by the press, lionised, fêted and honoured. He was made a Companion of Honour, a Companion of Literature, given an honorary degree at Oxford and, for his eightieth birthday, a Garrick Club dinner. His old friend Gerald Kelly, President of the Royal Academy, invited him to speak at the annual dinner at Burlington House where the other speakers were Attlee, Churchill, Samuel and Admiral Lord Cork and Orrery, despite which he stole the show. In 1955 he was asked again and sat next to the Queen. Syrie died that year mourned by her many friends but not by Maugham. The one sad note in this widespread celebration of his talent was an attempt by Heinemann to commission a *Festschrift*, most of the famous people and old friends approached declined to contribute and the project had to be abandoned.

Between 1948 and 1962 Maugham wrote five volumes of essays and reflections as the now Grand Old Man of English Letters, but he was becoming deeply unhappy despite which he clung to life. He visited Dr Niehans again for more rejuvenation, who was by then even more famous as he had been treating the Pope. Mauresque entertained further acquaintances such as Lord Beaverbrook and Freddy Ayer. Alan Searle, worried about his own future, secured new arrangements with the help of Liza. Maugham was made an Honorary Senator of the University of Heidelberg where he had been a student seventy years before.

Maugham's mind was failing, he had hysterical outbursts of hate, shouting at imaginary enemies. He feared for the safety of his pictures as there had been an outbreak of art thefts and decided to sell them, although most belonged to Liza. When she suggested that they discuss the matter he replied with a letter from his solicitors. He then threatened to sell Mauresque which belonged to her and where he had lived for thirty years and go to live in Lausanne but his lawyer told him he couldn't be turned out and that if he went to Switzerland 15% of his estate would have to go to his heirs. In April 1962 his pictures were sold at Sotheby's by Peter Wilson. The total realised was $1,466,864. Liza sued Sotheby's claiming $648,900 as her share backed by documentary evidence that many of them were hers. Liza's suit for her share of the sale was eventually settled out of court in January 1964 but she only got $250,000. Alan Searle was partly responsible for the increase in family troubles; as his influence on the failing

Maugham grew he tried to manipulate things to his own advantage.

Maugham was sinking into senile dementia. On a railway platform an old lady told Alan "You shold be gentle with this nice old man. He thinks he's Somerset Maugham". He wrote *Looking Back* in which he attacked Syrie in such shocking terms that his literary advisers wouldn't publish it and Alex Frere, Maugham's editor at Heinemanns, said "You can't let a man down when he gets to the end of his life and goes raving mad", however, some of it was serialised in the *Sunday Express* widening still further his estrangement from his daughter. He had deeply offended many of Syrie's friends including Cecil Beaton, Noel Coward, Beverly Nichols and Rebecca West. After Maugham's death Coward produced and acted in a play of his, *A Song at Twilight*, about a homosexual author, Sir Hugo Latymer with a secretary Perry Sheldon, who treated people with contempt because trying to hide his homosexuality had become such a strain that he had lost all feeling for other people.

In *The Summing Up* (1938) Maugham had said "I look forward to old age without dismay", and in the preface to *The Partial View* (1954) "old age liberates you from envy, hatred and malice", he was far too optimistic; fear, suspicion and mental deterioration were gaining a terrible ascendency. Fearing that Liza might have him certified to secure her inheritance, he tried to adopt Alan Searle as his son to guard against such an event but she challenged this successfully. Their affairs degenerated still further because his lawyers, in an attempt to gain their end, had questioned her legitimacy before the court. Protecting her mother's memory and the interests of her own family became her first objective. In his will he left Alan the contents of Mauresque, with all his royalties for life, some $50,000 a year, which were to go on his death to the Royal Literary Fund: the house went to Liza. His physical energy was still remarkable but he had become irrational and violent. Alan felt shut up with a madman. It was a sad long drawn-out end. Maugham had lived too long, he died in December 1965 just short of his ninety-second birthday. Perhaps Dr Paul Niehams was to blame.

Calder, Robin Lorin   *W. Somerset Maugham and the Quest for Freedom*
Heinemann, London, 1972.
Willie: The Life of W. Somerset Maugham   Heinemann, London, 1989.
Carter, Richard   *Medicine and W. Somerset Maugham*   Proc. Roy. Soc.
Med. 1967. 113. 713-716.
Editorial   *William Somerset Maugham (1874-1965) Playwright, Novelist,
Traveller*   J. Amer. Med. Ass. 1968. 204. 65-66.
Ford, John M.T.   *A Medical Student at St Thomas's Hospital. 1801-1802.
The Weekes Family Letters.*   Wellcome Institute for the History of
Medicine. 1987. Medical History Supplement No 7.
Laurie, J.B.   *William Somerset Maugham*   Med. Press. 1965. 11, 5-17.
Morgan, Ted   *Somerset Maugham*   Jonathan Cape, London 1980.
Ober, W.B.   *A Few Kind Words about W. Somerset Maugham*   N.Y. St. J.
Med. 1969. 69 2692-2701.
Raphael, Frederic   *Fiction and the Medical Mode* in *Cracks in the Ice*   W.H.
Allen.
Raphael, FredericReview of Robert Calder's   *Willie*   Times Literary
Supplement March 1989. 329.
Rogers, R.G.   *W. Somerset Maugham (1874-1965) A Medical Truant*
Trans Stud. Coll. Physicians Phila. 1966-7. 34. 103-112.

APPENDIX

Some Papers on British Doctor-Writers

GENERAL

Banks, Sir William Mitchell *Physic and Letters* Trans. Med. Soc. Lond. 1893, 16, 327-343

Bodansky, O. *Physicians who Abandoned Medicine for Literature* Proc. Rudolf Virchow Soc., City NY 1979, 33, 1-11

Bowers, J. Z. *Truants from Medicine* Pers. Biol. Med. 1979, 23, 83-92

Cooke, A. M. *Out of School* J. Roy. Coll. Physicians 1974, 9, 51-62

Cousins, Norman *The Physician in Literature* Ch. 10 W.B Saunders, Philadelphia, 1982

Dickson, H.E. *The M.Ds. Contribution to World Literature* J. Amer. Med. Ass. 1961, 175, 213-222

Edwards, L.F. *Medical Men as Pioneers in Non-Medical Fields* Ohio St. Med. J. 1942, 38, 461- 464

Findley, Palmer *The Doctor in Literature* Med. Life 1934, 41, 566-584

Gibson, W.C. *Creative Minds in Medicine* Ch. 10 Charles C. Thomas, Springfield, Illionois, 1963

Goss, Edmund *Personal Relations Between Medicine and Literature* (Abstract) Brit. Med. J. 1923, 2, 999-1000

Handley, W. S. *Medicine as a Liberal Education* Lancet, 1913, 2, 980-983

Hill, Brian *Practitioners in Poetry* Hist. Med. 1971, 3, 16-20

Kassel, Victor *The Secret Lives of Some Drs Mitty* Med. Times 1976, 104, 183-186

Kenner, R.C. *Contributions of Physicians to English and American Literature* Davis, Detroit, 1892

L'Etang, A. *Some Unusual Medical Truants* Practitioner, 1964, 193, 96-100

McDermot, J. H. *Greener Fields* Canad. Med. Ass. J. 1962, 86, 451-454

MacNalt, Sir Arthur *Medical Poets* St. Mary's Hosp. Gaz. 1959, 65, 31-34

Maidlow, W. H. *Some British Medical Men of Letters* Med. Press and Circular, Sept 1915 283-285 Jan 1916 29-32

Miller, C. J. *Children of Apollo* Ann. Med. Hist. 1930, 2, 227-235

Monro, T.K. *The Physician as a Man of Letters Science and Action* Jackson, Wylie, Glasgow 1933. E and S Livingstone, Edinburgh 1951

Moynihan, Lord *Truants* Cambridge University Press, 1936 Keynes Press, British Medical Ass. 1983

Nesbit, Louis *Physician-Authors of the Past and Present* Med. Life. 1935, 42, 643-670

Nova et Vetera *Doctors in British Fiction* Brit. Med. J. 1903, 1, 40-41

Nova et Vetera *Medical Poets* Brit. Med. J. 1945, 2, 698

Ober, W. B. *Drowsed with the Fume of Poppies* Bull, N.Y. Acad. Med. 1968, 44, 862-880

Owen, R. C. *Literary Physicians of the Twentieth Century* Prescriber, 1932, 25, 218-220

Pellegrino, E. D. *To Look Feelingly – The Attributes of Medicine and Literature* Literature and Med. 1982, 1, 18-22

Poynter, F. N. L. *The Doctor as Poet* MiddlesexHosp. J. 1961, 62, 137-139

Rabuzzi, K. A. *Literature and Medicine Towards a New Discipline* Vol 1 NY St. Univ. Press, 1982

Raphael, Frederic *Fiction and the Medical Mode in Cracks in the Ice* W. H. Allen ?1979

Rath, Gernot *The Physician and the Pen* Ciba Symp. 1962, 10, 86-89

Ready, W.B. *Medicine and Literature: Doctors in both Faculties* Bull. Med. Library Ass. 1962, 50, 57-66

Rolleston, Sir Humphrey *Poetry and Physic* Ann.Med. Hist. 1926, 8, 1-15

Royal College of Physicians *Physicians' Avocations* Exhibition Catalogue 1975

Sheridan, Niall *Doctors and Literature* Brit. Med. J., 1978, 3, 1779-1780

Smithers, D. W. *On Some Medico-literary Alliances* Brit. Med. J., 1985, 291, 1796-1801

Starrett, Vincent *Books Alive* Random House, New York, 1940

Thompson, W. M. *Medical Men who have Attained Fame in Other Fields of Endeavour* Illinois Med. J. 1923, 44, 49-52, 144-148, 296-302

Wilson, W. A. *Medical Truants* Trans. Pacific Cat. Oto-Ophthal Soc. 1977, 58, 1-20

Yates, E. L. *Some Medical Poets* Nurs. Mirror, 1966, 123, 1-3

PARTICULAR

ABSE
Cohen, J. *The Poetry of Dannie Abse* Robson Books, 1983
Lowbury, Edward *Blood and Roses* Brit. Med. J. 1989, 298, 1119

ABRAHAM
A.L.A. *John Johnson Abraham, Obituary* Ann. Roy. Coll. Surg. Eng. 1963, 33, 392-395

AKENSIDE
Charles, Sir John *Mark Akenside* Brit. Med. J. 1957, 2, 1449-1453
Miles, John *Mark Akenside (1721-1770)* Hist. Med. 1971, 22-23
Ober, W. B. *Mark Akenside M.D. (1721-1770)* N.Y. St. J. Med. 1968, 68, 3166-3180

ARBUTHNOT
Ober, W. B. *John Arbuthnot, M.D., F.R.S., F.R.C.P. (1667-1735)* N.Y. St. J. Med. 1966, 66, 276-281

ARMSTRONG
Knapp, L. M. *Dr John Armstron, Literature and Associate of Smollett, Thompson, Wilkes and other Celebrities* P,M,L,A, 1944, 59, 1019
Maloney, W. J. *John and George Armstrong at Edinburgh* Edin. Med. J. 1950, 57, 600
Ober, W. B. *John Armstrong, M.D. (1709-1779)* N.Y. St. J. Med. 1965, 56, 2711-2717

ASHER
Asher, Richard *A Sense of Asher* Edited by Ruth Holland. Keynes Press 1983. British Medical Association Paperback. 1984
Avery Jones, Sir Francis *Richard Asher. Talking Sense* Pitman Medical, London, 1972

COTTON

Hunter, R. A. and Wood, J. B. *Nathaniel Cotton M.D., Poet, Physician and Psychiatrist* Kings Coll. Hosp. Gaz. 1957, 36, 120-129

CRABBE

Editorial *Crabbe on Doctors* Brit. Med. J. 1910, 2, 26-27

Lewis, Paul *An Aldeburgh Apothecary* Hist Med. 1971, 3, 22-24

DENTON

Rowse, A. L. *Dear Dr Denton* In English Past, Macmillan, London, 1951

DOYLE

Aronson, M. E. *Sherlock Holmes, Father of Forensic Pathology* Trans. Stud. Coll. Physicians Phila. 1977-8, 45, 258-261

Beerman, H. *Sherlock Holmes and Medical History* Trans. Stud. Coll. Physicians Phila. 1977-8, 45, 243-248

Berg. Stanton O. *Sherlock Holmes, Father of Scientific Crime Detection* J. Criminal Law, Criminology and Police Science, 1970, 61, 446-452

Guthrie, D. *Sherlock Holmes and the Medical Profession* Baker St. J. 1947, 2, 465-471

Guthrie, D *Sherlock Holmes and Medicine* Canad. Med. Ass. J. 1961, 85, 996-1000

Hoffman, N. Y. *The Doctor and the Detective Story* J. Amer. Med. Ass. 1973, 224, 74-77

Liebow, E. M. *Dr. Joe Bell: Model for Sherlock Holmes* Bowling Green University Popular Press, Ohio, 1982

Ober, W. B. *Conan Doyle's Dying Detective* N.Y. St. J. Med. 1967, 67, 2141-2145

Rodin, A. E. *Journal of a Quest for the Elusive Doctor Arthur Conan Doyle* Davies Printing, Rochester, Minnesota, 1982

Rodin, A.E. and Key, J.D *Assessment and Significance of Arthur Conan Doyle's Writings* Southern Med. J. 1982, 75, 1392-1399

Rodin, A. E. and Key, J. D. *Medical Casebook of Doctor Arthur Conan Doyle* Robert Krieger, Malabar, Florida, 1984

Rodin, A. E. and Key, J. D. *Doctor Arthur Conan Doyle's Patients in Fact and Fiction* Med. Heritage, 1985, May/April, 80-98

Smith, Sir Sidney *Mostly Murder* Chap. 2. Companion Book Club, London, 1961

DRAKE

Snell, W. E. *Nathan Drake MD. A Literary Practitioner and His Illness* Proc. Roy. Soc. Med. 1963, 58, 263-266

FALLON

Editorial *John Fallon, M.D., Surgeon, Poet and Bibliophile* New Eng. J. Med. 1964, 271, 1272-1273

FERRIAR

Ruhräh, John *John Feriar (1761-1815)* Ann. Med. Hist. 1921, 3, 349-353

FLETCHER

Ober, W. B. *The Purple Island of Phineas Fletcher (1582-1650)* N.Y. St.J. Med. 1967, 67, 2630-2635

FREEMAN

Dirckx, J. H. *A Museum of Thorndykean Pathology* The Thorndyke File 1978, 5, 2-15

Donaldson, Norman *In Search of Dr Thorndyke* Bowling Green University Popular Press, Bowling Green, Ohio, 1971

Mayo, Oliver *R. Austin Freeman, The Anthropologist at Large* Investigator Press, Hawthorndene, S. Australia, 1980

Ober, W. B. *R. Austin Freeman and Dr Thorndyke* N.Y. St. J. Med. 1970, 70, 2242-2249
Stone, P. M. *5A KingsBench Walk* The Thorndyke File, 1977, 3, 37-51

GARTH
Cornog, W. H. *Sir Samuel Garth (1661- 1719) a Court Physician of the 18th Century* Isis, 1938, 19, 29-31
Ellis, F. H. *Garth's Harveian Oration* J. Hist. Med. 1963, 18, 9
Kelly, Michael *Samuel Garth (1661-1719) Physician and Poet* J. Hist. Med. 1964, 19, 162-165
McCue, D. *Samuel Garth, Physician and Man of Letters* Bull N.Y. Acad. Med. 1977, 53, 368-402

GAYTON
Bett, W. R. *Edmund Gayton (1608-1666) Physician, Poet and Pauper* Med. Press 1958, 240, 1164

GOGARTY
Fitzwilliam, M. *Gogarty, Doctor and Writer* Med. News. 1963, June 21, 17
Lyons, J. B. *Oliver St John Gogarty. The Early Phase* J. Irish Coll. Physicians and Surg. 1975, 3, 67-72
Ober, W. B. *Oliver St John Gogarty M.D. (1878-1957)* N.Y. St. J. Med. 1969, 69, 469-480
Scarlett, E. P. *Doctor out of Zebulum, The World of Oliver Gogarty* Arch. Int. Med. 1965, 116, 295-300
Wilson, T. G. *Oliver St John Gogarty* Arch. Otolaryngol. 1969, 90, 235-243

GOLDSMITH
Montgomery, James *Oliver Goldsmith, Doctor, Poet, Writer* Cent. African J. Med. 1984, 30, 303-308

GRAINGER
Ober, W. B. *James Grainger M.D. 1721- 1766 Poetry and Tropical Medicine* N.Y. St. J. Med. 1965, 1257-1260

HAKE
Bett W.R. *Thomas Golden Hake (1809-1895) Physician and Poet* Med. Press 1959, 241,223

KEATS
Brock, Lord *John Keats and Joseph Severn. The Tragedy of the Last Illness* Keats-Shelley Memorial Ass. 1973
Coellnicht, D. C. *The Poet-Physician. Keats and Medical Science* Pittsburgh University Press, 1984
Evans of Hungershall, Lord *Keats the Man, Medicine and Poetry* Brit. Med. J. 1969, 3, 7-11
Goodall, E. W. *Some Examples of the Knowledge of Medicine Exhibited in the Poems of John Keats* Guy's Hosp. Gaz. 1936, 50, 238-240
Hagelman, C. W. *Keats' Medical Training and the Last Stanza of the "Ode to Psyche"* Keats- Shelley J. 1962, 11, 73-82
Hale-White, Sir William *Keats as Doctor and Patient* Oxford Univ. Press, 1938
Holbrook, D. M. A. *John Keats: Student at the United Hospitals* St. Thomas's Hosp. Gaz. 1981, 79, 22-24
Walsh, W. *The Keatsian Paradox: The Hectic and the Healthy* Ann. Roy. Coll. Surg. Eng. 1984, 66, 139-144
Winston, George *John Keats and Joshua Waddinton, Contemporary Students at Guy's Hospital* Guy's Hosp. Rep. 1943, 92, 101-110

KEYNES
Harmer, M., LeFanu, W., Cornelius, E., Barker, N. and Murley, Sir Reginald *Sir Geoffrey Keynes 1887-1982, Surgeon and Scholar* Ann. Roy. Coll. Surg. Eng. Supp. 1984

Taylor, S., LeFanu, W., Whitteridge, G. and Barker, N. *Sir Geoffrey Keynes. Tributes on His 90th Birthday* Ann. Roy. Coll. Surg. Eng. 1977, 59, 307-312

KINLOCK
Ober, W. B. *David Kinlock 1559-1617. Early Scottish Physician and Poet* N.Y. St. J. Med. 1966, 66, 1931-1934

LATHAM
Royal College of Physicians *Physicians' Avocations* Exhibition Catalogue 1975

LETTSOM
Agnew, L. R. S. *Notes and Events. Lettsom, Morse and Sheridan* J. Hist. Med. 1966, 21, 412-418

LEYDEN
Guthrie, D. *Dr. John Leyden (1775-1811)* Scott. Soc. Hist. Med. Proc. 1963-4, 27-31
Eastwood, Martin *John Leyden, Poet and Linguist* Brit. Med. J. 1975, 3, 639-641

LHUYD
Jones, G. P. *Humphrey Lhuyd (1527-1568). A Sixteenth Century Welsh Physician* Proc. Roy. Soc. Med. 1956, 49, 521-528

LOCKE
Jeffreys, M. V. C. *John Locke* Brit. Med. J. 1974, 3, 34-35
Osler, Sir William *John Locke as Physician* Lancet, 1900, 2, 1116-1123

MAUGHAM
Carter, R. *Medicine and W. Somerset Maugham* Amer. J. Surg. 1967, 113, 713-716
Editorial *William Somerset Maugham (1874-1965) Playwright, Novelist, Traveller* J. Amer. Med. Ass. 1968, 204, 65-66

Laurie, J. B. *William Somerset Maugham* Med. Press. 1965, 11, 5-17
Ober, W. B. *A Few Kind Words About W. Somerset Maugham* N.Y. St. J. Med. 1969, 69, 2692- 2701
Rogers, R. B. *W. Somerset Maugham (1874-1965) A Medical Truant* Trans. Stud. Coll. Physicians Phila., 1966-7, 34, 103-112

MOFFET
Editorial *Thomas Moffet (1553-1604) Physician and Author* J. Amer. Med. Ass. 1970, 212, 315

PARSONS
Deranian, H. M. *Thomas W. Parsons 1819- 1892, Dentist, Poet and Devotee of Dante* Bull. Hist. Dent. 1964, 12, 38-45

PHAER
Ruhräh, John *Thomas Phaer* Ann. Med. Hist. 1919, 2, 334-347

RECORDE
Clarke, F. M. *New Light on Robert Recorde* Isis, 1926, 8, 50
Ober, W. B. and Hurwitz, R. M. *Robert Recorde M.D. (1510?-1558)* N.Y. St. J. Med. 1969, 69, 2159-2167
Ober, W. B. *Medical Polemic of 1651* N.Y. St. J. Med. 1971, 71 1880-1886

ROGET
Ober, W. B. *Peter Mark Roget M.D., F.R.S. (1779-1869)* N.Y. St. J. Med. 1965, 65, 1804-1807

ROGERS
Bell, W. J. *Autobiographical Verses by John Rogers M.D.* J. Hist. Med. 1966, 21, 413-414

SALTER
Innes-Smith, R. *A Doctor Digresses: The Salter Diaries* Country Life April 20th 1989, 212

SMOLLETT
Dobson, J. *Smollet the Surgeon* Ann. Roy. Coll. Surg. Eng. 1957, 20, 260-264

Drinker, C. K. *Doctor Smollett* Ann. Med. Hist. 1925, 7, 31-47

Jones, C. E. *Tobias Smollett (1721-1771) The Doctor as Man of Letters* J. Hist. Med. 1957, 12, 337-348

Musher, D. M. *The Medical Views of Dr. Tobias Smollett (1721-1771)* Bull. Hist. Med. 1967, 41, 455-462

Underwood, E. A. *Medicine and Science in the Writings of Smollett* Proc. Roy. Soc. Med. 1937, 30, 961-974

STAKELEY
Piggott, S. *William Stakely: Doctor, Divine and Antiquary* Brit. Med. J. 1974, 3, 725-727

THOMPSON
Moxon, R. K. *Doctors Afield. Sir Henry Thompson (1820-1904) Cremationist, Artist and Host Extraordinary* New Eng. J. Med. 1962, 267, 927-929

Ober, W. B. *Sir Henry Thompson (1820-1904) Victorian Virtues* N.Y. St. J. Med. 1968, 2571-2577

WILDE
Froggatt, P. *Sir William Wilde and the 1851 Census of Ireland* Hist. Med. 1965, 9, 302-327

WOLCOT
Butterfield, W. C. *John Wolcot (1738-1819)* J. Amer. Med. Ass. 1971, 216, 137-138

INDEX

REAL DOCTORS AND MEDICAL STUDENTS

FICTIONAL DOCTORS

GENERAL INDEX

Franklin, Sir John 157, 159
Frederick III 250
Frere, Alex 254
Fry, Christopher 174

Gaborian, Emile 221
Galitzine, Prince 23
Gardiner, Carey 37
Gardiner, Sir Thomas 37
Garrick, David 96, 110, 111, 114,
  117, 118
Gaskell, Elizabeth 17
Gauguin, Eugene 243, 244, 247
Gay, John 77, 78, 81
George III 109
Gielgud, John 246
Ginger, John 103, 119
Giometti 149
Gittings, Robert 100, 139, 140, 150,
  155
Goldsmith, Rev. Charles 104
Goldsmith, Henry 105
Gombrich, E.H. 60
Griffith, Arthur 182
Griffiths, Ralph 108, 109
Gurney, Hudson 124, 125, 132, 136,
  137

Haggard, Sir Henry Rider 19
Hall, S.C. 186, 187
Hals, Franz 58
Hamilton, Alexander 109
Hamilton, Bernice 12, 29
Hamilton, Duke of 90, 106
Hamilton, Sir David 72, 73
Hamilton, William Rowan 193, 197
Hampden, John 34
Handel, George Frederick 70
Hardinge, Mr Justice 75
Hardy, Thomas 248
Harley, Earl of Oxford 71, 78-80
Harris, Frank 182
Harte, Bret 188
Hastell, John 75
Hastings, Lady Flora 194
Hawkins, Jack 248
Hawkins, John 112
Hawtry, Charles 239
Haxton, Gerald 241, 243, 245, 247,
  249-252

Haycraft, Howard 218, 227
Haydon, Benjamin 148, 149
Hayworth, Rita 246
Hazlitt, William 14, 218
Heard, Gerald 251
Helmholtz, Herman von 136
Henrietta Maria, Queen 42
Henslow, Frances 162
Herbert, Thomas, Earl of Pembroke
  54
Hershal, D.J. 137
Hershman, D.J. 121
Higham, Charles 227
Hill, Birkbeck 112
Hilton 149
Hilton, Timothy 155
Hobbema, Meindert 58
Hobbs, Thomas 61
Hodgson, Brian 164
Hogarth 109
Holland, Merlin 26, 29
Holmes, Geoffrey 85
Hooke, Robert 51
Hooker, William Jackson 157, 176
Hope, Lord John 252
Hunt, Leigh 143, 146, 148, 149, 154
Hunter, Michael 68
Humboldt, Baron Friedrich von 161
Hume, David 89, 90, 99
Humphreys, A.R. 60
Humphreys, Samuel 70
Huston, Walter 246
Huxley, Aldous 251
Huxley, Leonard 179

Innes-Smith, Robert 22, 29
Irving, Ethel 239
Isherwood, Christopher 251

James II 43, 57, 58, 69
James, Henry 26
James, William 62, 68
Jeffrey, Josiah 124
Jeffreys, Judge 215
Jennings, Mrs John 142
John of Austria, Archduke 133
Johnson, Edgar 97, 98, 100
Johnson, Samuel 48, 53, 70, 74, 83,
  103, 110-117, 128, 173
Jones, C.E. 100

269